D0852713

The Hymnbook

The Hymnbook

Published by
Presbyterian Church in the United States
The United Presbyterian Church in the U.S.A.
Reformed Church in America

ATLANTA
PHILADELPHIA
NEW YORK

COPYRIGHT, MCMLV, BY JOHN RIDDLE

International Copyright Secured

Scripture quotations from the Revised Standard Version of the Bible are copyright, 1946 and 1952, by the Division of Christian Education of the National Council of Churches, and are used by permission.

Copying from this book by any process without written permission is forbidden. Where pages show credit line "Used by permission," permission to copy must be secured from the original source. On all other material in THE HYMNBOOK, application for permission to copy must be submitted in writing to Publishing Agent, THE HYMNBOOK, 925 Chestnut Street, Philadelphia, Pennsylvania 19107.

The publishers express their sincere gratitude to all who have granted permission to use hymns or tunes that they control. Individual notice of such permission is given below the hymns. Every effort has been made to ascertain what compositions, literary or musical, are copyrighted. If, however, through an oversight any copyrighted material has been used without permission, proper acknowledgment will be made in future printings after notice has been received.

PRINTED IN THE UNITED STATES OF AMERICA

24 25 26 27 28 29 30

PREFACE

The Christian religion is a singing faith, and thus stands in striking contrast to most of the great religions of mankind. From the dawn of creation, when "the morning stars sang together, and all the sons of God shouted for joy," psalms, hymns, and spiritual songs have been vehicles of the faith, the aspiration, and the joy of God's people. The corporate praise and choral prayer of a worshiping congregation have been characteristic expressions of its response to divine grace.

It is to strengthen and to broaden corporate worship among the congregations of the Presbyterian-Reformed family of Churches that this hymnbook has been prepared. The story of its beginnings is a fascinating one. In 1949, committees of the Reformed Church in America and the United Presbyterian Church of North America entered into correspondence with a view to exploring the possibility of jointly preparing a Psalter hymnal which should include metrical versions of the Biblical psalms and a selection of the great hymns of the Church with the needs of both communions in mind. The way was opened for such co-operation and the two committees labored for two years. In 1950 the General Assembly of the Presbyterian Church in the United States appointed a committee "to make approaches to other Presbyterian and Reformed bodies with an invitation to co-operate in the production of a hymnal for all Presbyterian and Reformed Churches." The Reformed Church in America and the United Presbyterian Church gladly accepted the invitation and shared the results of their two years of previous labors. The Associate Reformed Presbyterian Church and the Presbyterian Church in the United States of America joined promptly in the new undertaking, and appointed appropriate committees to co-operate with those already engaged in the task. Thus, THE HYMNBOOK is the product of the co-operative endeavor of five American Churches of the Presbyterian-Reformed tradition, representing a membership of three and a half million people.

The interweaving of the strands of worship from five denominations, each with its own peculiar and precious heritage, has added immeasurable richness to the book. It has been responsible for the inclusion of many of the psalms in meter, a happy recovery of one of the great sources of strength of both the Genevan and the Scottish tradition. With the exception of a few metrical psalms taken directly from the Scottish Psalter of 1650, the version used in this hymnbook is the revision prepared in 1909 by a joint committee representing nine Churches of the Presbyterian-Reformed family in the United States and Canada. This concerted effort of five Churches has also secured the admission of a representative body of so-called "gospel songs," which properly have a place in the devotional life of the Church. It has provided the working committee with a vast store of hymns and tunes from which to choose, out of the incredibly ample and ever-growing treasury of Christian hymnody. It has introduced helpful and stimulating viewpoints which might well

5

have been missed by a committee representing a narrower tradition. Though the task was made more complicated, and the pace of the work reduced, by the necessary blending of these various elements, THE HYMNBOOK is greatly the richer for this careful co-operative process.

Nor has the process been merely the sifting of the old and accepted. A number of new hymns and tunes have been included, wrought out of the Christian faith and devotion of our own time. Several tunes have been provided with descants which add to their beauty and impressiveness. The harmonic structure of others has been improved, without doing violence to their accepted and cherished melodies. In some cases two tunes have been used with a particular text in order to preserve the melodies known and loved by several groups. Much effort has been expended to secure the one best version of those hymns which have suffered many alterations in the course of time.

The Committee acknowledges the advice of many interested friends who have given generously of their time and thought toward the development of this book. Particularly we would thank Charles Grosvenor Osgood, who prepared the Topical Index; William Hallock Johnson, who prepared the Index of Scriptural Allusions; and Jean Woodward Steele, who, as secretary for the Committee, has rendered invaluable service. Throughout the production of this hymnbook we have constantly sought the guidance of the Holy Spirit. We are now sending it forth with the earnest prayer that it may help to enrich the spiritual life of our churches and to unite us in a larger bond of Christian fellowship as we "exalt His name together."

THE HYMNBOOK COMMITTEE

Associate Reformed Presbyterian Church
ARTHUR J. RANSON

Reformed Church in America
GERARD R. GNADE
BERNARD J. MULDER
WILLIAM A. WEBER

Presbyterian Church (U.S.A.)
EUGENE CARSON BLAKE
LEONARD V. BUSCHMAN
JOSEPH J. COPELAND
WALTER L. JENKINS
GEORGE LITCH KNIGHT
HAROLD R. MARTIN

United Presbyterian Church
RICHARD W. GRAVES
WILLIAM T. LYTLE
SAMUEL W. SHANE

Presbyterian Church (U.S.)
CAMERON D. DEANS
WILLIAM H. FOSTER, JR.
EDWARD D. GRANT
AUSTIN C. LOVELACE
STUART R. OGLESBY
HARMON B. RAMSEY
JAMES R. SYDNOR
HUBERT V. TAYLOR
W. TALIAFERRO THOMPSON
ALBERT J. KISSLING, *Chairman*

Editor: DAVID HUGH JONES
Publisher: JOHN RIBBLE

CONTENTS

Aids to Worship

Hymns

8 CONTENTS

Service Music

Scripture Readings

Indexes

AIDS TO WORSHIP

CALLS TO WORSHIP

O COME, let us sing unto the Lord: let us make a joyful noise to the rock of our salvation. Let us come before his presence with thanksgiving, and make a joyful noise unto him with psalms. (Ps. 95:1, 2) [1]

O COME, let us worship and bow down: let us kneel before the Lord our maker. For he is our God; and we are the people of his pasture, and the sheep of his hand. (Ps. 95:6, 7) [1]

SEEK ye the Lord while he may be found, call ye upon him while he is near: let the wicked forsake his way, and the unrighteous man his thoughts: and let him return unto the Lord, and he will have mercy upon him; and to our God, for he will abundantly pardon. (Isa. 55:6, 7) [1]

INVOCATIONS

O GOD, who art a Spirit, infinite, eternal, and unchangeable, in Thy being, wisdom, power, holiness, justice, goodness, and truth; we worship and adore Thee. All Thy works praise Thee in all places of Thy dominion, and Thy glory is revealed in Jesus Christ Thy Son. Wherefore we praise Thee, Father, Son, and Holy Spirit, one God, blessed for ever. Amen. (Alt.) [2]

ALMIGHTY God, from whom cometh every good and perfect gift, and who pourest out upon all who desire it the gift of grace and supplication, deliver us, when we draw nigh unto Thee, from coldness of heart and wanderings of mind, that with steadfast thoughts and kindled affections we may worship Thee in spirit and in truth; through Jesus Christ our Lord. Amen. (William Bright; alt.)

ALMIGHTY God, unto whom all hearts are open, all desires known, and from whom no secrets are hid; cleanse the thoughts of our hearts by the inspiration of Thy Holy Spirit, that we may perfectly love Thee, and worthily magnify Thy Holy Name; through Jesus Christ our Lord. Amen.

PRAYERS OF CONFESSION

ALMIGHTY and most merciful Father; We have erred and strayed from Thy ways like lost sheep. We have followed too much the devices and desires of our own hearts. We have offended against Thy holy laws. We have left undone those things which we ought to have done; And we have done those things which we ought not to have done; And there is no health in us. But Thou, O Lord, have mercy upon us, miserable offenders. Spare Thou those, O God, who confess their faults. Restore Thou those who are penitent; According to Thy promises declared unto mankind in Christ Jesus our Lord. And grant, O most merciful Father, for His sake; That we may hereafter live a godly, righteous, and sober life; To the glory of Thy holy name. Amen.

[1] From the King James Version.　　[2] From *The Book of Common Worship*, copyright, 1946, by the Board of Christian Education of the Presbyterian Church in the U.S.A.

Most holy and merciful Father; We acknowledge and confess before Thee; Our sinful nature prone to evil and slothful in good; And all our shortcomings and offenses. Thou alone knowest how often we have sinned; In wandering from Thy ways; In wasting Thy gifts; In forgetting Thy love. But Thou, O Lord, have mercy upon us; Who are ashamed and sorry for all wherein we have displeased Thee. Teach us to hate our errors; Cleanse us from our secret faults; And forgive our sins; For the sake of Thy dear Son. And O most holy and loving Father; Help us, we beseech Thee; To live in Thy light and walk in Thy ways; According to the commandments of Jesus Christ our Lord. Amen. (Henry van Dyke; alt.) [2]

O Lord Jesus Christ, who didst give Thy life for us that we might receive pardon and peace: Mercifully cleanse us from all sin, and evermore keep us in Thy favor and love, who livest and reignest with the Father and the Holy Spirit, ever one God, world without end. Amen.[3]

Have mercy upon us, O God, according to thy loving-kindness: according unto the multitude of thy tender mercies blot out our transgressions. Wash us thoroughly from our iniquities, and cleanse us from our sin. For we acknowledge our transgressions: and our sin is ever before us. Create in us clean hearts, O God; and renew a right spirit within us. Cast us not away from thy presence; and take not thy Holy Spirit from us. (Ps. 51, adapted) [1]

Assurances of Pardon

Almighty God, who doth freely pardon all who repent and turn to Him, now fulfill in every contrite heart the promise of redeeming grace; remitting all our sins, and cleansing us from an evil conscience; through the perfect sacrifice of Christ Jesus our Lord. Amen. (Henry van Dyke; alt.) [2]

The Lord is merciful and gracious, slow to anger, and plenteous in mercy. He hath not dealt with us after our sins, nor rewarded us according to our iniquities. As the heaven is high above the earth, so great is his mercy toward them that fear him. As far as the east is from the west, so far hath he removed our transgressions from us. Amen. (Ps. 103:8, 10–12) [1]

Prayers of Thanksgiving

Almighty God, Father of all mercies; We Thine unworthy servants; Do give Thee most humble and hearty thanks; For all Thy goodness and loving-kindness to us and to all men. We bless Thee for our creation, preservation, and all the blessings of this life; But above all for Thine inestimable love in the redemption of the world by our Lord Jesus Christ; For the means of grace, and for the hope of glory. And, we beseech Thee, give us that due sense of all Thy mercies; That our hearts may be unfeignedly thankful; And that we show forth Thy praise, not only with our lips, but in our lives; By giving up ourselves to Thy service; And by walking before Thee in righteousness all our days; Through Jesus Christ our Lord; To whom, with Thee and the Holy Spirit, be all honor and glory; World without end. Amen. (Richard Reynolds; alt.)

O Lord our God, the Author and Giver of all good things; We thank Thee for all Thy mercies, and for Thy loving care over all Thy creatures. We bless Thee for the gift of life; For Thy protection round about us; For Thy guiding hand upon us;

[3] From *A Chain of Prayer Across the Ages*, compiled by Selina Fitzherbert Fox; E. P. Dutton & Co., Inc., 1923.

And for all the tokens of Thy love. We thank Thee for friendship and duty; For good hopes and precious memories; For the joys that cheer us; And the trials that teach us to trust in Thee. Most of all we thank Thee for the saving knowledge of Thy Son our Saviour; For the living presence of Thy Spirit, the Comforter; For Thy Church, the Body of Christ (or Our Lord); For the ministry of Word and Sacrament; For all the means of grace; and for the hope of glory. In all these things, O Heavenly Father, make us wise unto a right use of Thy benefits; That we may render an acceptable thanksgiving unto Thee all the days of our life; Through Jesus Christ our Lord. Amen.[4]

ALMIGHTY and most merciful Father; From whom cometh every good and perfect gift; We give Thee praise and hearty thanks for all Thy mercies; For Thy goodness that hath created us; Thy bounty that hath sustained us; Thy Fatherly discipline that hath corrected us; Thy patience that hath borne with us; And Thy love that hath redeemed us. Grant unto us with Thy gifts a heart to love Thee; And enable us to show our thankfulness for all Thy benefits; By giving up ourselves to Thy service; And delighting in all things to do Thy blessed will; Through Jesus Christ our Lord. Amen. (Louis F. Benson; alt.) [2]

The Ten Commandments

GOD spake all these words, saying, I am the Lord thy God, which have brought thee out of the land of Egypt, out of the house of bondage.

1. Thou shalt have no other gods before me.

2. Thou shalt not make unto thee any graven image, or any likeness of any thing that is in heaven above, or that is in the earth beneath, or that is in the water under the earth; thou shalt not bow down thyself to them, nor serve them: for I, the Lord thy God, am a jealous God, visiting the iniquity of the fathers upon the children unto the third and fourth generation of them that hate me; and showing mercy unto thousands of them that love me, and keep my commandments.

3. Thou shalt not take the name of the Lord thy God in vain: for the Lord will not hold him guiltless that taketh his name in vain.

4. Remember the Sabbath Day, to keep it holy. Six days shalt thou labor, and do all thy work: but the seventh day is the Sabbath of the Lord thy God; in it thou shalt not do any work, thou, nor thy son, nor thy daughter, thy manservant, nor thy maidservant, nor thy cattle, nor thy stranger that is within thy gates: for in six days the Lord made heaven and earth, the sea, and all that in them is, and rested the seventh day; wherefore the Lord blessed the Sabbath Day, and hallowed it.

5. Honor thy father and thy mother: that thy days may be long upon the land which the Lord thy God giveth thee.

6. Thou shalt not kill.

7. Thou shalt not commit adultery.

8. Thou shalt not steal.

9. Thou shalt not bear false witness against thy neighbor.

10. Thou shalt not covet thy neighbor's house, thou shalt not covet thy neighbor's wife, nor his manservant, nor his maidservant, nor his ox, nor his ass, nor any thing that is thy neighbor's.

Hear also the words of our Lord Jesus, how He saith: Thou shalt love the Lord thy God with all thy heart, and with all thy soul, and with all thy mind. This is the first and great commandment. And the second is like unto it, Thou shalt love thy neighbor as thyself. On these two commandments hang all the law and the prophets.

[4] Altered from *The Book of Common Order.*

The Lord's Prayer

OUR Father, who art in heaven, Hallowed be Thy name. Thy kingdom come. Thy will be done on earth as it is in heaven. Give us this day our daily bread. And forgive us our debts, as we forgive our debtors. And lead us not into temptation, but deliver us from evil: For Thine is the kingdom, and the power, and the glory, for ever. Amen.

The Nicene Creed

I BELIEVE in one God the Father Almighty, Maker of heaven and earth, and of all things visible and invisible;

And in one Lord Jesus Christ, the only-begotten Son of God, begotten of His Father before all worlds; God of God; Light of Light; Very God of Very God; Begotten, not made; Being of one substance with the Father, by whom all things were made; Who for us men, and for our salvation, came down from heaven; And was incarnate by the Holy Ghost of the Virgin Mary, and was made man; And was crucified also for us under Pontius Pilate. He suffered and was buried; And the third day He rose again according to the Scriptures; And ascended into heaven; And sitteth on the right hand of the Father. And He shall come again with glory to judge both the quick and the dead; Whose kingdom shall have no end.

And I believe in the Holy Ghost; The Lord and Giver of Life; Who proceedeth from the Father and the Son; Who with the Father and the Son together is worshiped and glorified; Who spake by the prophets. And I believe one Holy Catholic and Apostolic Church. I acknowledge one Baptism for the remission of sins. And I look for the Resurrection of the dead; And the Life of the world to come. Amen.

The Apostles' Creed

I BELIEVE in God the Father Almighty, Maker of heaven and earth;

And in Jesus Christ His only Son our Lord; who was conceived by the Holy Ghost, born of the Virgin Mary, suffered under Pontius Pilate, was crucified, dead, and buried; He descended into hell;* the third day He rose again from the dead; He ascended into heaven, and sitteth on the right hand of God the Father Almighty; from thence He shall come to judge the quick and the dead.

I believe in the Holy Ghost; the holy Catholic Church; the communion of saints; the forgiveness of sins; the resurrection of the body; and the life everlasting. Amen.

* Some Churches omit this.

Praise Ye the Lord, the Almighty

1

From Psalms 103, 150
Joachim Neander, 1680
Trans. by Catherine Winkworth, 1863

LOBE DEN HERREN: 14. 14. 4. 7. 8.
Stralsund Gesangbuch, 1665
Arr. in *Praxis Pietatis Melica,* 1668

1. Praise ye the Lord, the Al - might - y, the King of cre - a - tion!
2. Praise ye the Lord, who o'er all things so won-drous-ly reign - eth,
3. Praise ye the Lord! O let all that is in me a - dore Him!

O my soul, praise Him, for He is thy health and sal - va - tion!
Shel - ters thee un - der His wings, yea, so gen - tly sus - tain - eth!
All that hath life and breath, come now with prais - es be - fore Him!

All ye who hear, Now to His tem - ple draw near;
Hast thou not seen How thy de - sires e'er have been
Let the A - men Sound from His peo - ple a - gain:

Join me in glad ad - o - ra - tion!
Grant - ed in what He or - dain - eth?
Glad - ly for aye we a - dore . . . . . Him. A - MEN.

WORSHIP: ADORATION AND PRAISE

[13]

2   For the Beauty of the Earth

DIX: 7. 7. 7. 7. 7. 7.
Abridged from chorale by
Conrad Kocher, 1838

Folliott S. Pierpoint, 1864

1. For the beau-ty of the earth, For the beau-ty of the skies,
2. For the won-der of each hour Of the day and of the night,
3. For the joy of ear and eye, For the heart and mind's de-light,
4. For the joy of hu-man love, Broth-er, sis-ter, par-ent, child,
5. For Thy Church that ev-er-more Lift-eth ho-ly hands a-bove,

For the love which from our birth O-ver and a-round us lies,
Hill and vale, and tree and flower, Sun and moon, and stars of light,
For the mys-tic har-mo-ny Link-ing sense to sound and sight,
Friends on earth, and friends a-bove, For all gen-tle thoughts and mild,
Offer-ing up on ev-ery shore Her pure sac-ri-fice of love,

REFRAIN

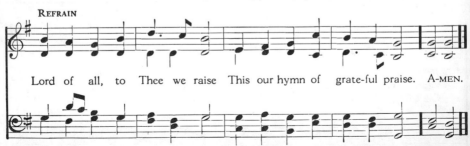

Lord of all, to Thee we raise This our hymn of grate-ful praise. A-MEN.

Words copyright. Used by permission of the author's estate and of Oxford University Press.

WORSHIP: ADORATION AND PRAISE

[14]

Praise the Lord: Ye Heavens, Adore Him

3

From Psalm 148
Foundling Hospital Collection, Stanzas 1 and 2, 1796
Edward Osler, Stanza 3, 1836

FABEN: 8. 7. 8. 7. D.
John H. Willcox, 1849

1. Praise the Lord: ye heavens, a-dore Him; Praise Him, an-gels in the height;
2. Praise the Lord, for He is glo-rious; Nev-er shall His prom-ise fail:
3. Wor-ship, hon-or, glo-ry, bless-ing, Lord, we of-fer un-to Thee;

Sun and moon, re-joice be-fore Him, Praise Him, all ye stars of light.
God hath made His saints vic-to-rious; Sin and death shall not pre-vail.
Young and old, Thy praise ex-press-ing, In glad hom-age bend the knee.

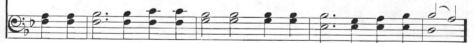

Praise the Lord, for He hath spo-ken; Worlds His might-y voice o-beyed:
Praise the God of our sal-va-tion; Hosts on high, His power pro-claim;
All the saints in heaven a-dore Thee; We would bow be-fore Thy throne:

Laws which nev-er shall be bro-ken For their guid-ance He hath made.
Heaven and earth and all cre-a-tion, Laud and mag-ni-fy His name.
As Thine an-gels serve be-fore Thee, So on earth Thy will be done. A-MEN.

Alternative tune, "Hyfrydol," Hymn 123.

[15]

WORSHIP: ADORATION AND PRAISE

4   Praise the Lord, His Glories Show

From Psalm 150
Henry Francis Lyte (1793-1847)

LLANFAIR: 7. 7. 7. 7. with Alleluias
Robert Williams, 1817
Har. by David Evans

1. Praise the Lord, His glo-ries show, Al - - le - lu - ia!
2. Earth to heaven, and heaven to earth, Al - - le - lu - ia!
3. Praise the Lord, His mer-cies trace, Al - - le - lu - ia!

Saints with-in His courts be-low, Al - - le - lu - ia!
Tell His won-ders, sing His worth, Al - - le - lu - ia!
Praise His prov-i-dence and grace, Al - - le - lu - ia!

An-gels round His throne a-bove, Al - - le - lu - ia!
Age to age and shore to shore, Al - - le - lu - ia!
All that He for man hath done, Al - - le - lu - ia!

All that see and share His love. Al - - le - lu - ia!
Praise Him, praise Him ev-er-more! Al - - le - lu - ia!
All He sends us through His Son. Al - - le - lu - ia! A-MEN.

Music from *The Church Hymnary*, Revised Edition. Used by permission of Oxford University Press.

WORSHIP: ADORATION AND PRAISE

[16]

O Lord, Thou Art My God and King

5

From Psalm 145
The Psalter, 1912

DUKE STREET: L. M.
John Hatton, d. 1793

1. O Lord, Thou art my God and King, And I will ev-er bless Thy name;
2. The Lord is great-ly to be praised, His great-ness is be-yond our thought;
3. Up-on Thy glo-rious maj-es-ty And won-drous works my mind shall dwell;
4. Thy match-less good-ness and Thy grace Thy peo-ple shall com-mem-o-rate,

I will ex-tol Thee ev-er-y day, And ev-er-more Thy praise pro-claim.
From age to age the sons of men Shall tell the won-ders God has wrought.
Thy deeds shall fill the world with awe, And of Thy great-ness I will tell.
And all Thy truth and right-eous-ness My joy-ful song shall cel-e-brate. A-MEN.

For lower key, see Hymn 496.

Heaven and Earth, and Sea and Air

6

GOTT SEI DANK DURCH ALLE WELT: 7. 7. 7. 7.
J. A. Freylinghausen's *Gesangbuch*
Halle, 1704

From Psalm 19
Joachim Neander (1650-1680)

1. Heaven and earth, and sea and air, All their Mak-er's praise de-clare;
2. See the glo-rious orb of day Break-ing through the clouds his way;
3. See how He hath ev-ery-where Made this earth so rich and fair;
4. Lord, great won-ders work-est Thou! To Thy sway all crea-tures bow;

Wake, my soul, a-wake and sing: Now thy grate-ful prais-es bring.
Moon and stars with sil-very light Praise Him through the si-lent night.
Hill and vale and fruit-ful land, All things liv-ing, show His hand.
Write Thou deep-ly in my heart What I am, and what Thou art. A-MEN.

Music from *The Oxford American Hymnal*. Used by permission of Oxford University Press, Inc.

WORSHIP: ADORATION AND PRAISE

7   Of the Father's Love Begotten

Aurelius Clemens Prudentius (348-413)
Trans. by John Mason Neale, 1854,
and Henry W. Baker, 1859

DIVINUM MYSTERIUM: 8. 7. 8. 7. 8. 7. 7.
Twelfth century plain song (Mode V)
Arr. by Charles Winfred Douglas, 1916

In unison

1. Of the Fa-ther's love be - got - ten, Ere the worlds be - gan to be,
2. O ye heights of heaven, a - dore Him; An - gel hosts, His prais - es sing;
3. Christ, to Thee with God the Fa - ther, And, O Ho - ly Ghost, to Thee,

He is Al - pha and O - me - ga, He the Source, the End - ing He,
Powers, do - min - ions, bow be - fore Him, And ex - tol our God and King;
Hymn and chant and high thanks-giv - ing And un - wea - ried prais - es be:

Of the things that are, that have . . . . . been, And that fu - ture
Let no tongue on earth be si - - lent, Ev - ery voice in
Hon - or, glo - ry, and do - min - - ion, And e - ter - nal

Music from *The New Hymnal*. Used by permission of Mrs. Charles Winfred Douglas.

WORSHIP: ADORATION AND PRAISE

[18]

Of the Father's Love Begotten

years shall see, Ev-er-more and ev-er-more!
con-cert ring, Ev-er-more and ev-er-more!
vic-to-ry, Ev-er-more and ev-er-more! A - MEN.

Bless, O My Soul! the Living God 8

From Psalm 103
Isaac Watts, 1719

PARK STREET: L. M.
Frederick M. A. Venua, c. 1810

1. Bless, O my soul! the liv-ing God; Call home thy thoughts that
2. Bless, O my soul! the God of grace; His fa-vors claim thy
3. 'Tis He, my soul! who sent His Son To die for crimes which
4. Let the whole earth His power con-fess, Let the whole earth a-

rove a-broad; Let all the powers with-in me join In work and
high-est praise: Why should the won-ders He hath wrought Be lost in
thou hast done: He owns the ran-som and for-gives The hour-ly
dore His grace; The Gen-tile with the Jew shall join In work and

wor-ship so di-vine, In work and wor-ship so di-vine.
si-lence and for-got, Be lost in si-lence and for-got?
fol-lies of our lives, The hour-ly fol-lies of our lives.
wor-ship so di-vine, In work and wor-ship so di-vine. A - MEN.

WORSHIP: ADORATION AND PRAISE

9

Now Thank We All Our God

Martin Rinkart, c. 1636
Trans. by Catherine Winkworth, 1858

NUN DANKET: 6. 7. 6. 7. 6. 6. 6. 6.
Johann Crüger, 1648

1. Now thank we all our God With heart and hands and voi - ces,
2. O may this boun - teous God Through all our life be near us,
3. All praise and thanks to God The Fa - ther now be giv - en,

Who won-drous things hath done, In whom His world re - joi - ces;
With ev - er - joy - ful hearts And bless - ed peace to cheer us;
The Son, and Him who reigns With Them in high - est heav - en,

Who, from our moth - ers' arms, Hath blessed us on our way
And keep us in His grace, And guide us when per - plexed,
The one e - ter - nal God, Whom earth and heaven a - dore;

With count-less gifts of love, And still is ours to - day.
And free us from all ills In this world and the next.
For thus it was, is now, And shall be ev - er - more. A - MEN.

WORSHIP: ADORATION AND PRAISE

Mighty God, While Angels Bless Thee

10

Robert Robinson, 1774

AUTUMN: 8. 7. 8. 7. D.
Ascribed to François H. Barthélémon (1741-1808)

1. Might - y God, while an - gels bless Thee, May a mor - tal sing Thy name?
2. For the gran - deur of Thy na - ture, Grand be - yond a ser - aph's thought;
3. Bright - ness of the Fa - ther's glo - ry, Shall Thy praise un - ut - tered lie?

Lord of men as well as an - gels, Thou art ev - ery crea - ture's theme.
For the won - ders of cre - a - tion, Works with skill and kind - ness wrought;
Break, my tongue, such guilt - y si - lence! Sing the Lord who came to die.

Lord of ev - ery land and na - tion, An - cient of e - ter - nal days,
For Thy prov - i - dence, that gov - erns, Thru Thine em - pire's wide do - main,
From the high - est throne of glo - ry To the cross of deep - est woe,

Sound - ed thru the wide cre - a - tion Be Thy just and end - less praise.
Wings an an - gel, guides a spar - row, Bless - ed be Thy gen - tle reign.
All to ran - som guilt - y cap - tives; Flow my praise, for - ev - er flow! A - MEN.

WORSHIP: ADORATION AND PRAISE

[21]

11   Holy, Holy, Holy! Lord God Almighty!

Reginald Heber, pub. 1826
Descant for Stanza 4

NICAEA: 11. 12. 12. 10.
John B. Dykes, 1861
Descant by David McK. Williams, 1948

1. Ho - ly, Ho - ly, Ho - ly! Lord God Al - might - y!
2. Ho - ly, Ho - ly, Ho - ly! All the saints a - dore Thee,
3. Ho - ly, Ho - ly, Ho - ly! Though the dark - ness hide Thee,
4. Ho - ly, Ho - ly, Ho - ly! Lord God Al - might - y!

Ear - ly in the morn - ing our song shall rise to Thee;
Cast - ing down their gold - en crowns a - round the glass - y sea;
Though the eye of sin - ful man Thy glo - ry may not see,
All Thy works shall praise Thy name, in earth and sky and sea;

Ho - ly, Ho - ly, Ho - ly! mer - ci - ful and might - y!
Cher - u - bim and ser - a - phim fall - ing down be - fore Thee,
On - ly Thou art ho - ly; there is none be - side Thee
Ho - ly, Ho - ly, Ho - ly! mer - ci - ful and might - y!

Descant copyright, 1948, by The H. W. Gray Company. Used by permission.

WORSHIP: ADORATION AND PRAISE

Holy, Holy, Holy! Lord God Almighty!

God in three Per-sons, bless-ed Trin - - i - ty. A-MEN.

God in three Per - sons, bless - ed Trin - i - ty!
Who wert, and art, and ev - er - more shalt be.
Per - fect in power, in love, and pu - ri - ty.
God in three Per - sons, bless - ed Trin - i - ty! A - MEN.

Lord of Health, Thou Life Within Us   12

IL BUON PASTOR: 8. 7. 8. 7. 7.
Adapted from melody in *Canzuns Spirituælas*, Upper Engadine, 1765
Four-part arr. for this book, 1953

Percy Dearmer (1867-1936)

1. Lord of health, Thou life with - in us, Strength of all that
2. Praise for all our work and lei - sure, Mirth and games and
3. Praise for joys, for sor - rows e - ven, All that leads us
4. Help us now, each mo - ment fill - ing, Keep us true to

lives and grows, Love that meets our hearts to win us, Beau - ty that a -
jol - li - ty, Stud - y, sci - ence, all the treas - ure That is stored by
up to Thee; Most of all that out from heav - en Came Thy Son to
Thee and wise; May our work be keen and will - ing, Power and serv - ice

round us glows, Take the praise that brims and flows.
mem - o - ry, Skill of mind and hand and eye.
set us free, Came to show us what to be.
be our prize, Till to Thy far hills we rise. A - MEN.

Words and music from *Songs of Praise*. Used by permission of Oxford University Press.

WORSHIP: ADORATION AND PRAISE

[23]

13

God Himself Is with Us

Gerhard Tersteegen. 1729
Trans. composite

ARNSBERG: 6. 6. 8. 6. 6. 8. 3. 3. 6. 6.
Joachim Neander's *Bundes-Lieder*, 1680

1. God Him-self is with us: Let us now a - dore Him, And with awe ap-
2. God Him-self is with us: Whom an-gel-ic le - gions Serve with awe in
3. Lord, come dwell with-in us, While on earth we tar - ry, Make us Thy blest

pear be - fore Him. God is in His tem - ple, All with - in keep
heaven-ly re - gions. "Ho - ly, Ho - ly, Ho - ly," Sing the hosts of
sanc - tu - a - ry, Grant us now Thy pres - ence, Un - to us draw

si - lence, And be-fore Him bow with rev - erence. Him a-lone, God we own;
heav - en, Praise to God be ev - er giv - en. Bow Thine ear To us here:
near - er, And re-veal Thy-self still clear - er. Where we are, Near or far,

To our Lord and Sav - iour Prais - es sing for - ev - er.
Hear, O Christ, the prais - es That Thy Church now rais - es.
Let us see Thy pow - er, Ev - ery day and hour. . . . A - MEN.

Words and music from *The Hymnal*. Used by permission of Eden Publishing House.

WORSHIP: ADORATION AND PRAISE

Lord of the Worlds Above

14

From Psalm 84
Isaac Watts, 1719
Stanza 4 alt.

DARWALL'S 148TH: 6. 6. 6. 6. 8. 8.
John Darwall, 1770

1. Lord of the worlds a - bove, How pleas - ant and how fair
2. O hap - py souls that pray Where God ap - points to hear!
3. They go from strength to strength, Through this dark vale of tears,
4. God is our Sun and Shield, Our Light and our De - fense;

The dwell - ings of Thy love, Thine earth - ly
O hap - py men that pay Their con - stant
Till each ar - rives at length, Till each in
With gifts His hands are filled: We draw our

tem - ples, are! To Thine a - bode my heart as - pires,
serv - ice there! They praise Thee still; and hap - py they
heaven ap - pears: O glo - rious seat, when God, our King,
bless - ings thence. Thrice hap - py he, O God of Hosts,

With warm de - sires to see my God.
That love the way to Zi - on's hill.
Shall thith - er bring our will - ing feet!
Whose spir - it trusts a - lone in Thee! A - MEN.

WORSHIP: ADORATION AND PRAISE

[25]

15 Sing Praise to God Who Reigns Above

Johann J. Schütz (1640-1690)
Trans. by Frances E. Cox (1812-1897)

MIT FREUDEN ZART: 8. 7. 8. 7 8. 8. 7.
Pre-Reformation melody
From the Bohemian Brethren's *Gesangbuch*, 1566

1. Sing praise to God who reigns a - bove, The God of all cre - a - tion,
2. What God's al-might-y power hath made, His gra-cious mer - cy keep-eth;
3. The Lord is nev - er far a - way, But, through all grief dis - tress-ing,
4. Thus, all my toil-some way a - long, I sing a-loud Thy prais - es,

The God of power, the God of love, The God of our sal - va - tion;
By morn - ing glow or eve - ning shade His watch-ful eye ne'er sleep - eth;
An ev - er - pres - ent help and stay, Our peace, and joy, and bless - ing;
That men may hear the grate - ful song My voice un - wea - ried rais - es;

With heal-ing balm my soul He fills, And ev - ery faith-less mur - mur stills:
With - in the king-dom of His might, Lo! all is just and all is right:
As with a moth-er's ten - der hand, He leads His own, His cho - sen band:
Be joy - ful in the Lord, my heart, Both soul and bod - y bear your part:

To God all praise and glo - ry.
To God all praise and glo - ry.
To God all praise and glo - ry.
To God all praise and glo - ry. A - MEN.

Alternative tune. "Nun Freut Euch," opposite page.

WORSHIP: ADORATION AND PRAISE

[26]

We Come Unto Our Fathers' God

NUN FREUT EUCH: 8. 7. 8. 7. 8. 8. 7.
Melody by Martin Luther in
Geistliche Lieder, Wittenberg, 1535

Thomas H. Gill, 1868

16

1. We come un-to our fa-thers' God, Their Rock is our sal - va - tion;
2. Their joy un-to their Lord we bring, Their song to us de - scend-eth;
3. Ye saints to come, take up the strain, The same sweet theme en - deav-or;

Th'e-ter-nal arms, their dear a-bode, We make our hab - i - ta - tion.
The Spir-it who in them did sing To us His mu - sic lend-eth:
Un-bro-ken be the gold-en chain! Keep on the song for - ev - er!

We bring Thee, Lord, the praise they brought, We seek Thee as Thy
His song in them, in us, is one; We raise it high, we
Safe in the same dear dwell - ing place, Rich with the same e -

saints have sought In ev - ery gen - e - ra - tion.
send it on— The song that nev - er end - eth.
ter - nal grace, Bless the same bound - less Giv - er. A - men.

Words copyright by E. W. B. Gill. Used by permission.
Alternative tune, "Mit Freuden Zart," opposite page.

WORSHIP: ADORATION AND PRAISE

We Praise Thee, O God, Our Redeemer

KREMSER: 12. 11. 12. 11.
Old Netherlands melody in
The Collection, Adrianus Valerius, 1625

Julia C. Cory

1. We praise Thee, O God, our Re-deem-er, Cre-a-tor,
2. We wor-ship Thee, God of our fa-thers, we bless Thee;
3. With voic-es u-nit-ed our prais-es we of-fer,

In grate-ful de-vo-tion our trib-ute we bring.
Through life's storm and tem-pest our Guide hast Thou been.
And glad-ly our song of true wor-ship we raise;

We lay it be-fore Thee, we kneel and a-dore Thee,
When per-ils o'er-take us, es-cape Thou wilt make us,
Our sins now con-fess-ing, we pray for Thy bless-ing,

We bless Thy ho-ly name, glad prais-es we sing.
And with Thy help, O Lord, life's bat-tles we win.
To Thee, our great Re-deem-er, ev-er be praise. A-MEN.

Words used by permission of the author.

WORSHIP: ADORATION AND PRAISE

We Gather Together to Ask the Lord's Blessing 18

Netherlands folk song
Trans. by Theodore Baker

1 We gather together to ask the Lord's blessing;
   He chastens and hastens His will to make known;
   The wicked oppressing now cease from distressing,
      Sing praises to His name; He forgets not His own.

2 Beside us to guide us, our God with us joining,
   Ordaining, maintaining His Kingdom divine;
   So from the beginning the fight we were winning;
      Thou, Lord, wast at our side; all glory be Thine!

3 We all do extol Thee, Thou Leader triumphant,
   And pray that Thou still our Defender wilt be.
   Let Thy congregation escape tribulation;
      Thy name be ever praised! O Lord, make us free! AMEN.

This hymn may be sung to the tune "Kremser," on opposite page.

Praise God, Ye Servants of the Lord 19

From Psalm 113
The Psalter, 1912

ANDRE: L. M.
William B. Bradbury (1816-1868)

1. Praise God, ye serv-ants of the Lord, O praise His name with
2. From ris-ing un-to set-ting sun Praised be the Lord, the
3. On whom but God can we re-ly, The Lord our God who
4. He lifts the poor and makes them great, With joy He fills the

one ac-cord; Bless ye the Lord, His name a-dore From this time
Might-y One; He reigns o'er all, su-preme in might, A-bove the
reigns on high, Who con-de-scends to see and know The things of
des-o-late; Praise ye the Lord and bless His name, His mer-cy

forth for-ev-er-more, From this time forth for-ev-er-more.
heavens in glo-ry bright, A-bove the heavens in glo-ry bright.
heaven and earth be-low, The things of heaven and earth be-low?
and His might pro-claim, His mer-cy and His might pro-claim. A-MEN.

WORSHIP: ADORATION AND PRAISE

[29]

20 It Is Good to Sing Thy Praises

From Psalm 92
The Psalter, 1912

ELLESDIE: 8. 7. 8. 7. D.
Attributed to Wolfgang A. Mozart (1756-1791)
Arr. by Hubert P. Main, 1872

1. It is good to sing Thy prais-es And to thank Thee, O Most High,
2. Thou hast filled my heart with glad-ness Thro' the works Thy hands have wrought;
3. But the good shall live be-fore Thee, Plant-ed in Thy dwell-ing place,

Show - ing forth Thy lov - ing - kind-ness When the morn-ing lights the sky.
Thou hast made my life vic - to - rious, Great Thy works and deep Thy thought.
Fruit - ful trees and ev - er ver-dant, Nour-ished by Thy bound-less grace.

It is good when night is fall - ing Of Thy faith-ful - ness to tell,
Thou, O Lord, on high ex - alt - ed, Reign-est ev - er - more in might;
In His good-ness to the right-eous God His right-eous - ness dis - plays;

While with sweet, me-lo-dious prais-es Songs of ad - o - ra - tion swell.
All Thy en - e - mies shall per - ish, Sin be ban - ished from Thy sight.
God my rock, my strength and ref-uge, Just and true are all His ways. A-MEN.

Alternative tune. "Hyfrydol," Hymn 123.

WORSHIP: ADORATION AND PRAISE

Joyful, Joyful, We Adore Thee

Henry van Dyke, 1907

HYMN TO JOY: 8. 7. 8. 7. D.
Ludwig van Beethoven, 1824
Arr. by Edward Hodges (1796-1867)

1. Joy - ful, joy - ful, we a - dore Thee, God of glo - ry, Lord of love;
2. All Thy works with joy sur - round Thee, Earth and heaven re - flect Thy rays,
3. Thou art giv - ing and for - giv - ing, Ev - er bless - ing, ev - er blest,
4. Mor - tals, join the hap - py cho - rus Which the morn - ing stars be - gan;

Hearts un - fold like flowers be - fore Thee, O - pening to the sun a - bove.
Stars and an - gels sing a - round Thee, Cen - ter of un - bro - ken praise.
Well - spring of the joy of liv - ing, O - cean depth of hap - py rest!
Fa - ther love is reign - ing o'er us, Broth - er love binds man to man.

Melt the clouds of sin and sad - ness, Drive the dark of doubt a - way;
Field and for - est, vale and moun - tain, Flow - ery mead - ow, flash - ing sea,
Thou our Fa - ther, Christ our Broth - er, All who live in love are Thine;
Ev - er sing - ing, march we on - ward, Vic - tors in the midst of strife,

Giv - er of im - mor - tal glad - ness, Fill us with the light of day.
Chant - ing bird and flow - ing foun - tain, Call us to re - joice in Thee.
Teach us how to love each oth - er, Lift us to the Joy di - vine.
Joy - ful mu - sic leads us Sun - ward In the tri - umph song of life. A-MEN.

Words reprinted from *The Poems of Henry van Dyke:* copyright. 1911. by Charles Scribner's Sons. 1939. by Tertius van Dyke. Used by permission of the publishers.

WORSHIP: ADORATION AND PRAISE

22 Let All the World in Every Corner Sing

George Herbert, 1633

HIGH ROAD: 10. 4. 6. 6. 6. 6. 10. 4.
Martin Shaw, 1915

1. Let all the world in ev - ery cor - ner sing, My God and King!
2. Let all the world in ev - ery cor - ner sing, My God and King!

The heavens are not too high, His praise may thith - er fly;
The Church with psalms must shout, No door can keep them out;

The earth is not too low, His prais - es there may grow.
But, a - bove all, the heart Must bear the long - est part.

Let all the world in ev - ery cor - ner sing, My God and King!
Let all the world in ev - ery cor - ner sing, My God and King! A-MEN.

Music by permission, from Curwen Edition No. 6300, published by J. Curwen & Sons, Ltd., 24 Berners Street, London, W. I.

WORSHIP: ADORATION AND PRAISE

All Nature's Works His Praise Declare

Henry Ware. Jr., 1822
Stanza 3 alt.

BETHLEHEM: C. M. D.
Gottfried W. Fink. 1842

1. All na - ture's works His praise de - clare, To whom they all be - long;
2. To God the tribes of o - cean cry, And birds up - on the wing;
3. Great God, to Thee we con - se - crate Our voi - ces and our skill;

There is a voice in ev - ery star, In ev - ery breeze a song.
To God the powers that dwell on high Their tune - ful trib - ute bring.
We bid the peal - ing or - gan wait To speak a - lone Thy will.

Sweet mu - sic fills the world a - broad With strains of love and power;
Like them, let man the throne sur - round, With them loud cho - rus raise,
Lord, while the mu - sic round us floats May earth - born pas - sions die;

The storm - y sea sings praise to God, The thun - der and the shower.
While in - stru - ments of loft - ier sound As - sist his fee - ble praise.
O grant its rich and swell - ing notes May lift our souls on high! A-MEN.

WORSHIP: ADORATION AND PRAISE

All People That on Earth Do Dwell

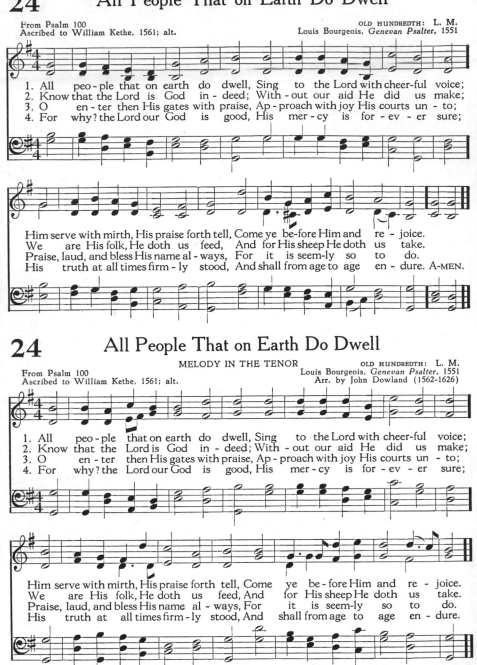

From Psalm 100
Ascribed to William Kethe, 1561; alt.

OLD HUNDREDTH: L. M.
Louis Bourgeois, *Genevan Psalter*, 1551

1. All peo-ple that on earth do dwell, Sing to the Lord with cheer-ful voice;
2. Know that the Lord is God in - deed; With - out our aid He did us make;
3. O en - ter then His gates with praise, Ap - proach with joy His courts un - to;
4. For why? the Lord our God is good, His mer - cy is for - ev - er sure;

Him serve with mirth, His praise forth tell, Come ye be-fore Him and re - joice.
We are His folk, He doth us feed, And for His sheep He doth us take.
Praise, laud, and bless His name al - ways, For it is seem-ly so to do.
His truth at all times firm - ly stood, And shall from age to age en - dure. A-MEN.

24 All People That on Earth Do Dwell

MELODY IN THE TENOR

OLD HUNDREDTH: L. M.
Louis Bourgeois, *Genevan Psalter*, 1551
Arr. by John Dowland (1562-1626)

From Psalm 100
Ascribed to William Kethe, 1561; alt.

1. All peo-ple that on earth do dwell, Sing to the Lord with cheer-ful voice;
2. Know that the Lord is God in - deed; With - out our aid He did us make;
3. O en - ter then His gates with praise, Ap - proach with joy His courts un - to;
4. For why? the Lord our God is good, His mer - cy is for - ev - er sure;

Him serve with mirth, His praise forth tell, Come ye be-fore Him and re - joice.
We are His folk, He doth us feed, And for His sheep He doth us take.
Praise, laud, and bless His name al - ways, For it is seem-ly so to do.
His truth at all times firm - ly stood, And shall from age to age en - dure.

This alternative arrangement may be used for one or more stanzas, the congregation singing the melody only.

WORSHIP: ADORATION AND PRAISE

We Worship Thee, Almighty Lord   25

Johann Olaf Wallin (1779-1839)
Trans. by Charles Wharton Stork, 1925

WALLIN: 8. 8. 10. 10.
Melody of 1529

Unison

1. We wor - ship Thee, al - might - y Lord.
2. Up - on a moun - tain build - ed high,
3. Through her shall ev - ery land pro - claim
4. All na - tions to Thy throne shall throng

Our hearts re - vere Thy gra - cious word When it goes forth from
Thy Church doth in Thy strength re - ly, And stand - eth sure while
The sa - cred might of Je - sus' name, And all re - joice with
And raise on high the vic - tory song, While cher - u - bim re -

Harmony

heaven o'er all the earth. Ho - ly, ho - ly,
earth and time en - dure. Ho - ly, ho - ly,
Chris - tian heart and voice. Ho - ly, ho - ly,
ply to ser - a - phim, "Ho - ly, ho - ly,

Unison

ho - ly art Thou, O God!
ho - ly art Thou, O God!
ho - ly art Thou, O God!
ho - ly art Thou, O God!" A - MEN.

Words used by permission of the author.

WORSHIP: ADORATION AND PRAISE

[35]

26 O Worship the King All Glorious Above

From Psalm 104
Robert Grant, 1833

LYONS: 10. 10. 11. 11.
Adapted from J. Michael Haydn (1737-1806)

1. O wor-ship the King all glo-rious a-bove, O grate-ful-ly sing His
2. O tell of His might, O sing of His grace, Whose robe is the light, whose
3. The earth with its store of won-ders un-told, Al-might-y, Thy power hath
4. Thy boun-ti-ful care what tongue can re-cite? It breathes in the air, it
5. Frail chil-dren of dust, and fee-ble as frail, In Thee do we trust, nor

power and His love; Our Shield and De-fend-er, the An-cient of Days,
can-o-py space. His char-iots of wrath the deep thun-der-clouds form,
found-ed of old; Hath stab-lished it fast by a change-less de-cree,
shines in the light; It streams from the hills, it de-scends to the plain,
find Thee to fail; Thy mer-cies how ten-der, how firm to the end,

Pa - vil-ioned in splen-dor, and gird-ed with praise.
And dark is His path on the wings of the storm.
And round it hath cast, like a man-tle, the sea.
And sweet-ly dis-tills in the dew and the rain.
Our Mak-er, De-fend-er, Re-deem-er, and Friend. A-MEN.

Alternative tune, "Hanover," below.

27 Ye Servants of God, Your Master Proclaim

Charles Wesley, 1744; alt.

HANOVER: 10. 10. 11. 11.
William Croft, Supplement to the New Version, 1708

1. Ye serv-ants of God, your Mas-ter pro-claim, And pub-lish a-
2. God rul-eth on high, al-might-y to save; And still He is
3. "Sal-va-tion to God, who sits on the throne," Let all cry a-
4. Then let us a-dore, and give Him His right, All glo-ry and

WORSHIP: ADORATION AND PRAISE   [36]

Ye Servants of God, Your Master Proclaim

broad His won - der - ful name; The name all vic - to - rious of
nigh— His pres - ence we have; The great con - gre - ga - tion His
loud, and hon - or the Son; The prais - es of Je - sus the
power, all wis - dom and might; All hon - or and bless - ing, with

Je - sus ex - tol; His King-dom is glo-rious, He rules o - ver all.
tri-umph shall sing, As - crib-ing sal - va - tion to Je - sus our King.
an - gels pro - claim, Fall down on their fa - ces, and wor-ship the Lamb.
an - gels a - bove, And thanks nev-er ceas-ing, and in - fi - nite love. A - MEN.

Alternative tune, "Lyons," opposite page.

Let Us with a Gladsome Mind
28

From Psalm 136
John Milton, 1623; alt.

MONKLAND: 7. 7. 7. 7.
Anon., Manchester, 1824
Arr. by John B. Wilkes, 1861

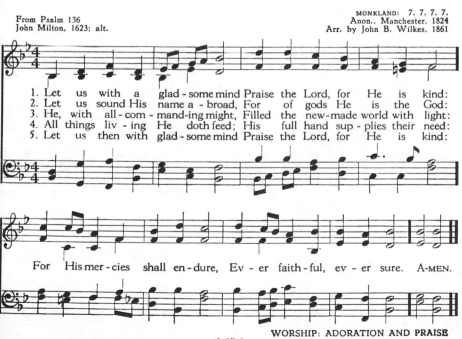

1. Let us with a glad - some mind Praise the Lord, for He is kind:
2. Let us sound His name a - broad, For of gods He is the God:
3. He, with all - com - mand-ing might, Filled the new-made world with light:
4. All things liv - ing He doth feed; His full hand sup - plies their need:
5. Let us then with glad - some mind Praise the Lord, for He is kind:

For His mer - cies shall en - dure, Ev - er faith - ful, ev - er sure. A - MEN.

WORSHIP: ADORATION AND PRAISE

[37]

29 — O Come and Sing Unto the Lord

(FIRST TUNE)

From Psalm 95
The Psalter, 1912; alt.

IRISH: C. M.
Melody from *A Collection of Hymns and Sacred Poems*, Dublin, 1749

1. O come and sing un-to the Lord, To Him our voi-ces raise;
2. Be-fore His pres-ence let us come With praise and thank-ful voice;
3. The Lord our God is King of Kings, A-bove all gods His throne;
4. To Him the spa-cious sea be-longs, He made its waves and tides;
5. O come, and bow-ing down to Him Our wor-ship let us bring;

Let us in our most joy-ful songs The Lord, our Sav-iour, praise.
Let us sing psalms to Him with grace, With grate-ful hearts re-joice.
The depths of earth are in His hand, The moun-tains are His own.
And by His hand the ris-ing land Was formed, and still a-bides.
Yea, let us kneel be-fore the Lord, Our Mak-er and our King. A-MEN.

29 — O Come and Sing Unto the Lord

(SECOND TUNE)

From Psalm 95
The Psalter, 1912; alt.

CHOPIN: C. M.
Isaac B. Woodbury (1819-1858)

1. O come and sing un-to the Lord, To Him our voi-ces raise;
2. Be-fore His pres-ence let us come With praise and thank-ful voice;
3. The Lord our God is King of Kings, A-bove all gods His throne;
4. To Him the spa-cious sea be-longs, He made its waves and tides;
5. O come, and bow-ing down to Him Our wor-ship let us bring;

Let us in our most joy-ful songs The Lord, our
Let us sing psalms to Him with grace, With grate-ful
The depths of earth are in His hand, The moun-tains
And by His hand the ris-ing land Was formed, and
Yea, let us kneel be-fore the Lord, Our Mak-er

O Come and Sing Unto the Lord

Sav - iour, praise, The Lord, our Sav - iour, praise.
hearts re - joice, With grate - ful hearts re - joice.
are His own, The moun-tains are His own.
still a - bides, Was formed, and still a - bides.
and our King, Our Mak - er and our King. A - MEN.

Angel Voices, Ever Singing

30

Francis Pott, 1861

ANGEL VOICES: 8. 5. 8. 5. 8. 7.
Arthur S. Sullivan, 1872

1. An - gel voi - ces, ev - er sing - ing Round Thy throne of light,
2. Lord, we know Thy love re - joi - ces O'er each work of Thine;
3. Here, great God, to - day we of - fer Of Thine own to Thee;
4. Hon - or, glo - ry, might, and mer - it, Thine shall ev - er be,

An - gel harps, for - ev - er ring - ing, Rest not day nor night;
Thou didst ears and hands and voi - ces For Thy praise com-bine;
And for Thine ac - cept - ance prof - fer, All un - wor - thi - ly,
Fa - ther, Son, and Ho - ly Spir - it, Bless - ed Trin - i - ty:

Thou - sands on - ly live to bless Thee, And con - fess Thee Lord of might.
Crafts-man's art and mu-sic's meas-ure For Thy pleas - ure didst de - sign.
Hearts and minds, and hands and voi-ces, In our choic - est mel - o - dy.
Of the best that Thou hast giv - en Earth and heav - en ren - der Thee. A - MEN.

Words copyright by the Proprietors of *Hymns Ancient and Modern*. Used by permission.

WORSHIP: ADORATION AND PRAISE

31 Praise, My Soul, the King of Heaven

From Psalm 103
Henry Francis Lyte, 1834; alt.

LAUDA ANIMA (BENEDIC ANIMA MEA): 8. 7. 8. 7. 8. 7.
John Goss, 1869

1. Praise, my soul, the King of heav - en; To His feet thy
2. Praise Him for His grace and fa - vor To our fa - thers
3. Fa - ther - like He tends and spares us; Well our fee - ble
4. An - gels, help us to a - dore Him; Ye be - hold Him

trib - ute bring; Ran - somed, healed, re - stored, for - giv - en,
in dis - tress; Praise Him still the same as ev - er,
frame He knows; In His hands He gen - tly bears us,
face to face; Sun and moon, bow down be - fore Him,

Ev - er - more His prais - es sing: Al - le - lu - ia!
Slow to chide, and swift to bless: Al - le - lu - ia!
Res - cues us from all our foes. Al - le - lu - ia!
Dwell - ers all in time and space. Al - le - lu - ia!

Al - le - lu - ia! Praise the ev - er - last - ing King.
Al - le - lu - ia! Glo - rious in His faith - ful - ness.
Al - le - lu - ia! Wide - ly yet His mer - cy flows.
Al - le - lu - ia! Praise with us the God of grace. A - MEN.

Alternative tune, "Regent Square," Hymn 168.

WORSHIP: ADORATION AND PRAISE

[40]

Praise, My Soul, the King of Heaven   31

ALTERNATIVE HARMONIZATION

LAUDA ANIMA (BENEDIC ANIMA MEA): 8. 7. 8. 7. 8. 7.
John Goss, 1869

This version may be used for one or more stanzas, the congregation and the choir singing the melody.

What Shall I Render to the Lord   32

From Psalm 116
The Psalter, 1912

LAMBETH: C. M.
Wilhelm A. F. Schulthes, 1871

1. What shall I ren - der to the Lord, What shall my of - fering be,
2. Sal - va - tion's cup my soul will take While to the Lord I pray,
3. Not light - ly does the Lord per - mit His cho - sen saints to die;
4. With - in His house, the house of prayer, My soul shall bless the Lord,

For all the gra - cious ben - e - fits He has be - stowed on me?
And with His peo - ple I will meet, My thank - ful vows to pay.
From death Thou hast de - liv - ered me, Thy serv - ant, Lord, am I.
And prais - es to His ho - ly name Let all His saints ac - cord.   A - MEN.

WORSHIP: ADORATION AND PRAISE

33 From All That Dwell Below the Skies

From Psalm 117
Isaac Watts. 1719

LASST UNS ERFREUEN: 8. 8. 4. 4. 8. 8. with Alleluias
Geistliche Kirchengesäng, Cologne. 1623

Unison

1. From all that dwell be - low the skies Let the Cre - a - tor's praise a -
2. In ev - ery land be - gin the song, To ev - ery land the strains be -
3. E - ter - nal are Thy mer - cies, Lord; E - ter - nal truth at - tends Thy

Harmony   *Unison*

rise: Al - le - lu - ia! Al - le - lu - ia! Let the Re - deem - er's
long: Al - le - lu - ia! Al - le - lu - ia! In cheer - ful sound all
word. Al - le - lu - ia! Al - le - lu - ia! Thy praise shall sound from

Harmony

name be sung Through ev - ery land, in ev - ery tongue. Al - le - lu - ia!
voi - ces raise And fill the world with joy - ful praise. Al - le - lu - ia!
shore to shore, Till suns shall rise and set no . more. Al - le - lu - ia!

Unison   *Harmony*

Al - le - lu - ia! Al - le - lu - ia! Al - le - lu - ia! Al - le - lu - ia!
Al - le - lu - ia! Al - le - lu - ia! Al - le - lu - ia! Al - le - lu - ia!
Al - le - lu - ia! Al - le - lu - ia! Al - le - lu - ia! Al - le - lu - ia! A - MEN.

Music from *The English Hymnal.* Used by permission of Oxford University Press.
Alternative tune. "Duke Street." Hymn 5. If this is used, omit "Alleluias."

WORSHIP: ADORATION AND PRAISE

Ye Watchers and Ye Holy Ones

34

Athelstan Riley, 1906

1 Ye watchers and ye holy ones,
  Bright seraphs, cherubim, and thrones,
    Raise the glad strain, Alleluia!
  Cry out, dominions, princedoms, powers,
  Virtues, archangels, angels' choirs,
Alleluia, Alleluia, Alleluia, Alleluia, Alleluia!

2 O higher than the cherubim,
  More glorious than the seraphim,
    Lead their praises, Alleluia!
  Thou bearer of the eternal Word,
  Most gracious, magnify the Lord,
Alleluia, Alleluia, Alleluia, Alleluia, Alleluia!

3 Respond, ye souls in endless rest,
  Ye patriarchs and prophets blest,
    Alleluia, Alleluia!
  Ye holy twelve, ye martyrs strong,
  All saints triumphant, raise the song,
Alleluia, Alleluia, Alleluia, Alleluia, Alleluia!

4 O friends, in gladness let us sing,
  Supernal anthems echoing,
    Alleluia, Alleluia!
  To God the Father, God the Son,
  And God the Spirit, Three in One,
Alleluia, Alleluia, Alleluia, Alleluia, Alleluia!
AMEN.

From *The English Hymnal.* Used by permission of Oxford University Press.
This hymn may be sung to the tune "Lasst uns erfreuen." on opposite page.

All Ye That Fear God's Holy Name

35

From Psalm 22
The Psalter, 1912; alt.

PARK STREET: L. M.
Frederick M. A. Venua, c. 1810

1. All ye that fear God's ho - ly name, His glo - ry tell, His
2. The suf-fering one He has not spurned Who un - to Him for
3. O Lord, Thy good - ness makes me raise A - mid Thy peo - ple
4. For all the meek Thou wilt pro - vide, They shall be fed and

praise pro - claim; Ye chil - dren of His cho - sen race, Stand ye in
suc - cor turned; From him He has not hid His face, But an-swered
songs of praise; Be - fore all them that fear Thee, now I wor - ship
sat - is - fied; All they that seek the Lord shall live And nev - er-

awe be - fore His face, Stand ye in awe be - fore His face.
his re - quest in grace, But an-swered his re - quest in grace.
Thee and pay my vow, I wor-ship Thee and pay my vow.
end - ing prais - es give, And nev - er - end - ing prais - es give. A - MEN.

WORSHIP: ADORATION AND PRAISE

36 Praise Ye the Lord, for It Is Good

From Psalm 147
The Psalter, 1912

MINERVA: C. M. D.
John H. Stockton (1813-1877)
Har. for this book, 1953

1. Praise ye the Lord, for it is good To sing un - to our God;
2. Our Lord is great, He calls by name And counts the stars of night;
3. No hu - man might, no earth - ly pride, De - lights the Lord a - bove;

'Tis right and pleas - ant for His saints To tell His praise a - broad.
His wis - dom is un - search - a - ble, And won - drous is His might.
In them that fear Him He de - lights, In them that trust His love.

The Lord our God builds up His Church, He seeks her wan - dering sons;
The Lord up - holds the poor and meek, He brings the wick - ed low;
O Zi - on, praise the Lord thy God, His won - drous love con - fess;

He binds their wounds and gent - ly heals The bro - ken-heart - ed ones.
Sing praise to Him and give Him thanks And all His good-ness show.
He is thy glo - ry and thy strength, He will thy chil - dren bless. A-MEN.

Music copyright, 1955, by John Ribble.

WORSHIP: ADORATION AND PRAISE

[44]

O Sing a New Song to the Lord 37

SONG 67 (Gibbons): C. M.
Orlando Gibbons (1583-1625)
Arr. by Henry Smart (1813-1879)

From Psalm 96
Scottish Psalter, 1650; alt.

1. O sing a new song to the Lord: Sing, all the earth, to God,
2. Great hon-or is be-fore His face, And maj-es-ty di-vine;
3. Do ye as-cribe un-to the Lord, Of peo-ple ev-ery tribe,
4. Give ye the glo-ry to the Lord That to His name is due;
5. In beau-ty of His ho-li-ness, O do the Lord a-dore;

To God sing, bless His name, show still His sav-ing health a-broad.
Strength is with-in His ho-ly place, And there doth beau-ty shine.
Glo-ry do ye un-to the Lord And might-y power as-cribe.
Come ye in-to His courts, and bring An of-fer-ing with you.
Like-wise let all the earth through-out Trem-ble His face be-fore. A-MEN.

The Earth, with All That Dwell Therein 38

BOARDMAN: C. M.
Arr. from L. Devereux

From Psalm 24
The Psalter, 1912

1. The earth, with all that dwell there-in, With all its wealth un-told,
2. What man shall stand be-fore the Lord On Zi-on's ho-ly hill?
3. Ye ev-er-last-ing doors, give way, Lift up your heads, ye gates!
4. Who is this glo-rious King that comes To claim His right-ful throne?

Be-longs to God, who found-ed it Up-on the seas of old.
The clean of hand, the pure of heart, The just who does His will.
For now, be-hold, to en-ter in The King of glo-ry waits.
The Lord of Hosts, He is the King Of glo-ry, God a-lone. A-MEN.

WORSHIP: ADORATION AND PRAISE

[45]

39 Come, Ye People, Rise and Sing

BOUNDLESS MERCY: 7. 6. 7. 6. D.
From *Union Harmony*
Har. by Hilton Rufty, 1934

Cyril Argentine Alington, b. 1872

1. Come, ye peo-ple, rise and sing Praise to God, who made you,
2. Praise we God the Fa-ther's name For our world's cre-a-tion,
3. Praise we God the on-ly Son, Who in mer-cy sought us;
4. Grant us, Ho-ly Ghost, we pray, More and more to know Him,
5. Fa-ther, Son, and Ho-ly Ghost, Help us to a-dore Thee,

And to heaven's e-ter-nal King Bring the prayers He bade you;
And His sav-ing health pro-claim Un-to ev-ery na-tion;
Born to save a world un-done, Out of death He brought us;
More and more and ev-ery day In our lives to show Him;
Till, with all the an-gel host, Low we fall be-fore Thee;

Bring your praise for mer-cies past, All His love con-fess-ing,
Till, His name by all con-fessed, Ev-ery heart en-throne Him,
Here a-while He showed His love, Suf-fered un-com-plain-ing,
That with hearts by Thee made brave, Strong and wise and ten-der,
Till, through-out our earth-ly days Guid-ed, loved, for-giv-en,

And on life, while life shall last, Ask your Fa-ther's bless-ing.
And from farth-est east and west All His chil-dren own Him.
Now He pleads for us a-bove, Risen, as-cend-ed, reign-ing!
We, with all the powers we have, Serv-ice meet may ren-der.
We can blend our songs of praise With the song of heav-en! A-MEN.

Words copyright by C. A. Alington. Used by permission. Music copyright, 1934, by J. Fischer & Bro. Used by permission.

WORSHIP: ADORATION AND PRAISE

Open Now Thy Gates of Beauty

Benjamin Schmolck, 1732
Trans. by Catherine Winkworth, 1863; alt.

UNSER HERRSCHER (NEANDER): 8. 7. 8. 7. 7. 7.
Joachim Neander, 1680
Descant by Geoffrey Shaw (1879-1943)

Descant for Stanza 3

1. O - pen now thy gates of beau - ty, Zi - on, let me en - ter there,
2. Gra - cious God, I come be - fore Thee, Come Thou al - so down to me;
3. Speak, O Lord, and I will hear Thee, Let Thy will be done in - deed;

Where my soul in joy - ful du - ty Waits for Him who an - swers prayer:
Where we find Thee and a - dore Thee, There a heaven on earth must be:
May I un - dis-turbed draw near Thee While Thou dost Thy peo - ple feed.

O how bless-ed is this place, Filled with sol - ace, light, and grace!
To my heart O en - ter Thou, Let it be Thy tem - ple now.
Here of life the foun - tain flows, Here is balm for all our woes. A-MEN.

Descant used by permission of Novello & Co., Ltd.

WORSHIP: ADORATION AND PRAISE

41 When Morning Gilds the Skies

Anon., German. c. 1800
Trans. by Edward Caswall, 1853. 1858

LAUDES DOMINI: 6. 6. 6. 6. 6. 6.
Joseph Barnby, 1868

1. When morn-ing gilds the skies, My heart a-wak-ing cries,
2. The night be-comes as day When from the heart we say,
3. Ye na-tions of man-kind, In this your con-cord find,
4. Be this, while life is mine, My can-ti-cle di-vine,

May Je-sus Christ be praised: A-like at work and prayer
May Je-sus Christ be praised: The powers of dark-ness fear
May Je-sus Christ be praised: Let all the earth a-round
May Je-sus Christ be praised: Be this th'e-ter-nal song,

To Je-sus I re-pair; May Je-sus Christ be praised!
When this sweet chant they hear, May Je-sus Christ be praised!
Ring joy-ous with the sound, May Je-sus Christ be praised!
Through all the a-ges long, May Je-sus Christ be praised! A-MEN.

42 As the Sun Doth Daily Rise

Trans. from the Latin by O. B. C.
Alt. by Horatio Nelson, 1864

INNOCENTS: 7. 7. 7. 7.
The Parish Choir, 1850

1. As the sun doth dai-ly rise, Bright-ening all the morn-ing skies,
2. Day by day pro-vide us food, For from Thee come all things good;
3. Be our Guard in sin and strife; Be the Lead-er of our life;
4. Quick-ened by the Spir-it's grace All Thy ho-ly will to trace

WORSHIP: MORNING

As the Sun Doth Daily Rise

So to Thee with one ac - cord Lift we up our hearts, O Lord!
Strength un - to our souls af - ford From Thy liv - ing Bread, O Lord!
Lest from Thee we stray a - broad, Stay our way-ward feet, O Lord!
While we dai - ly search Thy Word, Wis - dom true im - part, O Lord! A-MEN.

Father, We Praise Thee, Now the Night Is Over 43

Gregory I (540-604)
Trans. by Percy Dearmer, 1906

CHRISTE SANCTORUM: 11. 11. 11. 5.
French church melody, 1782
In La Feillée's *Méthode du plain-chant*, 1808

1. Fa - ther, we praise Thee, now the night is o - ver; Ac - tive and
2. Mon - arch of all things, fit us for Thy man - sions; Ban - ish our
3. All ho - ly Fa - ther, Son and e - qual Spir - it, Trin - i - ty

watch - ful, stand we all be - fore Thee; Sing - ing, we of - fer
weak - ness, health and whole-ness send - ing; Bring us to heav - en,
bless - ed, send us Thy sal - va - tion; Thine is the glo - ry,

prayer and med - i - ta - tion: Thus we a - dore Thee.
where Thy saints u - nit - ed Joy with - out end - ing.
gleam - ing and re - sound - ing Through all cre - a - tion. A - MEN.

Words from *The English Hymnal*. Used by permission of Oxford University Press. Music from *The Harvard University Hymn Book*. Used by permission of Harvard University Press.

WORSHIP: MORNING

[49]

44   Come, My Soul, Thou Must Be Waking

Friedrich R. L. von Canitz, 1700
Trans. by Henry J. Buckoll, 1838

HAYDN: 8. 4. 7. 8. 4. 7.
Arr. from Franz Joseph Haydn, 1791

1. Come, my soul, thou must be waking; Now is break - ing O'er the earth an - oth - er day: Come to Him who made this splen - dor; See thou ren - der All thy fee - ble powers can pay.

2. Thou, too, hail the light re - turn - ing; Read - y burn - ing Be the in - cense of thy powers; For the night is safe - ly end - ed, God hath tend - ed With His care thy help - less hours.

3. Pray that He may pros - per ev - er Each en - deav - or, When thine aim is good and true; But that He may ev - er thwart thee, And con - vert thee, When thou e - vil wouldst pur - sue.

4. On - ly God's free gifts a - buse not, Light re - fuse not, But His Spir - it's voice o - bey; Thou with Him shalt dwell, be - hold - ing Light en - fold - ing All things in un - cloud - ed day. A - MEN.

WORSHIP: MORNING

New Every Morning Is the Love

45

John Keble, 1827

MELCOMBE: L. M.
Samuel Webbe, 1782

1. New ev - ery morn-ing is the love Our wak-ening and up - ris - ing prove;
2. New mer - cies, each re - turn-ing day, Hov - er a - round us while we pray;
3. If, on our dai - ly course, our mind Be set to hal - low all we find,
4. On - ly, O Lord, in Thy dear love, Fit us for per - fect rest a - bove,

Thru sleep and dark-ness safe-ly brought, Re-stored to life and power and thought.
New per - ils past, new sins for-given, New thoughts of God, new hopes of heaven.
New treas-ures still, of count-less price, God will pro - vide for sac - ri - fice.
And help us, this and ev - ery day, To live more near - ly as we pray. A-MEN.

O Splendor of God's Glory Bright

46

PUER NOBIS NASCITUR: L. M.
Composed or adapted by Michael Praetorius (1571-1621)
Har. for *Songs of Praise*, 1925

Ambrose of Milan (340-397)
Trans. composite

1. O Splen-dor of God's glo - ry bright, From light e - ter - nal bring-ing light;
2. Con-firm our will to do the right, And keep our hearts from en-vy's blight;
3. O joy - ful be the pass-ing day With thoughts as clear as morn-ing's ray,
4. Dawn's glo-ry gilds the earth and skies; Do Thou, our per - fect Morn, a - rise;

Thou Light of life, light's liv-ing Spring, True Day, all days il - lu - min - ing.
Let faith her ea - ger fires re - new, And hate the false, and love the true.
With faith like noon-tide shin-ing bright, Our souls un-shad-owed by the night.
The Fa-ther's help His chil-dren claim, And sing the Fa-ther's glo-rious name. A-MEN.

Music from *Songs of Praise*, Enlarged Edition. Used by permission of Oxford University Press.

WORSHIP: MORNING

47 Christ, Whose Glory Fills the Skies

Charles Wesley, 1740

LUX PRIMA: 7. 7. 7. 7. 7. 7.
Charles F. Gounod, 1872

1. Christ, whose glo - ry fills the skies; Christ, the true, the
2. Dark and cheer - less is the morn Un - ac - com - pa -
3. Vis - it, then, this soul of mine; Pierce the gloom of

on - ly Light, Sun of Right - eous - ness, a - rise,
nied by Thee; Joy - less is the day's re - turn
sin and grief; Fill me, Ra - dian - cy di - vine;

Tri - umph o'er the shades of night; Day - spring from on
Till Thy mer - cy's beams I see; Till they in - ward
Scat - ter all my un - be - lief; More and more Thy -

high, be near; Day - star, in my heart ap - pear.
light im - part, Glad my eyes and warm my heart.
self dis - play, Shin - ing to the per - fect day. A - MEN.

WORSHIP; MORNING

[52]

Hear My Words, O Gracious Lord 48

From Psalm 5
The Psalter, 1912; alt., 1950

INNOCENTS: 7. 7. 7. 7.
The Parish Choir, 1850

1. Hear my words, O gra-cious Lord, To my thoughts at-ten-tive be;
2. With the morn-ing light, O Lord, Thou shalt hear my voice a-rise,
3. Thou art ho-ly, O my God, Thou de-light-est not in sin;
4. In the full-ness of Thy grace To Thy house I will re-pair;

Hear my cry, my King, my God, I will make my prayer to Thee.
And ex-pect-ant I will bring Prayer as morn-ing sac-ri-fice.
E-vil shall not dwell with Thee, Nor the proud Thy fa-vor win.
Bow-ing toward Thy ho-ly place, In Thy fear will wor-ship there. A-MEN.

When Morning Lights the Eastern Skies 49

From Psalm 143
The Psalter, 1912

ST. STEPHEN: C. M.
William Jones, 1789

1. When morn-ing lights the east-ern skies, O Lord, Thy mer-cy show;
2. Teach me the way that I should go; I lift my soul to Thee;
3. Thou art my God; to Thee I pray: Teach me Thy will to heed;
4. For Thy name's sake, O gra-cious Lord, Re-vive my soul and bless,

On Thee a-lone my hope re-lies, Let me Thy kind-ness know.
For ref-uge from my cru-el foe To Thee, O Lord, I flee.
And in the right and per-fect way May Thy good Spir-it lead.
And in Thy faith-ful-ness and love Re-deem me from dis-tress. A-MEN.

WORSHIP: MORNING

[53]

50 Awake, My Soul, and with the Sun

Thomas Ken, 1695, 1709

MORNING HYMN: L. M.
François H. Barthélémon, 1785

1. A - wake, my soul, and with the sun Thy dai - ly stage of du - ty run:
2. Lord, I my vows to Thee re - new: Dis - perse my sins as morn-ing dew,
3. Di - rect, con - trol, sug - gest, this day, All I de - sign, or do, or say;
4. Praise God from whom all bless-ings flow; Praise Him, all crea-tures here be - low;

Shake off dull sloth, and joy-ful rise To pay thy morn-ing sac - ri - fice.
Guard my first springs of thought and will, And with Thy - self my spir - it fill.
That all my powers, with all their might, In Thy sole glo - ry may u - nite.
Praise Him a - bove, ye heaven-ly host: Praise Fa - ther, Son, and Ho - ly Ghost. A-MEN.

51 Now the Day Is Over

Sabine Baring-Gould, 1865

MERRIAL: 6. 5. 6. 5.
Joseph Barnby, 1868

1. Now the day is o - ver, Night is draw - ing nigh,
2. Je - sus, give the wea - ry Calm and sweet re - pose;
3. Grant to lit - tle chil - dren Vi - sions bright of Thee;
4. Com - fort ev - ery suf - ferer Watch - ing late in pain;
5. Through the long night watch - es, May Thine an - gels spread
6. When the morn - ing wak - ens, Then may I a - rise

Shad - ows of the eve - ning Steal a - cross the sky.
With Thy ten - derest bless - ing May mine eye - lids close.
Guard the sail - ors toss - ing On the deep blue sea.
Those who plan some e - vil From their sin re - strain.
Their white wings a - bove me, Watch - ing round my bed.
Pure, and fresh, and sin - less In Thy ho - ly eyes. A - MEN.

Words copyright by J. Curwen & Sons, Ltd. Used by permission.

On the Good and Faithful

From Psalm 4
The Psalter, 1912

PENITENCE: 6. 5. 6. 5. D.
Spencer Lane. 1879

1. On the good and faith - ful God has set His love;
2. Lay up - on God's al - tar Good and lov - ing deeds,
3. In God's love a - bid - ing, I have joy and peace

When they call He sends them Bless - ings from a - bove.
And in all things trust Him To sup - ply your needs.
More than all the wick - ed, Though their wealth in - crease.

Stand in awe, and sin not, Bid your heart be still;
Anx - ious and de - spair - ing, Man - y walk in night;
In His care con - fid - ing, I will sweet - ly sleep,

Through the si - lent watch - es Think up - on His will.
But to those that fear Him God will send His light.
For the Lord, my Sav - iour, Will in safe - ty keep. A-MEN.

For lower key, see Hymn 394.

WORSHIP: EVENING

53 Now God Be with Us, for the Night Is Closing

Petrus Herbert, 1566
Trans. by Catherine Winkworth, 1863

FLEMMING: 11. 11. 11. 5.
Friedrich F. Flemming, 1811

1. Now God be with us, for the night is clos-ing: The light and
2. Let ho-ly thoughts be ours when sleep o'er-takes us, Our ear-liest
3. We have no ref-uge, none on earth to aid us, Save Thee, O
4. Fa-ther, Thy name be praised, Thy King-dom giv-en, Thy will be

dark-ness are of His dis-pos-ing, And 'neath His shad-ow
thoughts be Thine when morn-ing wakes us, All day serve Thee, in
Fa-ther, who Thine own hast made us; But Thy dear pres-ence
done on earth as 'tis in heav-en; Keep us in life, for-

here to rest we yield us, For He will shield us.
all that we are do-ing, Thy praise pur-su-ing.
will not leave them lone-ly Who seek Thee on-ly.
give our sins, de-liv-er Us now and ev-er! A-MEN.

54 Saviour, Breathe an Evening Blessing

James Edmeston, 1820

EVENING PRAYER (Stebbins): 8. 7. 8. 7.
George C. Stebbins, 1878

1. Sav-iour, breathe an eve-ning bless-ing, Ere re-pose our spir-its seal;
2. Though de-struc-tion walk a-round us, Though the ar-row past us fly,
3. Though the night be dark and drear-y, Dark-ness can-not hide from Thee;
4. Should swift death this night o'er-take us, And our couch be-come our tomb,

WORSHIP: EVENING

[56]

Saviour, Breathe an Evening Blessing

Sin and want we come con-fess-ing: Thou canst save, and Thou canst heal.
An-gel guards from Thee sur-round us: We are safe if Thou art nigh.
Thou art He who, nev-er wea-ry, Watch-est where Thy peo-ple be.
May the morn in heaven a-wake us, Clad in light and death-less bloom. A-MEN.

At Even, When the Sun Was Set

55

ANGELUS: L. M.
Georg Joseph
Heilige Seelenlust, 1657

Henry Twells, 1868

1. At e-ven, when the sun was set, The sick, O
2. Once more 'tis e-ven-tide, and we, Op-pressed with
3. O Sav-iour Christ, our woes dis-pel: For some are
4. O Sav-iour Christ, Thou too art man; Thou hast been
5. Thy touch has still its an-cient power; No word from

Lord, a-round Thee lay; O in what di-vers pains they met!
var-ious ills, draw near: What if Thy form we can-not see?
sick, and some are sad, And some have nev-er loved Thee well,
trou-bled, tempt-ed, tried; Thy kind but search-ing glance can scan
Thee can fruit-less fall: Hear in this sol-emn eve-ning hour,

O with what joy they went a-way!
We know and feel that Thou art here.
And some have lost the love they had.
The ver-y wounds that shame would hide.
And in Thy mer-cy heal us all. A-MEN.

WORSHIP: EVENING

56 Sun of My Soul, Thou Saviour Dear

John Keble, 1820

HURSLEY: L. M.

Katholisches Gesangbuch, Vienna, c. 1774

1. Sun of my soul, Thou Sav-iour dear, It is not night if Thou be near;
2. When the soft dews of kind-ly sleep My wea-ried eye-lids gen-tly steep,
3. A - bide with me from morn till eve, For with-out Thee I can-not live;
4. Watch by the sick; en-rich the poor With bless-ings from Thy bound-less store;
5. Come near and bless us when we wake, Ere through the world our way we take,

O may no earth-born cloud a-rise To hide Thee from Thy serv-ant's eyes.
Be my last thought, how sweet to rest For-ev-er on my Sav-iour's breast.
A - bide with me when night is nigh, For with-out Thee I dare not die.
Be ev-ery mourn-er's sleep to-night, Like in-fants' slum-bers, pure and light.
Till in the o - cean of Thy love We lose our-selves in heaven a-bove. A-MEN.

57 Before the Day Draws Near Its Ending

John Ellerton, 1880

SUNSET: 9. 8. 9. 8.

George Gilbert Stocks, 1924

Unison

1. Be - fore the day draws near its end-ing, And eve-ning steals o'er earth and sky,
2. O Light all clear, O Truth most ho - ly, O bound-less Mer-cy par-doning all,
3. When we no more on earth a-dore Thee, And oth-ers wor-ship here in turn,

Harmony

Once more to Thee our hymns as-cend-ing Shall speak Thy prais-es, Lord Most High.
Be - fore Thy feet, a-bashed and low-ly, With one last prayer Thy chil-dren fall.
O may we sing that song be-fore Thee, Which none but Thy re-deemed can learn. A-MEN.

Music copyright by the Repton School. Used by permission.

WORSHIP: EVENING

God, That Madest Earth and Heaven

58

Stanza 1, Reginald Heber. 1827
Stanza 2, William Mercer. 1864
Stanza 3, Richard Whately (1787-1863)

AR HYD Y NOS: 8. 4. 8. 4. 8. 8. 8. 4.
Traditional Welsh melody
Har. by L. O. Emerson, 1906

1. God, that mad-est earth and heav-en, Dark-ness and light;
2. And when morn a-gain shall call us To run life's way,
3. Guard us wak-ing, guard us sleep-ing, And when we die,

Who the day for toil hast giv-en, For rest the night;
May we still, what-e'er be-fall us, Thy will o-bey.
May we in Thy might-y keep-ing All peace-ful lie;

May Thine an-gel guards de-fend us, Slum-ber sweet Thy mer-cy send us;
From the power of e-vil hide us, In the nar-row path-way guide us,
When the last dread call shall wake us, Do not Thou, our God, for-sake us,

Ho-ly dreams and hopes at-tend us, This live-long night.
Nor Thy smile be e'er de-nied us The live-long day.
But to reign in glo-ry take us With Thee on high. A-MEN.

WORSHIP: EVENING

[59]

59 The Day Thou Gavest, Lord, Is Ended

(FIRST TUNE)

John Ellerton, 1870

COMMANDMENTS: 9. 8. 9. 8.
Louis Bourgeois, 1543

1. The day Thou gav - est, Lord, is end - ed, The dark-ness falls at Thy be - hest; To Thee our morn - ing hymns as - cend - ed, Thy praise shall hal - low now our rest.
2. We thank Thee that Thy Church un - sleep - ing, While earth rolls on - ward in - to light, Through all the world her watch is keep - ing, And rests not now by day or night.
3. As o'er each con - ti - nent and is - land The dawn leads on an - oth - er day, The voice of prayer is nev - er si - lent, Nor dies the strain of praise a - way.
4. The sun that bids us rest is wak - ing Our breth - ren 'neath the west - ern sky, And hour by hour fresh lips are mak - ing Thy won - drous do - ings heard on high.
5. So be it, Lord; Thy throne shall nev - er, Like earth's proud em-pires, pass a - way; Thy King - dom stands, and grows for - ev - er Till all Thy crea - tures own Thy sway. A - MEN.

59 The Day Thou Gavest, Lord, Is Ended

(SECOND TUNE)

John Ellerton, 1870

ST. CLEMENT: 9. 8. 9. 8.
Clement C. Scholefield, 1874

1. The day Thou gav - est, Lord, is end - ed, The dark - ness
2. We thank Thee that Thy Church un - sleep - ing, While earth rolls
3. As o'er each con - ti - nent and is - land The dawn leads
4. The sun that bids us rest is wak - ing Our breth - ren
5. So be it, Lord; Thy throne shall nev - er, Like earth's proud

The Day Thou Gavest, Lord, Is Ended

falls at Thy be - hest; To Thee our morn - ing hymns as -
on - ward in - to light, Through all the world her watch is
on an - oth - er day, The voice of prayer is nev - er
'neath the west - ern sky, And hour by hour fresh lips are
em - pires, pass a - way; Thy King - dom stands, and grows for -

cend - ed, Thy praise shall hal - low now our rest.
keep - ing, And rests not now by day or night.
si - lent, Nor dies the strain of praise a - way.
mak - ing Thy won - drous do - ings heard on high.
ev - er, Till all Thy crea - tures own Thy sway. A - MEN.

Softly Now the Light of Day 60

George W. Doane, 1824

SEYMOUR: 7. 7. 7. 7.
Arr. from Carl M. von Weber, 1826

1. Soft - ly now the light of day Fades up - on my sight a - way;
2. Thou, whose all - per - vad - ing eye Nought es - capes, with - out, with - in,
3. Soon for me the light of day Shall for - ev - er pass a - way;
4. Thou who, sin - less, yet hast known All of man's in - fir - mi - ty;

Free from care, from la - bor free, Lord, I would com - mune with Thee.
Par - don each in - fir - mi - ty, O - pen fault, and se - cret sin.
Then, from sin and sor - row free, Take me, Lord, to dwell with Thee.
Then, from Thine e - ter - nal throne, Je - sus, look with pity - ing eye. A - MEN.

WORSHIP: EVENING

[61]

61   O Gladsome Light

Greek, third century
Trans. by Robert Bridges, 1899

NUNC DIMITTIS: 6. 6. 7. 6. 6. 7.
Melody by Louis Bourgeois, 1549
Har. by Claude Goudimel

1. O glad-some light, O grace Of God the Fa-ther's face, Th'e-
2. Now, ere day fad - eth quite, We see the eve-ning light, Our
3. To Thee of right be - longs All praise of ho - ly songs, O

ter - nal splen - dor wear - ing; Ce - les - tial, ho - ly, blest, Our
wont - ed hymn out - pour - ing; Fa - ther of might un - known, Thee,
Son of God, Life - giv - er; Thee, there - fore, O Most High, The

Sav - iour Je - sus Christ, Joy - ful in Thine ap - pear - ing.
His in - car - nate Son, And Ho - ly Spirit a - dor - ing.
world doth glo - ri - fy, And shall ex - alt for - ev - er. A - MEN.

Words from *The Yattendon Hymnal*, edited by Robert Bridges and H. Ellis Wooldridge. Used by permission of the Clarendon Press, Oxford.

62   Again, as Evening's Shadow Falls

Samuel Longfellow (1819-1892)

ABENDS: L. M.
Herbert S. Oakeley (1830-1903)

1. A - gain, as ev-ening's shad-ow falls, We gath-er in these hal-lowed walls;
2. May strug-gling hearts that seek re - lease Here find the rest of God's own peace;
3. O God, our light! to Thee we bow; With-in all shad-ows stand-est Thou;
4. Life's tu-mult we must meet a - gain, We can-not at the shrine re-main;

WORSHIP: EVENING

[62]

Again, as Evening's Shadow Falls

And ves-per hymn and ves - per prayer Rise min-gling on the ho - ly air.
And, strengthened here by hymn and prayer, Lay down the bur-den and the care.
Give deep-er calm than night can bring; Give sweet-er songs than lips can sing.
But in the spir - it's se - cret cell May hymn and prayer for-ev-er dwell. A-MEN.

Alternative tune, "Canonbury," Hymn 298.

All Praise to Thee, My God, This Night   63

Thomas Ken. 1695, 1709

TALLIS' CANON: L. M.
Thomas Tallis, c. 1567

1. All praise to Thee, my God, this night, For all the bless-ings of the light!
2. For-give me, Lord, for Thy dear Son, The ill that I this day have done,
3. Teach me to live, that I may dread The grave as lit - tle as my bed;
4. O may my soul on Thee re - pose, And with sweet sleep mine eye - lids close;
5. Praise God, from whom all bless-ings flow; Praise Him, all crea-tures here be - low;

Keep me, O keep me, King of kings, Be-neath Thine own al - might-y wings!
That with the world, my - self, and Thee, I, ere I sleep, at peace may be.
Teach me to die, that so I may Rise glo - rious at the Judg-ment Day.
Sleep that may me more vig-orous make To serve my God when I a - wake.
Praise Him a - bove, ye heaven-ly host; Praise Fa-ther, Son, and Ho - ly Ghost. A-MEN.

*Canon begins here.   [63]   WORSHIP: EVENING

64   Abide with Me: Fast Falls the Eventide

Henry F. Lyte. 1820

EVENTIDE: 10. 10. 10. 10.
William H. Monk. 1861

1. A - bide with me: fast falls the e - ven - tide;
2. Swift to its close ebbs out life's lit - tle day;
3. I need Thy pres - ence ev - ery pass - ing hour;
4. I fear no foe, with Thee at hand to bless:
5. Hold Thou Thy cross be - fore my clos - ing eyes;

The dark - ness deep - ens; Lord, with me a - bide!
Earth's joys grow dim, its glo - ries pass a - way;
What but Thy grace can foil the tempt - er's power?
Ills have no weight, and tears no bit - ter - ness.
Shine through the gloom and point me to the skies:

When oth - er help - ers fail, and com - forts flee,
Change and de - cay in all a - round I see.
Who, like Thy - self, my guide and stay can be?
Where is death's sting? Where, grave, thy vic - to - ry?
Heaven's morn - ing breaks, and earth's vain shad - ows flee;

Help of the help - less, O a - bide with me.
O Thou, who chang - est not, a - bide with me.
Through cloud and sun - shine, Lord, a - bide with me.
I tri - umph still, if Thou a - bide with me.
In life, in death, O Lord, a - bide with me. A - MEN.

WORSHIP: EVENING

[64]

Day Is Dying in the West

65

Mary A. Lathbury, 1877

CHAUTAUQUA (EVENING PRAISE): 7. 7. 7. 7. 4.
William F. Sherwin, 1877

1. Day is dy - ing in the west; Heaven is touch - ing
2. Lord of life, be - neath the dome Of the u - ni -
3. When for - ev - er from our sight Pass the stars, the

earth with rest: Wait and wor - ship while the night
verse, Thy home, Gath - er us who seek Thy face
day, the night, Lord of an - gels, on our eyes

Sets her eve - ning lamps a - light Through all the sky.
To the fold of Thy em - brace, For Thou art nigh.
Let e - ter - nal morn - ing rise, And shad - ows end.

REFRAIN

Ho - ly, ho - ly, ho - ly Lord God of Hosts! Heaven and earth are full of Thee!

Heaven and earth are prais - ing Thee, O Lord Most High! A - MEN.

Words and music used by permission of the Chautauqua Institution, Chautauqua, New York.

WORSHIP: EVENING

66   Now Woods and Wolds Are Sleeping

INNSBRUCK: **7. 7. 6. 7. 7. 8.**

Paul Gerhardt (1607-1676)
Trans. by George R. Woodward, 1910

Melody ascribed to Heinrich Isaak, 1539
Har. by Johann Sebastian Bach (1685-1750)

1. Now woods and wolds are sleep-ing, And dark-ness fast is
2. Ye al-so, O my dear-est, My friends and kin-dred

creep-ing O'er byre, hearth, and hall; But thou, my
near-est, God rest you safe from harm! His an-gel

soul, ere slum-ber, For bless-ings pass-ing
hosts at-tend ye, Their gold-en shields de-

num-ber Ex-alt the Giv-er of them all.
fend ye, From night-ly dan-ger and a-larm. A-MEN.

Words used by permission of J. Meredith Tatton, copyright owner, and Messrs. Schott & Co., Ltd.

WORSHIP: EVENING

Now, on Land and Sea Descending

67

Samuel Longfellow, 1859; alt.

VESPER HYMN: 8. 7. 8. 7. 8. 6. 8. 7.
Dimitri S. Bortniansky, 1818

1. Now, on land and sea de-scend-ing, Brings the night its peace pro-found;
2. Soon as dies the sun-set glo-ry, Stars of heaven shine out a-bove,
3. Now, our wants and bur-dens leav-ing To His care who cares for all,
4. As the dark-ness deep-ens o'er us, Lo! e-ter-nal stars a-rise;

Let our ves-per hymn be blend-ing With the ho-ly calm a-round.
Tell-ing still the an-cient sto-ry— Their Cre-a-tor's change-less love.
Cease we fear-ing, cease we griev-ing: At His touch our bur-dens fall.
Hope and faith and love rise glo-rious, Shin-ing in the spir-it's skies.

Ju-bi-la-te! Ju-bi-la-te! Ju-bi-la-te! A-men!

Let our ves-per hymn be blend-ing With the ho-ly calm a-round.
Tell-ing still the an-cient sto-ry— Their Cre-a-tor's change-less love.
Cease we fear-ing, cease we griev-ing: At His touch our bur-dens fall.
Hope and faith and love rise glo-rious, Shin-ing in the spir-it's skies. A-MEN.

WORSHIP: EVENING

[67]

68 When in the Night I Meditate

From Psalm 16
The Psalter, 1912

MAITLAND: C. M.
George N. Allen (1812-1877)

1. When in the night I med - i - tate On mer - cies mul - ti - plied,
2. For - ev - er in my thought the Lord Be - fore my face shall stand;
3. My in - most be - ing thrills with joy And glad - ness fills my breast;
4. I know that I shall not be left For - got - ten in the grave,
5. The path of life Thou show - est me; Of joy a bound - less store

My grate - ful heart in - spires my tongue To bless the Lord, my Guide.
Se - cure, un - moved, I shall re - main, With Him at my right hand.
Be - cause on Him my trust is stayed, My flesh in hope shall rest.
And from cor - rup - tion, Thou, O Lord, Thy ho - ly one wilt save.
Is ev - er found at Thy right hand, And pleas - ures ev - er - more. A-MEN.

WORSHIP: EVENING

69 This Is the Day the Lord Hath Made

From Psalm 118
Isaac Watts, 1719

ARLINGTON: C. M.
Thomas A. Arne, 1762

1. This is the day the Lord hath made; He calls the hours His own;
2. To - day He rose and left the dead, And Sa - tan's em - pire fell;
3. Ho - san - na to th' a - noint - ed King, To Da - vid's ho - ly Son!
4. Ho - san - na in the high - est strains The Church on earth can raise!

Let heaven re - joice, let earth be glad, And praise sur - round the throne.
To - day the saints His tri - umphs spread, And all His won - ders tell.
Help us, O Lord; de - scend and bring Sal - va - tion from the throne.
The high - est heavens in which He reigns Shall give Him no - bler praise. A-MEN.

WORSHIP: THE LORD'S DAY

[68]

O Day of Rest and Gladness

70

MENDEBRAS: 7. 6. 7. 6. D.
Old German melody
Arr. by Lowell Mason, 1839

Christopher Wordsworth, 1862

1. O day of rest and glad-ness, O day of joy and light,
2. On thee, at the Cre - a - tion, The light first had its birth;
3. New gra - ces ev - er gain-ing From this our day of rest,

O balm of care and sad-ness, Most beau - ti - ful, most bright;
On thee, for our sal - va - tion, Christ rose from depths of earth;
We reach the rest re - main-ing To spir - its of the blest.

On thee the high and low - ly, Through a - ges joined in tune,
On thee our Lord, vic - to - rious, The Spir - it sent from heaven;
To Ho - ly Ghost be prais - es, To Fa - ther, and to Son;

Sing ho - ly, ho - ly, ho - ly, To the great God Tri - une.
And thus on thee, most glo - rious, A tri - ple light was given.
The Church her voice up - rais - es To Thee, blest Three in One. A-MEN.

WORSHIP: THE LORD'S DAY

[69]

The Glorious Gates of Righteousness

From Psalm 118
The Psalter, 1912; alt.

ZERAH: C. M.
Lowell Mason, 1837

1. The glo - rious gates of right - eous-ness Throw o - pen un - to me,
2. This is Thy tem - ple gate, O Lord, The just shall en - ter there;
3. The stone re - ject - ed and de-spised Is now the cor - ner - stone;
4. In this the day that Thou hast made Tri - um - phant - ly we sing;
5. Ho - san - na! Ev - er blest be He That com - eth in God's name,

And I will en - ter them with praise, O Lord, my God, to Thee,
My Sav - iour, I will give Thee thanks, O Thou that hear-est prayer,
How won - drous are the ways of God, Un - fath - omed and un - known!
Send now pros - per - i - ty, O Lord, O Lord, sal - va - tion bring,
The bless - ing of the House of God Up - on you we pro - claim,

And I will en - ter them with praise, O Lord, my God, to Thee.
My Sav-iour, I will give Thee thanks, O Thou that hear - est prayer.
How won-drous are the ways of God, Un-fath-omed and un-known!
Send now pros - per - i - ty, O Lord, O Lord, sal - va - tion bring.
The bless-ing of the House of God Up-on you we pro - claim. A - MEN.

This Is the Day of Light

SWABIA: S. M.
Johann M. Spiess
Davids Harpffen-Spiel, Heidelberg, 1745
Arr. by William H. Havergal, 1847

John Ellerton, 1867

1. This is the day of light: Let there be light to - day;
2. This is the day of rest: Our fail - ing strength re - new;
3. This is the day of peace: Thy peace our spir - its fill;
4. This is the day of prayer: Let earth to heaven draw near;

WORSHIP: THE LORD'S DAY

This Is the Day of Light

O Day-spring, rise up-on our night And chase its gloom a - way.
On wea - ry brain and trou-bled breast Shed Thou Thy fresh-ening dew.
Bid Thou the blasts of dis - cord cease, The waves of strife be still.
Lift up our hearts to seek Thee there, Come down to meet us here. A-MEN.

Alternative tune, "Franconia," Hymn 94.

Light of Light, Enlighten Me 73

Benjamin Schmolck, 1714
Trans. by Catherine Winkworth, 1858

HINCHMAN: 7. 8. 7. 8. 7. 7.
Uzziah C. Burnap, 1869

1. Light of light, en - light-en me, Now a - new the day is dawn - ing;
2. Let me with my heart to-day, Ho - ly, ho - ly, ho - ly, sing - ing,
3. Hence all care, all van - i - ty! For the day to God is ho - ly;

Sun of grace, the shad-ows flee; Bright-en Thou my Sab-bath morn - ing;
Rapt a - while from earth a - way, All my soul to Thee up-spring-ing,
Come, Thou glo - rious Maj-es - ty, Deign to fill this tem - ple low - ly;

With Thy joy - ous sun-shine blest, Hap-py is my day of rest.
Have a fore-taste in - ly given How they wor - ship Thee in heaven.
Nought to-day my soul shall move, Sim - ply rest - ing in Thy love. A-MEN.

Alternative tune, "Liebster Jesu," Hymn 248.

WORSHIP: THE LORD'S DAY

74 Safely Through Another Week

John Newton, 1774; alt.

SABBATH: 7. 7. 7. 7. D.
Lowell Mason, 1824

1. Safe - ly through an - oth - er week, God has brought us on our way;
2. While we pray for par-doning grace, Through the dear Re-deem-er's name,
3. Here we come Thy name to praise; Let us feel Thy pres-ence near:
4. May Thy gos-pel's joy-ful sound Con - quer sin - ners, com-fort saints;

Let us now a bless-ing seek, Wait-ing in His courts to - day:
Show Thy rec - on - cil - ed face, Take a - way our sin and shame;
May Thy glo - ry meet our eyes, While we in Thy house ap - pear:
Make the fruits of grace a - bound, Bring re - lief for all com-plaints:

Day of all the week the best, Em - blem of e - ter - nal rest;
From our world - ly cares set free, May we rest this day in Thee;
Here af - ford us, Lord, a taste Of our ev - er - last - ing feast;
Thus may all our Sab-baths prove, Till we join the Church a - bove;

Day of all the week the best, Em - blem of e - ter - nal rest.
From our world - ly cares set free, May we rest this day in Thee.
Here af - ford us, Lord, a taste Of our ev - er - last - ing feast.
Thus may all our Sab-baths prove, Till we join the Church a - bove. A - MEN.

WORSHIP: THE LORD'S DAY

[72]

Praise Our Father for This Sunday

75

T. C. Chao, 1931
Trans. by Frank W. Price, 1952

P'U T'O: 8. 8. 7. 8.
Chinese melody
Arr. by Bliss Wiant, 1936; alt.

1. Praise our Fa-ther for this Sun-day, Praise His good-ness now and al-way.
2. Af-ter toil-ing through the long week Now we gath-er to hear Thee speak.
3. Some-times we bear pain and sor-row, Some-times dark-ness hides the mor-row;
4. Some-times we find peace and glad-ness, Calm and hope in joy and sad-ness;
5. Here we come our lives to of-fer, Hearts and minds we hum-bly prof-fer.

Praise His grace that loves men thus, Praise His mer-cy that for-gives us.
In Thy house may all be blest, Here may all gain strength and find rest.
Fa-ther, Fa-ther, leave us not When sore trou-ble be-comes our lot.
On our way God sheds His light, Loves us ev-er, day and dark night.
Fa-ther, hear us while we pray, And re-ceive us, now and for aye. A-MEN.

Translation copyright, 1953, by Frank W. Price. Used by permission. Music from *Hymns of Universal Praise.* Used by permission.

WORSHIP: THE LORD'S DAY

May the Grace of Christ Our Saviour

76

John Newton, 1779

EVENING PRAYER (Stainer): 8. 7. 8. 7.
John Stainer, 1898

1. May the grace of Christ our Sav-iour And the Fa-ther's bound-less love,
2. Thus may we a-bide in un-ion With each oth-er and the Lord,

With the Ho-ly Spir-it's fa-vor, Rest up-on us from a-bove.
And pos-sess, in sweet com-mun-ion, Joys which earth can-not af-ford. A-MEN.

WORSHIP: CLOSING

77 Saviour, Again to Thy Dear Name We Raise

John Ellerton, 1866

ELLERS: 10. 10. 10. 10.
Edward J. Hopkins, 1869

1. Sav - iour, a - gain to Thy dear name we raise
2. Grant us Thy peace up - on our home - ward way;
3. Grant us Thy peace, Lord, through the com - ing night;
4. Grant us Thy peace through - out our earth - ly life,

With one ac - cord our part - ing hymn of praise;
With Thee be - gan, with Thee shall end the day:
Turn Thou for us its dark - ness in - to light;
Our balm in sor - row, and our stay in strife;

We stand to bless Thee ere our wor - ship cease;
Guard Thou the lips from sin, the hearts from shame,
From harm and dan - ger keep Thy chil - dren free,
Then, when Thy voice shall bid our con - flict cease,

Then, low - ly kneel - ing, wait Thy word of peace.
That in this house have called up - on Thy name.
For dark and light are both a - like to Thee.
Call us, O Lord, to Thine e - ter - nal peace. A - MEN.

WORSHIP: CLOSING

God Be with You Till We Meet Again · 78

(FIRST TUNE)

Jeremiah E. Rankin (1828-1904)

RANDOLPH: 9. 8. 8. 9.
R. Vaughan Williams, 1906

Unison · *Harmony*

1. God be with you till we meet a-gain; By His coun-sels guide, up-hold you,
2. God be with you till we meet a-gain; 'Neath His wings pro-tect-ing hide you,
3. God be with you till we meet a-gain; When life's per-ils thick con-found you,
4. God be with you till we meet a-gain; Keep love's ban-ner float-ing o'er you,

Unison · *Harmony*

With His sheep se-cure-ly fold you: God be with you till we meet a-gain.
Dai - ly man-na still pro-vide you: God be with you till we meet a-gain.
Put His arms un - fail-ing round you: God be with you till we meet a-gain.
Smite death's threat-ening wave be-fore you: God be with you till we meet a-gain. A-MEN.

Music from *The English Hymnal.* Used by permission of Oxford University Press.

God Be with You Till We Meet Again · 78

(SECOND TUNE)

Jeremiah E. Rankin (1828-1904)

GOD BE WITH YOU: 9. 8. 8. 9.
William G. Tomer (1832-1896)

1. God be with you till we meet a - gain; By His coun-sels guide, up-hold you,
2. God be with you till we meet a - gain; 'Neath His wings pro-tect-ing hide you,
3. God be with you till we meet a - gain; When life's per - ils thick con-found you,
4. God be with you till we meet a - gain; Keep love's ban - ner float-ing o'er you,

ritard.

With His sheep se-cure - ly fold you: God be with you till we meet a - gain.
Dai - ly man-na still pro-vide you: God be with you till we meet a - gain.
Put His arms un-fail-ing round you: God be with you till we meet a - gain.
Smite death's threat-ening wave be-fore you: God be with you till we meet a - gain. A-MEN.

WORSHIP: CLOSING

79 Lord, Dismiss Us with Thy Blessing

Ascribed to John Fawcett (1740-1817)
Stanza 1, line 6. alt.; stanza 3 alt. by
Godfrey Thring (1823-1903)

SICILIAN MARINERS: 8. 7. 8. 7. 8. 7.
Arr. from a Sicilian melody

1. Lord, dis - miss us with Thy bless - ing; Fill our hearts with
2. Thanks we give and ad - o - ra - tion For Thy gos - pel's
3. So that when Thy love shall call us, Sav - iour, from the

joy and peace; Let us each, Thy love pos - sess - ing,
joy - ful sound; May the fruits of Thy sal - va - tion
world a - way, Let no fear of death ap - pall us,

Tri - umph in re - deem - ing grace: O re - fresh us,
In our hearts and lives a - bound: Ev - er faith - ful,
Glad Thy sum - mons to o - bey: May we ev - er,

O re - fresh us, Trav - eling through this wil - der - ness.
Ev - er faith - ful To the truth may we be found;
May we ev - er Reign with Thee in end - less day. A - MEN.

WORSHIP: CLOSING

[76]

On Our Way Rejoicing

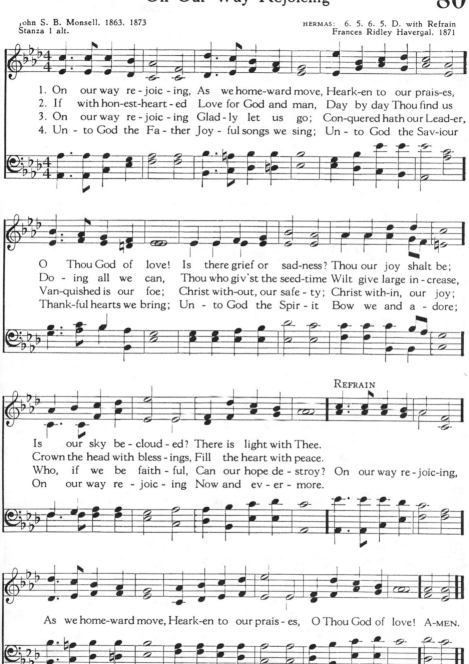

John S. B. Monsell, 1863, 1873
Stanza 1 alt.

HERMAS: 6. 5. 6. 5. D. with Refrain
Frances Ridley Havergal, 1871

80

1. On our way re-joic-ing, As we home-ward move, Heark-en to our prais-es,
2. If with hon-est-heart-ed Love for God and man, Day by day Thou find us
3. On our way re-joic-ing Glad-ly let us go; Con-quered hath our Lead-er,
4. Un-to God the Fa-ther Joy-ful songs we sing; Un-to God the Sav-iour

O Thou God of love! Is there grief or sad-ness? Thou our joy shalt be;
Do-ing all we can, Thou who giv'st the seed-time Wilt give large in-crease,
Van-quished is our foe; Christ with-out, our safe-ty; Christ with-in, our joy;
Thank-ful hearts we bring; Un-to God the Spir-it Bow we and a-dore;

Is our sky be-cloud-ed? There is light with Thee.
Crown the head with bless-ings, Fill the heart with peace.
Who, if we be faith-ful, Can our hope de-stroy? On our way re-joic-ing,
On our way re-joic-ing Now and ev-er-more.

REFRAIN

As we home-ward move, Heark-en to our prais-es, O Thou God of love! A-MEN.

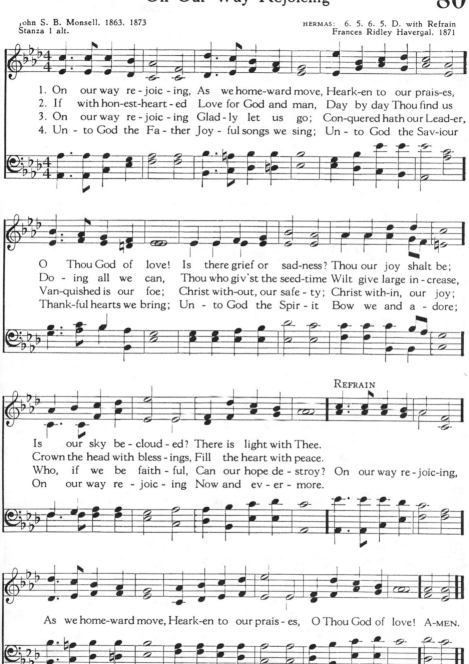

WORSHIP: CLOSING

81 Before Jehovah's Awful Throne

From Psalm 100
Isaac Watts, 1705, 1719; alt.
Stanza 1 alt. by John Wesley, 1737

PARK STREET: L. M.
Frederick M. A. Venua, c. 1810

1. Be - fore Je - ho - vah's aw - ful throne, Ye na - tions, bow with
2. His sov-ereign power, with-out our aid, Made us of clay, and
3. We'll crowd His gates with thank - ful songs, High as the heavens our
4. Wide as the world is His com-mand, Vast as e - ter - ni-

sa - cred joy; Know that the Lord is God a - lone, He can cre-
formed us men; And when like wan-dering sheep we strayed, He brought us
voi - ces raise; And earth, with her ten thou-sand tongues, Shall fill His
ty His love; Firm as a rock His truth shall stand, When roll - ing

ate, and He de - stroy; He can cre - ate, and He de - stroy.
to His fold a - gain, He brought us to His fold a - gain.
courts with sound-ing praise, Shall fill His courts with sound-ing praise.
years shall cease to move, When roll - ing years shall cease to move. A - MEN.

82 Thy Mercy and Thy Truth, O Lord

From Psalm 36
The Psalter, 1912

CADDO: C. M.
William B. Bradbury (1816-1868)

1. Thy mer - cy and Thy truth, O Lord, Tran-scend the loft - y sky;
2. Lord, Thou pre-serv - est man and beast; Since Thou art ev - er kind,
3. With the a - bun-dance of Thy house We shall be sat - is - fied,
4. The foun-tain of e - ter - nal life Is found a - lone with Thee,
5. From those that know Thee may Thy love And mer - cy ne'er de - part,

GOD: HIS ETERNITY AND POWER

[78]

Thy Mercy and Thy Truth, O Lord

Thy judg-ments are a might-y deep, And as the moun-tains high.
Be - neath the shad-ow of Thy wings We may a ref - uge find.
From riv - ers of un - fail - ing joy Our thirst shall be sup-plied.
And in the bright-ness of Thy light We clear - ly light shall see.
And may Thy jus - tice still pro-tect And bless the up - right heart. A - MEN.

The Lord Is King! Lift Up Thy Voice   83

Josiah Conder (1789-1855); abridged

DEUS TUORUM MILITUM: L. M.
Grenoble church melody

1. The Lord is King! lift up thy voice, O earth, and all ye heavens, re-joice!
2. The Lord is King! who then shall dare Re - sist His will, dis-trust His care,
3. The Lord is King! child of the dust, The Judge of all the earth is just;
4. A - like per - vad - ed by His eye, All parts of His do-min - ion lie—
5. One Lord, one em - pire, all se - cures; He reigns, and life and death are yours:

From world to world the joy shall ring, The Lord Om - nip - o - tent is King.
Or mur-mur at His wise de-crees, Or doubt His roy - al prom - is - es?
Ho - ly and true are all His ways, Let ev - ery crea-ture speak His praise.
This world of ours, and worlds un-seen, And thin the bound-a - ry be-tween.
Thru earth and heaven one song shall ring, The Lord Om - nip - o - tent is King. A - MEN.

GOD: HIS ETERNITY AND POWER

I Sing the Mighty Power of God

(FIRST TUNE)

ELLACOMBE: C. M. D.

Isaac Watts, 1709
Stanza 3 alt.

Gesangbuch der Herzogl. Wirtembergischen
Katholischen Hofkapelle, 1784

1. I sing the might-y power of God, That made the moun-tains rise;
2. I sing the good-ness of the Lord, That filled the earth with food;
3. There's not a plant or flower be-low, But makes Thy glo-ries known;

That spread the flow-ing seas a-broad, And built the loft-y skies.
He formed the crea-tures with His word, And then pro-nounced them good.
And clouds a-rise, and tem-pests blow, By or-der from Thy throne;

I sing the Wis-dom that or-dained The sun to rule the day;
Lord, how Thy won-ders are dis-played, Wher-e'er I turn my eye:
While all that bor-rows life from Thee Is ev-er in Thy care,

The moon shines full at His com-mand, And all the stars o-bey.
If I sur-vey the ground I tread, Or gaze up-on the sky!
And ev-ery-where that man can be, Thou, God, art pres-ent there. A-MEN.

GOD: HIS ETERNITY AND POWER

I Sing the Mighty Power of God

(SECOND TUNE)

84

Isaac Watts, 1709
Stanza 3 alt.

ZERAH: C. M.
Lowell Mason, 1837

1. I sing the might - y power of God, That made the moun - tains rise; That spread the flow - ing seas a - broad, And built the loft - y skies, That spread the flow - ing seas a - broad, And built the loft - y skies.

2. I sing the good - ness of the Lord, That filled the earth with food; He formed the crea - tures with His word, And then pro-nounced them good, He formed the crea - tures with His word, And then pro-nounced them good.

3. There's not a plant or flower be - low, But makes Thy glo - ries known; And clouds a - rise, and tem - pests blow, By or - der from Thy throne; And clouds a - rise, and tem-pests blow, By or - der from Thy throne. A - MEN.

GOD: HIS ETERNITY AND POWER

[81]

85   Immortal, Invisible, God Only Wise

Walter Chalmers Smith (1824-1908)

JOANNA: 11. 11. 11. 11.
Welsh hymn melody

1. Im - mor - tal, in - vis - i - ble, God on - ly wise,
2. Un - rest - ing, un - hast - ing, and si - lent as light,
3. To all, life Thou giv - est— to both great and small;
4. Great Fa - ther of glo - ry, pure Fa - ther of light,

In light in - ac - ces - si - ble hid from our eyes,
Nor want - ing, nor wast - ing, Thou rul - est in might;
In all life Thou liv - est, the true life of all;
Thine an - gels a - dore Thee, all veil - ing their sight;

Most bless - ed, most glo - rious, the An - cient of Days,
Thy jus - tice like moun - tains high soar - ing a - bove
We blos - som and flour - ish as leaves on the tree,
All praise we would ren - der; O help us to see

Al - might - y, vic - to - rious, Thy great name we praise.
Thy clouds which are foun - tains of good - ness and love.
And with - er and per - ish— but nought chang - eth Thee.
'Tis on - ly the splen - dor of light hid - eth Thee! A - MEN.

Words used by permission of the Executors of the late W. Chalmers Smith and Oxford University Press.

GOD: HIS ETERNITY AND POWER

[82]

Begin, My Tongue, Some Heavenly Theme 86

Isaac Watts. 1707

MANOAH: C. M.
Henry W. Greatorex's
Collection, Boston, 1851

1. Be - gin, my tongue, some heaven-ly theme, And speak some bound - less thing,
2. Tell of His won-drous faith - ful - ness, And sound His power a - broad;
3. His ver - y word of grace is strong As that which built the skies;
4. O might I hear Thy heaven-ly tongue But whis - per, "Thou art Mine,"

The might-y works, or might - ier name, Of our e - ter - nal King.
Sing the sweet prom-ise of His grace, And our re - deem - ing God.
The voice that rolls the stars a - long Speaks all the prom - is - es.
Those gen - tle words should raise my song To notes al - most di - vine. A - MEN.

Lord of All Being, Throned Afar 87

Oliver Wendell Holmes, 1848

ARIZONA: L. M.
Robert Henry Earnshaw (1856-1929)

1. Lord of all be - ing, throned a - far, Thy glo - ry flames from sun and star;
2. Sun of our life, Thy quick-ening ray Sheds on our path the glow of day;
3. Our mid-night is Thy smile with-drawn; Our noon-tide is Thy gra - cious dawn;
4. Grant us Thy truth to make us free, And kind-ling hearts that burn for Thee;

Cen-ter and soul of ev-ery sphere, Yet to each lov - ing heart how near!
Star of our hope, Thy soft-ened light Cheers the long watch-es of the night.
Our rain-bow arch, Thy mer-cy's sign; All, save the clouds of sin, are Thine.
Till all Thy liv - ing al - tars claim One ho - ly light, one heaven-ly flame. A-MEN.

Words used by permission of Houghton Mifflin Company, authorized publishers. Music used by permission of Miss J. Edgar.

GOD: HIS ETERNITY AND POWER

88 Lord, Thou Hast Been Our Dwelling Place

From Psalm 90
The Psalter, 1912

ST. CATHERINE: 8. 8. 8. 8. 8. 8.
Henri F. Hemy, 1865
Alt. by James G. Walton, 1871

1. Lord, Thou hast been our dwell - ing place Through all the
2. O teach Thou us to count our days And set our
3. O send the day of joy and light, For long has
4. So let there be on us be - stowed The beau - ty

a - ges of our race; Be - fore the moun - tains had their birth,
hearts on wis - dom's ways; Turn, Lord, to us in our dis - tress,
been our sor - row's night; Af - flict - ed through the wea - ry years,
of the Lord our God; The work ac - com - plished by our hand

Or ev - er Thou hadst formed the earth, From ev - er - last - ing
In pit - y now Thy serv - ants bless; Let mer - cy's dawn dis -
We wait un - til Thy help ap - pears; With us and with our
Es - tab - lish Thou, and make it stand; Yea, let our hope - ful

Thou art God, To ev - er - last - ing our a - bode.
pel our night, And all our day with joy be bright.
sons a - bide, In us let God be glo - ri - fied.
la - bor be Es - tab - lished ev - er - more by Thee. A - MEN.

GOD: HIS ETERNITY AND POWER

[84]

Revised version of the Yigdal
Daniel ben Judah, 14th century
Trans. by Max Landsberg and Newton Mann, 1885; alt.

YIGDAL (LEONI): 6. 6. 8. 4. D.
Adapted from a Hebrew melody

1. The God of A - braham praise, All prais - ed be His name,
2. His spir - it flow - eth free, High surg - ing where it will:
3. He hath e - ter - nal life Im - plant - ed in the soul;

Who was, and is, and is to be, For aye the same!
In proph - et's word He spoke of old—He speak - eth still.
His love shall be our strength and stay, While a - ges roll.

The one e - ter - nal God, Ere aught that now ap - pears;
Es - tab - lished is His law, And change - less it shall stand,
Praise to the liv - ing God! All prais - ed be His name

The First, the Last: be - yond all thought His time - less years!
Deep writ up - on the hu - man heart, On sea, or land.
Who was, and is, and is to be, For aye the same! A-MEN.

GOD: HIS ETERNITY AND POWER

90 God, the Lord, a King Remaineth

From Psalm 93
John Keble, 1839; alt.

BRYN CALFARIA: 8. 7. 8. 7. 4. 7.
William Owen (1814-1893)

1. God, the Lord, a King re-main-eth, Robed in His own glo-rious light;
2. In her ev-er-last-ing sta-tion Earth is poised, to swerve no more;
3. With all tones of wa-ters blend-ing, Glo-rious is the break-ing deep;
4. Lord, the words Thy lips are tell-ing Are the per-fect ver-i-ty;

God hath robed Him-self and reign-eth; He hath girt Him-self with might.
Thou hast laid Thy throne's foun-da-tion From all time where thought can soar.
Glo-rious, beau-teous, with-out end-ing, God, who reigns on heaven's high steep.
Of Thine high e-ter-nal dwell-ing, Ho-li-ness shall in-mate be:

Al-le-lu-ia! Al-le-lu-ia! Al-le-lu-ia!
Al-le-lu-ia! Al-le-lu-ia! Al-le-lu-ia!
Al-le-lu-ia! Al-le-lu-ia! Al-le-lu-ia!
Al-le-lu-ia! Al-le-lu-ia! Al-le-lu-ia!

God is King in depth and height! God is King in depth and height!
Lord, Thou art for-ev-er-more! Lord, Thou art for-ev-er-more!
Songs of o-cean nev-er sleep. Songs of o-cean nev-er sleep.
Pure is all that lives with Thee. Pure is all that lives with Thee. A-MEN.

GOD: HIS ETERNITY AND POWER

A Mighty Fortress Is Our God

From Psalm 46
Martin Luther, 1529
Trans. by Frederick H. Hedge, 1853

EIN' FESTE BURG: 8. 7. 8. 7. 6. 6. 6. 6. 7.
Martin Luther, 1529

1. A might-y For-tress is our God, A Bul-wark nev-er fail-ing;
2. Did we in our own strength con-fide, Our striv-ing would be los-ing;
3. And though this world, with dev-ils filled, Should threat-en to un-do us,
4. That word a-bove all earth-ly powers, No thanks to them, a-bid-eth;

Our Help-er He a-mid the flood Of mor-tal ills pre-vail-ing.
Were not the right man on our side, The man of God's own choos-ing.
We will not fear, for God hath willed His truth to tri-umph through us.
The Spir-it and the gifts are ours Through Him who with us sid-eth;

For still our an-cient foe Doth seek to work us woe; His craft and power are
Dost ask who that may be? Christ Je-sus, it is He, Lord Sab-a-oth His
The prince of dark-ness grim, We trem-ble not for him; His rage we can en-
Let goods and kin-dred go, This mor-tal life al-so; The bod-y they may

great; And, armed with cru-el hate, On earth is not his e-qual.
name, From age to age the same, And He must win the bat-tle.
dure, For lo! his doom is sure; One lit-tle word shall fell him.
kill: God's truth a-bid-eth still; His King-dom is for-ev-er. A-MEN.

GOD: HIS ETERNITY AND POWER

92 O God, the Rock of Ages

MIRIAM: 7. 6. 7. 6. D.

Edward H. Bickersteth, 1860

Joseph P. Holbrook, 1865

1. O God, the Rock of A - ges, Who ev - er - more hast been,
2. Our years are like the shad - ows On sun - ny hills that lie,
3. O Thou, who dost not slum - ber, Whose light grows nev - er pale,

What time the tem - pest ra - ges, Our dwell - ing place se - rene:
Or grass - es in the mead - ows That blos - som but to die;
Teach us a - right to num - ber Our years be - fore they fail;

Be - fore Thy first cre - a - tions, O Lord, the same as now,
A sleep, a dream, a sto - ry By stran - gers quick - ly told,
On us Thy mer - cy light - en, On us Thy good - ness rest,

To end - less gen - er - a - tions The Ev - er - last - ing Thou!
An un - re - main - ing glo - ry Of things that soon are old.
And let Thy Spir - it bright - en The hearts Thy - self hast blessed. A - MEN.

Words copyright by the Church Society. Used by permission.

GOD: HIS ETERNITY AND POWER

O God, Thou Art the Father

93

Columba (521-597)
Trans. by Duncan Macgregor (1854-1923)

DURROW: 7. 6. 7. 6. D.
Traditional Irish melody
Har. by David Evans, 1927

1. O God, Thou art the Fa - ther Of all that have be - lieved:
2. High in the heaven-ly Zi - on Thou reign - est God a - dored;
3. Thou to the meek and low - ly Thy se - crets dost un - fold;

From whom all hosts of an - gels Have life and power re - ceived.
And in the com - ing glo - ry Thou shalt be Sov - ereign Lord.
O God, Thou do - est all things, All things both new and old.

O God, Thou art the Mak - er Of all cre - a - ted things,
Be - yond our ken Thou shin - est, The ev - er - last - ing Light;
I walk se - cure and bless - ed In ev - ery clime or coast,

The right-eous Judge of jud - ges, Th'al-might-y King of kings.
In - ef - fa - ble in lov - ing, Un - think - a - ble in might.
In name of God the Fa - ther, And Son, and Ho - ly Ghost. A-MEN.

Music from *The Church Hymnary*, Revised Edition. Used by permission of Oxford University Press.

GOD: HIS ETERNITY AND POWER

[89]

94 The Lord Almighty Reigns

FRANCONIA: S. M.

From Psalm 93
The Psalter, 1912; alt.

Johann B. König, 1738
Arr. by William H. Havergal, 1840

1. The Lord Al - might - y reigns In maj - es - ty most bright,
2. The world es - tab - lished stands On its foun - da - tions broad;
3. The floods have lift - ed up Their voice in maj - es - ty,
4. Thy tes - ti - mo - nies, Lord, In faith - ful - ness ex - cel.

Ap - par - eled in om - nip - o - tence, And gird - ed round with might.
His throne is fixed, He reigns su - preme, The ev - er - last - ing God.
But might - y is the Lord our God A - bove the rag - ing sea.
And ho - ly must Thy serv - ants be Who in Thy tem - ple dwell. A-MEN.

95 O Lord, Our Lord, in All the Earth

From Psalm 8
The Psalter, 1912

DUNFERMLINE: C. M.
Scottish Psalter, 1615

1. O Lord, our Lord, in all the earth How ex - cel - lent Thy name!
2. When I re - gard the won-drous heavens, Thy hand - i - work on high,
3. Oh, what is man, in Thy re - gard To hold so large a place!
4. On man Thy wis-dom hath be-stowed A power well nigh di - vine;
5. Thy might - y works and won-drous grace Thy glo - ry, Lord, pro - claim.

Thy glo - ry Thou hast spread a - far In all the star - ry frame.
The moon and stars or - dained by Thee, Oh, what is man! I cry.
And what the son of man, that Thou Dost vis - it him in grace!
With hon - or Thou hast crowned his head With glo - ry like to Thine.
O Lord, our Lord, in all the earth How ex - cel - lent Thy name! A-MEN.

GOD: HIS ETERNITY AND POWER

All Beautiful the March of Days

96

FOREST GREEN: C. M. D.
Traditional English melody
Arr. by R. Vaughan Williams, 1906

Frances Whitmarsh Wile, 1912

1. All beau-ti-ful the march of days, As sea-sons come and go;
2. O'er white ex-pans-es spar-kling pure The ra-diant morns un-fold;
3. O Thou from whose un-fath-omed law The year in beau-ty flows,

The Hand that shaped the rose hath wrought The crys-tal of the snow;
The sol-emn splen-dors of the night Burn bright-er through the cold;
Thy-self the vi-sion pass-ing by In crys-tal and in rose,

Hath sent the hoar-y frost of heaven, The flow-ing wa-ters sealed,
Life mounts in ev-ery throb-bing vein, Love deep-ens round the hearth,
Day un-to day doth ut-ter speech, And night to night pro-claim,

And laid a si-lent love-li-ness On hill and wood and field.
And clear-er sounds the an-gel hymn, "Good will to men on earth."
In ev-er-chang-ing words of light, The won-der of Thy name. A-MEN.

Words used by permission of Dorothy M. W. Bean. Music from *The English Hymnal.* Used by permission of Oxford University Press.
For lower key, see Hymn 256.

GOD: IN NATURE

[91]

97 The Spacious Firmament on High

Joseph Addison, 1712

CREATION: L. M. D.
Franz Joseph Haydn, 1798

1 The spa-cious fir-ma-ment on high, With all the
2. Soon as the eve-ning shades pre-vail, The moon takes
3. What though in sol-emn si-lence all Move round this

blue e-the-real sky, And span-gled heavens, a shin-ing frame,
up the won-drous tale, And night-ly to the lis-tening earth
dark ter-res-trial ball? What though no re-al voice nor sound

Their great O-rig-i-nal pro-claim: Th'un-wea-ried sun, from
Re-peats the sto-ry of her birth; Whilst all the stars that
A-midst the ra-diant orbs be found? In rea-son's ear they

day to day, Does his Cre-a-tor's power dis-play, And pub-lish-
round her burn, And all the plan-ets in their turn, Con-firm the
all re-joice, And ut-ter forth a glo-rious voice; For-ev-er

es to ev-ery land The work of an al-might-y hand.
ti-dings as they roll, And spread the truth from pole to pole.
sing-ing, as they shine, "The hand that made us is di-vine." A-MEN.

GOD: IN NATURE

[92]

Praise Ye, Praise Ye the Lord

98

From Psalm 148
The Psalter, 1912

COLUMBIA: 6. 6. 6. 6. 8. 8.
Leonard Cooper Blanton, 1951; alt.

1. Praise ye, praise ye the Lord . . . In yon-der heaven-ly
2. Praise Him, ye high-est heavens, . Praise Him, ye clouds that
3. Ye crea-tures in the sea . . . And crea-tures on the
4. Ye hills and moun-tains, praise, . Each tree and beast and
5. By all let God be praised, . . For He a-lone is

height; . . . Ye an-gels, all His hosts, ... In
roll, ... Cre - at - ed by His power . . . . And
earth, ... Your might - y Mak - er praise . . . . And
bird; . . . . Ye kings and realms of earth, ... Now
great; . . . . A - bove the earth and heaven . . . He

joy - ful praise u - nite; . . . . O sun and moon, de -
un - der His con-trol, ... Ye heavens that stand e -
tell His match-less worth; . . . . Praise Him, ye storm - y
let your praise be heard; . . . . By high and low, by
reigns in glo - rious state; . . . Praise Him, ye saints, who

clare His might, Show forth His praise, ye stars of light.
ter - nal - ly, Es - tab-lished by His firm de - cree.
winds that blow, Ye fire and hail, ye rain and snow.
young and old, Be all His praise and glo - ry told.
know His grace And ev - er dwell be - fore His face. A-MEN.

Music copyright, 1951, by the composer. Used by permission.
Alternative tune, "Darwall's 148th," Hymn 14.

GOD: IN NATURE

99 Thy Might Sets Fast the Mountains

From Psalm 65
The Psalter, 1912

WEBB: 7. 6. 7. 6. D.
George J. Webb, 1837

1. Thy might sets fast the moun - tains; Strength girds Thee ev - er - more
2. To bless the earth Thou send - est From Thy a - bun - dant store
3. The year with good Thou crown - est, The earth Thy mer - cy fills,

To calm the rag - ing peo - ples And still the o - cean's roar.
The wa - ters of the spring - time, En - rich - ing it once more.
The wil - der - ness is fruit - ful, And joy - ful are the hills;

Thy maj - es - ty and great - ness Are through all lands con - fessed,
The seed by Thee pro - vid - ed Is sown o'er hill and plain,
With corn the vales are cov - ered, The flocks in pas - tures graze;

And joy on earth Thou send - est A - far, from east to west.
And Thou with gen - tle show - ers Dost bless the spring-ing grain.
All na - ture joins in sing - ing A joy - ful song of praise. A-MEN.

GOD: IN NATURE

All Creatures of Our God and King
100

Francis of Assisi, 1225
Para. by William H. Draper, 1926

LASST UNS ERFREUEN: 8. 8. 4. 4. 8. 8. with Alleluias
Geistliche Kirchengesäng, Cologne. 1623

1. All crea-tures of our God and King, Lift up your voice and with us sing, Al-le-lu-ia! Al-le-lu-ia! Thou burn-ing sun with gold-en beam, Thou sil-ver moon with soft-er gleam, Oh, praise Him! Oh, praise Him! Al-le-lu-ia! Al-le-lu-ia! Al-le-lu-ia! A-MEN.
2. Thou rush-ing wind that art so strong, Ye clouds that sail in heaven a-long, Oh, praise Him! Al-le-lu-ia! Thou ris-ing morn, in praise re-joice, Ye lights of eve-ning, find a voice!
3. Thou flow-ing wa-ter, pure and clear, Make mu-sic for thy Lord to hear, Al-le-lu-ia! Al-le-lu-ia! Thou fire so mas-ter-ful and bright, That giv-est man both warmth and light,
4. Dear moth-er earth, who day by day Un-fold-est bless-ings on our way, Oh, praise Him! Al-le-lu-ia! The flowers and fruits that in thee grow, Let them His glo-ry al-so show!
5. And all ye men of ten-der heart, For-giv-ing oth-ers, take your part. Oh, sing ye! Al-le-lu-ia! Ye who long pain and sor-row bear, Praise God and on Him cast your care!
6. Let all things their Cre-a-tor bless, And wor-ship Him in hum-ble-ness. Oh, praise Him! Al-le-lu-ia! Praise, praise the Fa-ther, praise the Son, And praise the Spir-it, Three in One!

Words by permission, from Curwen Edition No. 80649, published by J. Curwen & Sons. Ltd.. 24 Berners Street, London, W. 1, England. Music from *The English Hymnal*. Used by permission of Oxford University Press.

[95]

GOD: IN NATURE

101   This Is My Father's World

TERRA BEATA: S. M. D.
Franklin L. Sheppard, 1915
Har. for this book, 1953

Maltbie D. Babcock, 1901

1. This is my Fa-ther's world, And to my lis-tening ears All na-ture sings, and round me rings The mu-sic of the spheres.
2. This is my Fa-ther's world: The birds their car-ols raise, The morn-ing light, the lil-y white, De-clare their Mak-er's praise.
3. This is my Fa-ther's world: Oh, let me ne'er for-get That though the wrong seems oft so strong, God is the Rul-er yet.

This is my Fa-ther's world: I rest me in the thought Of rocks and trees, of skies and seas; His hand the won-ders wrought.
This is my Fa-ther's world: He shines in all that's fair; In the rus-tling grass I hear Him pass, He speaks to me ev-ery-where.
This is my Fa-ther's world: The bat-tle is not done; Je-sus who died shall be sat-is-fied, And earth and heaven be one. A-MEN.

Words reprinted from *Thoughts for Everyday Living,* by Maltbie D. Babcock; copyright, 1901, by Charles Scribner's Sons, 1929, by Katharine T. Babcock. Used by permission of the publishers.

GOD: IN NATURE

God, Who Touchest Earth with Beauty 102

Mary S. Edgar. 1925. 1939

BULLINGER: 8. 5. 8. 5.
Ethelbert W. Bullinger, 1874; alt.

1. God, who touch - est earth with beau - ty, Make my heart a - new;
2. Like Thy springs and run - ning wa - ters Make me crys - tal pure;
3. Like Thy danc - ing waves in sun - light Make me glad and free;
4. Like the arch - ing of the heav - ens Lift my thoughts a - bove;
5. God, who touch - est earth with beau - ty, Make my heart a - new;

With Thy Spir - it re - cre - ate me, Pure and strong and true.
Like Thy rocks of tow - ering gran-deur Make me strong and sure.
Like the straight-ness of the pine trees Let me up - right be.
Turn my dreams to no - ble ac - tion—Min - is - tries of love.
Keep me ev - er, by Thy Spir - it, Pure and strong and true. A-MEN.

Words copyright by Mary S. Edgar. Used by permission.

GOD: IN NATURE

God Is Love; His Mercy Brightens 103

SUSSEX: 8. 7. 8. 7.
Traditional English melody
Adapted by R. Vaughan Williams, 1906

John Bowring (1792-1872)

1. God is Love; His mer - cy bright-ens All the path in which we rove;
2. Chance and change are bus - y ev - er; Man de - cays, and a - ges move;
3. E'en the hour that dark - est seem-eth Will His change-less good-ness prove;
4. He with earth - ly cares en - twin-eth Hope and com - fort from a - bove;

Bliss He wakes, and woe He light-ens: God is Wis - dom, God is Love.
But His mer - cy wan-eth nev - er: God is Wis - dom, God is Love.
From the mist His bright-ness stream-eth: God is Wis - dom, God is Love.
Ev - ery - where His glo - ry shin-eth: God is Wis - dom, God is Love. A-MEN.

Music from *The English Hymnal.* Used by permission of Oxford University Press.
Alternative tune. "Stuttgart." Hymn 151, second tune.

GOD: HIS LOVE AND FATHERHOOD

104

The Lord's My Shepherd
(FIRST TUNE)

From Psalm 23
Scottish Psalter, 1650

EVAN: C. M.
William H. Havergal. 1846

1. The Lord's my Shep-herd, I'll not want; He makes me down to lie
2. My soul He doth re-store a-gain; And me to walk doth make
3. Yea, though I walk in death's dark vale, Yet will I fear none ill;
4. My ta-ble Thou hast fur-nish-ed In pres-ence of my foes;
5. Good-ness and mer-cy all my life Shall sure-ly fol-low me;

In pas-tures green; He lead-eth me The qui-et wa-ters by.
With-in the paths of right-eous-ness, E'en for His own name's sake.
For Thou art with me; and Thy rod And staff me com-fort still.
My head Thou dost with oil a-noint, And my cup o-ver-flows.
And in God's house for - ev-er-more My dwell-ing place shall be. A-MEN.

104

The Lord's My Shepherd
(SECOND TUNE)

From Psalm 23
Scottish Psalter, 1650

CRIMOND: C. M.
Jessie Seymour Irvine (1836-1887)
Har. by T. C. L. Pritchard, 1929; alt.

1. The Lord's my Shep-herd, I'll not want; He makes me down to lie
2. My soul He doth re-store a-gain; And me to walk doth make
3. Yea, though I walk in death's dark vale, Yet will I fear none ill;
4. My ta-ble Thou hast fur-nish-ed In pres-ence of my foes;
5. Good-ness and mer-cy all my life Shall sure-ly fol-low me;

In pas-tures green; He lead-eth me The qui-et wa-ters by.
With-in the paths of right-eous-ness, E'en for His own name's sake.
For Thou art with me; and Thy rod And staff me com-fort still.
My head Thou dost with oil a-noint, And my cup o-ver-flows.
And in God's house for - ev-er-more My dwell-ing place shall be. A-MEN.

Music from *The BBC Hymn Book* (slightly altered). Used by permission of Oxford University Press.
GOD: HIS LOVE AND FATHERHOOD   [98]

The Lord's My Shepherd

(THIRD TUNE)

104

BELMONT: C. M.
Arr. from William Gardiner's
Sacred Melodies, 1812

From Psalm 23
Scottish Psalter, 1650

1. The Lord's my Shep-herd, I'll not want; He makes me down to lie
2. My soul He doth re - store a - gain; And me to walk doth make
3. Yea, though I walk in death's dark vale, Yet will I fear none ill;
4. My ta - ble Thou hast fur - nish - ed In pres-ence of my foes;
5. Good - ness and mer - cy all my life Shall sure - ly fol - low me;

In pas-tures green; He lead - eth me The qui - et wa - ters by.
With - in the paths of right-eous-ness, E'en for His own name's sake.
For Thou art with me; and Thy rod And staff me com - fort still.
My head Thou dost with oil a-noint, And my cup o - ver - flows.
And in God's house for - ev - er-more My dwell-ing place shall be. A - MEN.

How Gentle God's Commands

105

DENNIS: S. M.
Hans G. Nägeli (1773-1836)
Arr. by Lowell Mason, 1845

Philip Doddridge, 1755

1. How gen - tle God's com-mands, How kind His pre - cepts are!
2. Be - neath His watch - ful eye His saints se - cure - ly dwell;
3. Why should this anx - ious load Press down your wea - ry mind?
4. His good - ness stands ap-proved, Down to the pres - ent day;

Come, cast your bur - dens on the Lord, And trust His con - stant care.
That hand which bears all na - ture up Shall guide His chil - dren well.
Haste to your Heaven-ly Fa-ther's throne, And sweet re - fresh-ment find.
I'll drop my bur - den at His feet, And bear a song a - way. A - MEN.

[99]   GOD: HIS LOVE AND FATHERHOOD

106 The King of Love My Shepherd Is

From Psalm 23
Henry W. Baker, 1868

(FIRST TUNE)

DOMINUS REGIT ME: 8. 7. 8. 7.
John B. Dykes, 1868

1. The King of love my Shep-herd is, Whose good-ness fail-eth nev - er;
2. Where streams of liv - ing wa - ter flow My ran-somed soul He lead - eth,
3. Per - verse and fool-ish oft I strayed, But yet in love He sought me,
4. In death's dark vale I fear no ill With Thee, dear Lord, be - side me;
5. Thou spreadest a ta - ble in my sight; Thy unc - tion grace be - stow - eth;
6. And so through all the length of days Thy good-ness fail-eth nev - er:

I noth-ing lack if I am His And He is mine for - ev - er.
And where the ver-dant pas - tures grow, With food ce - les - tial feed - eth.
And on His shoul-der gent - ly laid, And home, re - joic-ing, brought me.
Thy rod and staff my com - fort still, Thy cross be-fore to guide me.
And O what trans-port of de - light From Thy pure chal-ice flow - eth!
Good Shep-herd, may I sing Thy praise With-in Thy house for - ev - er. A-MEN.

106 The King of Love My Shepherd Is

From Psalm 23
Henry W. Baker, 1868

(SECOND TUNE)

ST. COLUMBA: 8. 7. 8. 7.
Ancient Irish melody

1. The King of love my Shep-herd is, Whose good-ness fail-eth nev - er;

I noth-ing lack if I am His And He is mine for-ev - er. A - MEN.

Music used by permission of Stainer & Bell. Ltd.
GOD: HIS LOVE AND FATHERHOOD   [100]

Father, Long Before Creation

107

Chinese; anon., c. 1952
Trans. by Francis P. Jones, 1953

MILLER CHAPEL: 8. 7. 8. 7. 4. 4. 7.
David Hugh Jones, 1954

1. Fa - ther, long be - fore cre - a - tion Thou hadst cho - sen us in love;
2. Though the world may change its fash - ion, Yet our God is e'er the same;
3. God's com - pas - sion is my sto - ry, Is my boast - ing all the day;
4. Lov - ing Fa - ther, now be - fore Thee We will ev - er praise Thy love;

And that love, so deep, so mov-ing, Draws us close to Christ a - bove.
His com - pas - sion and His cov-enant Through all a - ges will re-main.
Mer - cy free and nev - er fail - ing Moves my will, di - rects my way.
And our song will sound un - ceas-ing Till we reach our home a - bove,

Still it keeps us, Still it keeps us, Firm - ly fixed in Christ a - lone.
God's own chil-dren, God's own chil-dren, Must for-ev - er praise His name.
God so loved us, God so loved us, That His on - ly Son He gave.
Giv - ing glo - ry, Giv - ing glo - ry, To our God and to the Lamb. A - MEN.

Words used by permission of the translator. Music copyright, 1954, by John Ribble.

GOD: HIS LOVE AND FATHERHOOD

[101]

108 God of Our Life, Through All the Circling Years

Hugh T. Kerr, 1917; alt.

SANDON: 10. 4. 10. 4. 10. 10.
Charles Henry Purday (1799-1885)

1. God of our life, through all the cir - cling years, We trust in Thee;
2. God of the past, our times are in Thy hand; With us a - bide.
3. God of the com - ing years, through paths un-known We fol - low Thee;

In all the past, through all our hopes and fears, Thy hand we see.
Lead us by faith to hope's true Prom-ised Land; Be Thou our guide.
When we are strong, Lord, leave us not a - lone; Our ref - uge be.

With each new day, when morn - ing lifts the veil,
With Thee to bless, the dark - ness shines as light,
Be Thou for us in life our Dai - ly Bread,

We own Thy mer - cies, Lord, which nev - er fail.
And faith's fair vi - sion chan - ges in - to sight.
Our heart's true Home when all our years have sped. A - MEN.

Words from *The Church School Hymnal for Youth,* copyright, 1928, by F. M. Braselman. Used by permission.

GOD: HIS LOVE AND FATHERHOOD

I Bow My Forehead to the Dust

PENTATONE: C. M. D.

John Greenleaf Whittier, 1867

Henry Walford Davies, 1923

1. I bow my fore-head to the dust, I veil mine eyes for shame,
2. I know not what the fu - ture hath Of mar - vel or sur - prise,
3. I know not where His is - lands lift Their frond - ed palms in air;

And urge, in trem - bling self - dis - trust, A prayer with - out a claim.
As - sured a - lone that life and death His mer - cy un - der - lies.
I on - ly know I can - not drift Be - yond His love and care.

No of - fering of mine own I have, No works my faith to prove;
And so be - side the si - lent sea I wait the muf - fled oar:
And Thou, O Lord, by whom are seen Thy crea - tures as they be,

I can but give the gifts He gave, And plead His love for love.
No harm from Him can come to me On o - cean or on shore.
For - give me if too close I lean My hu - man heart on Thee. A - MEN.

Words used by permission of Houghton Mifflin Company, authorized publishers. Music from *A Students'
Hymnal.* Used by permission of Oxford University Press.

GOD: HIS LOVE AND FATHERHOOD

110 There's a Wideness in God's Mercy
(FIRST TUNE)

Frederick W. Faber, 1854

IN BABILONE: 8. 7. 8. 7. D.
Traditional Dutch melody

1. There's a wide-ness in God's mer-cy, Like the wide-ness of the sea;
2. For the love of God is broad-er Than the meas-ures of man's mind;

There's a kind-ness in His jus-tice, Which is more than lib-er-ty.
And the heart of the E-ter-nal Is most won-der-ful-ly kind.

There is no place where earth's sor-rows Are more felt than up in heaven;
If our love were but more sim-ple, We should take Him at His word;

There is no place where earth's fail-ings Have such kind-ly judg-ment given.
And our lives would be all sun-shine In the sweet-ness of our Lord. A-MEN.

Music used by permission of Engelbert Roentgen.

GOD: HIS LOVE AND FATHERHOOD

There's a Wideness in God's Mercy

(SECOND TUNE)

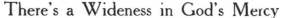

110

Frederick W. Faber. 1854

WELLESLEY: 8. 7. 8. 7.
Lizzie S. Tourjée. 1878

1. There's a wide-ness in God's mer-cy, Like the wide-ness of the sea;
2. There is no place where earth's sor-rows Are more felt than up in heaven;
3. For the love of God is broad-er Than the meas-ures of man's mind;
4. If our love were but more sim-ple, We should take Him at His word;

There's a kind-ness in His jus-tice, Which is more than lib-er-ty.
There is no place where earth's fail-ings Have such kind-ly judg-ment given.
And the heart of the E-ter-nal Is most won-der-ful-ly kind.
And our lives would be all sun-shine In the sweet-ness of our Lord. A-MEN.

GOD: HIS LOVE AND FATHERHOOD

O God, Our Help in Ages Past

111

From Psalm 90
Isaac Watts. 1719; alt.

ST. ANNE: C. M.
Ascribed to William Croft
Supplement to the New Version. 1708

1. O God, our Help in a-ges past, Our Hope for years to come,
2. Be-fore the hills in or-der stood, Or earth re-ceived her frame,
3. A thou-sand a-ges in Thy sight Are like an eve-ning gone;
4. Time, like an ev-er-roll-ing stream, Bears all its sons a-way;
5. O God, our Help in a-ges past, Our Hope for years to come,

Our Shel-ter from the storm-y blast, And our e-ter-nal Home:
From ev-er-last-ing Thou art God, To end-less years the same.
Short as the watch that ends the night Be-fore the ris-ing sun.
They fly for-got-ten, as a dream Dies at the o-pening day.
Be Thou our Guard while life shall last, And our e-ter-nal Home. A-MEN.

GOD: HIS PRESENCE

112 God Moves in a Mysterious Way

DUNDEE (FRENCH): C. M.
Scottish Psalter, 1615

William Cowper, 1774

1. God moves in a mys - te - rious way His won-ders to per - form;
2. Deep in un - fath - om - a - ble mines Of nev - er - fail - ing skill
3. Ye fear - ful saints, fresh cour-age take; The clouds ye so much dread
4. Blind un - be - lief is sure to err, And scan His work in vain;

He plants His foot-steps in the sea, And rides up - on the storm.
He treas-ures up His bright de - signs, And works His sov-ereign will.
Are big with mer - cy, and shall break In bless - ings on your head.
God is His own In - ter - pre - ter, And He will make it plain. A-MEN.

112 God Moves in a Mysterious Way

MELODY IN THE TENOR

DUNDEE (FRENCH): C. M.
Scottish Psalter, 1615
Arr by Thomas Ravenscroft, 1621

This alternative arrangement may be used for one or more stanzas, the congregation singing the melody only.

113 My Soul with Expectation

From Psalm 62
Scottish Psalter, 1650

ST. FLAVIAN: C. M.
Day's Psalter, 1563

1. My soul with ex - pec - ta - tion doth De - pend on God in - deed;
2. He on - ly my sal - va - tion is, And my strong Rock is He;
3. In God my glo - ry pla - ced is, And my sal - va - tion sure;
4. Ye peo - ple, place your con - fi - dence In Him con - tin - ual - ly;

My Soul with Expectation

My strength and my sal - va - tion do From Him a - lone pro - ceed.
He on - ly is my sure de - fense: I shall not mov - ed be.
In God the Rock is of my strength, My ref - uge most se - cure.
Be - fore Him pour ye out your heart: God is our ref - uge high. A-MEN.

I Look to Thee in Every Need **114**

Samuel Longfellow, 1864

O JESU: 8. 6. 8. 6. 8. 8.
Melody from *Hirschberg Gesangbuch*, 1741

1. I look to Thee in ev - ery need, And nev - er look in vain;
2. Dis - cour - aged in the work of life, Dis - heart - ened by its load,
3. Thy calm - ness bends se - rene a - bove, My rest - less - ness to still;
4. En - fold - ed deep in Thy dear love, Held in Thy law, I stand;

I feel Thy strong and ten - der love, And all is well a - gain:
Shamed by its fail - ures or its fears, I sink be - side the road;
A - round me flows Thy quick - ening life, To nerve my fal - tering will;
Thy hand in all things I be - hold, And all things in Thy hand;

The thought of Thee is might-ier far Than sin and pain and sor - row are.
But let me on - ly think of Thee And then new heart springs up in me.
Thy pres-ence fills my sol - i - tude; Thy prov-i-dence turns all to good.
Thou lead - est me by un-sought ways, And turnest my mourn-ing in - to praise. A-MEN.

GOD: HIS PRESENCE

[107]

115 Praise the Lord, for He Is Good

From Psalm 107
The Psalter, 1912; alt., 1950

HALLE: 7. 7. 7. 7. 7. 7.
Ascribed to Franz Joseph Haydn (1732-1809)

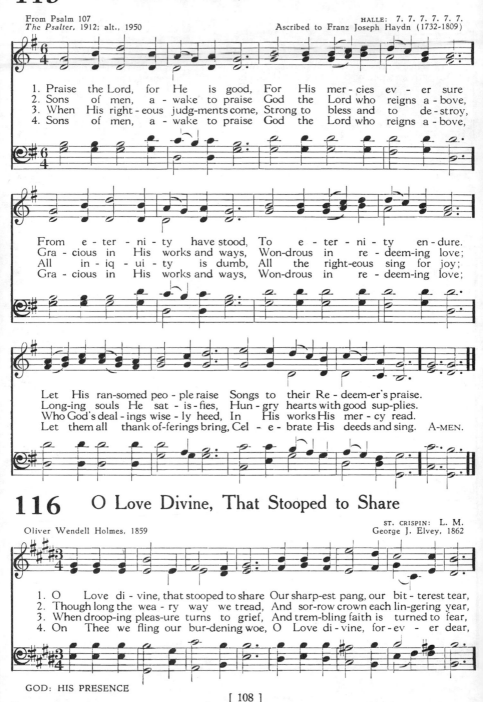

1. Praise the Lord, for He is good, For His mer-cies ev-er sure
2. Sons of men, a-wake to praise God the Lord who reigns a-bove,
3. When His right-eous judg-ments come, Strong to bless and to de-stroy,
4. Sons of men, a-wake to praise God the Lord who reigns a-bove,

From e-ter-ni-ty have stood, To e-ter-ni-ty en-dure.
Gra-cious in His works and ways, Won-drous in re-deem-ing love;
All in-iq-ui-ty is dumb, All the right-eous sing for joy;
Gra-cious in His works and ways, Won-drous in re-deem-ing love;

Let His ran-somed peo-ple raise Songs to their Re-deem-er's praise.
Long-ing souls He sat-is-fies, Hun-gry hearts with good sup-plies.
Who God's deal-ings wise-ly heed, In His works His mer-cy read.
Let them all thank of-fer-ings bring, Cel-e-brate His deeds and sing. A-MEN.

116 O Love Divine, That Stooped to Share

Oliver Wendell Holmes, 1859

ST. CRISPIN: L. M.
George J. Elvey, 1862

1. O Love di-vine, that stooped to share Our sharp-est pang, our bit-ter-est tear,
2. Though long the wea-ry way we tread, And sor-row crown each lin-ger-ing year,
3. When droop-ing pleas-ure turns to grief, And trem-bling faith is turned to fear,
4. On Thee we fling our bur-den-ing woe, O Love di-vine, for-ev-er dear,

GOD: HIS PRESENCE

O Love Divine, That Stooped to Share

On Thee we cast each earth-born care; We smile at pain while Thou art near.
No path we shun, no dark-ness dread, Our hearts still whis-pering, Thou art near.
The mur-muring wind, the quiv-ering leaf, Shall soft-ly tell us, Thou art near.
Con - tent to suf-fer, while we know, Liv - ing and dy - ing, Thou art near. A-MEN.

Words used by permission of Houghton Mifflin Company, authorized publishers.

By All Whom Thou Hast Made 117

From Psalm 86
The Psalter, 1912

AVIEMORE: 6. 6. 4. 6. 6. 6. 4,
Roger M. Hickman

1. By all whom Thou hast made Be praise and wor - ship paid
2. Help me Thy will to do, Thy truth I will pur - sue,
3. How great Thy love ap - pears That bade death's gloom - y fears

Through earth a - broad; Thy name be glo - ri - fied, There is none
Teach me to fear; Give me the sin - gle eye Thy name to
No more dis - may; O God, to an - ger slow, Save me from

great be - side, Match-less Thy works a - bide, For Thou art God.
glo - ri - fy, O Lord, my God Most High, With heart sin - cere.
ev - ery foe, Thy lov - ing - kind - ness show, Thy truth dis - play. A - MEN.

GOD: HIS PRESENCE

[109]

118

O Love of God Most Full

AYLESBURY: S. M.
Melody from *Hesperian Harp*, 1848
Harmonized by Louise McAllister, 1951

Oscar Clute (1837-1901)

1. O Love of God most full, O Love of God most free,
2. Warm as the glow-ing sun So shines Thy love on me,
3. The wild-est sea is calm, The tem-pest brings no fear,
4. O Love of God most full, O Love of God most free,

Come warm my heart, come fill my soul, Come lead me un-to Thee!
It wraps me round with kind-ly care, It draws me un-to Thee.
The dark-est night is full of light, Be-cause Thy love is near.
Thou warmest my heart, Thou fillest my soul, With might Thou strength-enest me. A-MEN.

Music copyright, 1953, by Louise McAllister. Used by permission.

119

When All Thy Mercies, O My God

TALLIS' ORDINAL: C. M.
Thomas Tallis, c. 1567

Joseph Addison, 1712

1. When all Thy mer-cies, O my God, My ris-ing soul sur-veys,
2. Un-num-bered com-forts to my soul Thy ten-der care be-stowed,
3. Ten thou-sand thou-sand pre-cious gifts My dai-ly thanks em-ploy,
4. Through all e-ter-ni-ty to Thee A joy-ful song I'll raise;

Trans-port-ed with the view, I'm lost In won-der, love, and praise.
Be-fore my in-fant heart con-ceived From whom those comforts flowed.
Nor is the least a cheer-ful heart That tastes those gifts with joy.
For, oh, e-ter-ni-ty's too short To ut-ter all Thy praise! A-MEN.

Alternative tune, "St. Peter," Hymn 130.

GOD: HIS PRESENCE

Behold the Amazing Gift of Love

120

Isaac Watts, 1709
Para. by William Cameron, 1781

ST. STEPHEN: C. M.
William Jones, 1789

1. Be - hold th' a - maz - ing gift of love The Fa - ther hath be - stowed
2. Con - cealed as yet this hon - or lies, By this dark world un - known,
3. High is the rank we now pos - sess; But high - er we shall rise;
4. Our souls, we know, when He ap - pears, Shall bear His im - age bright;
5. A hope so great, and so di - vine, May tri - als well en - dure;

On us, the sin - ful sons of men, To call us sons of God!
A world that knew not when He came, Even God's e - ter - nal Son.
Though what we shall here - aft - er be Is hid from mor - tal eyes:
For all His glo - ry, full dis-closed, Shall o - pen to our sight.
And purge the soul from sense and sin, As Christ Him-self is pure. A-MEN.

O Thou My Soul, Bless God the Lord

121

From Psalm 103
Scottish Psalter, 1650

HOWARD: C. M.
Elizabeth H. Cuthbert, c. 1810

1. O thou my soul, bless God the Lord; And all that in me is
2. Bless, O my soul, the Lord thy God, And not for - get - ful be
3. All thine in - iq - ui - ties who doth Most gra - cious - ly for - give;
4. Who doth re - deem thy life, that thou To death mayst not go down;
5. Who with a - bun-dance of good things Doth sat - is - fy thy mouth;

Be stir - red up His ho - ly name To mag - ni - fy and bless.
Of all His gra - cious ben - e - fits He hath be - stowed on thee:
Who thy dis - eas - es all and pains Doth heal, and thee re-lieve:
Who thee with lov - ing-kind-ness doth And ten - der mer - cies crown:
So that, even as the ea - gle's age, Re - new - ed is thy youth. A - MEN.

GOD: HIS PRESENCE

122 God of Compassion, in Mercy Befriend Us

John J. Moment, b. 1875

O QUANTA QUALIA: 11. 11. 11. 11.
La Feillée's *Méthode du plain-chant*, 1808

1. God of com - pas - sion, in mer - cy be - friend us;
2. Wan - dering and lost, Thou hast sought us and found us,
3. How shall we stray, with Thy hand to di - rect us,

Giv - er of grace for our needs all - a - vail - ing,
Stilled our rude hearts with Thy word of con - sol - ing;
Thou who the stars in their cours - es art guid - ing?

Wis - dom and strength for each day do Thou send us,
Wrap now Thy peace, like a man - tle, a - round us,
What shall we fear, with Thy power to pro - tect us,

Pa - tience un - tir - ing and cour - age un - fail - ing.
Guard - ing our thoughts and our pas - sions con - troll - ing.
We who walk forth in Thy great - ness con - fid - ing? A - MEN.

Words used by permission of the author.

GOD: HIS PRESENCE

[112]

Call Jehovah Thy Salvation

From Psalm 91
James Montgomery, 1822

HYFRYDOL: 8. 7. 8. 7. D.
Rowland Hugh Prichard, 1855

1. Call Je - ho - vah thy Sal - va - tion, Rest be-neath th' Al-might - y's shade,
2. From the sword at noon-day wast-ing, From the noi - some pes - ti - lence,
3. Since, with pure and firm af - fec - tion, Thou on God hast set thy love,

In His se - cret hab - i - ta - tion Dwell, and nev - er be dis-mayed:
In the depth of mid - night blast-ing, God shall be thy sure De-fense:
With the wings of His pro - tec - tion He will shield thee from a - bove:

There no tu - mult shall a - larm thee, Thou shalt dread no hid - den snare;
He shall charge His an - gel le - gions Watch and ward o'er thee to keep;
Thou shalt call on Him in trou - ble, He will heark-en, He will save;

Guile nor vi - o - lence can harm thee, In e - ter - nal safe-guard there.
Though thou walk through hos-tile re - gions, Though in des-ert wilds thou sleep.
Here for grief re - ward thee dou - ble, Crown with life be - yond the grave. A-MEN.

Alternative tune, "Autumn," Hymn 10.

GOD: HIS PRESENCE

124 Be Not Dismayed Whate'er Betide

Civilla D. Martin, 1905

MARTIN: 8. 6. 8. 6. with Refrain
W. Stillman Martin, 1905

1. Be not dis - mayed what-e'er be - tide, God will take care of you;
2. Through days of toil when heart doth fail, God will take care of you;
3. All you may need He will pro - vide, God will take care of you;
4. No mat - ter what may be the test, God will take care of you;

Be - neath His wings of love a - bide, God will take care of you.
When dan - gers fierce your path as - sail, God will take care of you.
Noth - ing you ask will be de - nied, God will take care of you.
Lean, wea - ry one, up - on His breast, God will take care of you.

REFRAIN

God will take care of you, Through ev - ery day, O'er all the way;

He will take care of you, God will take care of you. A - MEN.

Words and music copyright, 1905; renewal, 1933, by W. S. Martin. Assigned to Hope Publishing Company. Used by permission.

GOD: HIS PRESENCE

Come, Let Us to the Lord Our God   125

John Morison
Scottish Paraphrases, 1781

KILMARNOCK: C. M.
Neil Dougall (1776-1862)

1. Come, let us to the Lord our God With con - trite hearts re - turn;
2. His voice com-mands the tem - pest forth And stills the storm-y wave;
3. Long hath the night of sor - row reigned; The dawn shall bring us light;
4. Our hearts, if God we seek to know, Shall know Him, and re - joice;
5. As dew up - on the ten - der herb, Dif - fus - ing fra - grance round,
6. So shall His pres - ence bless our souls, And shed a joy - ful light;

Our God is gra - cious, nor will leave The des - o - late to mourn.
And though His arm be strong to smite, 'Tis al - so strong to save.
God shall ap - pear, and we shall rise With glad - ness in His sight.
His com - ing like the morn shall be, Like morn - ing songs His voice.
As showers that ush - er in the spring, And cheer the thirst-y ground,
That hal - lowed morn shall chase a - way The sor - rows of the night. A-MEN.

In Sweet Communion, Lord, with Thee   126

From Psalm 73
The Psalter, 1912

PRAYER: C. M.
William U. Butcher

1. In sweet com - mun - ion, Lord, with Thee I con - stant - ly a - bide;
2. Thy coun - sel through my earth - ly way Shall guide me and con - trol,
3. Whom have I, Lord, in heaven but Thee, To whom my thoughts as - pire?
4. Though flesh and heart should faint and fail, The Lord will ev - er be
5. To live a - part from God is death, 'Tis good His face to seek;

My hand Thou hold-est in Thy own To keep me near Thy side.
And then to glo - ry aft - er - ward Thou wilt re - ceive my soul.
And, hav - ing Thee, on earth is nought That I can yet de - sire.
The strength and por - tion of my heart, My God e - ter - nal - ly.
My ref - uge is the liv - ing God, His praise I long to speak. A-MEN.

GOD: HIS PRESENCE

127 O Lord, by Thee Delivered

From Psalm 30
The Psalter, 1912; alt., 1953

CRUCIFIX: 7. 6. 7. 6. D.
Arr. by C. C. Converse, 1896; alt.
Har. for this book, 1953

1. O Lord, by Thee de - liv - ered, I Thee with songs ex - tol;
2. His ho - ly name re - mem - ber, Ye saints, give thanks and praise;
3. My grief is turned to glad - ness, To Thee my thanks I raise,

My foes Thou hast not suf - fered To glo - ry o'er my fall.
His an - ger lasts a mo - ment, His fa - vor all our days;
Who hast re - moved my sor - row And gird - ed me with praise;

O Lord, my God, I sought Thee, And Thou didst heal and save;
For sor - row, like a pil - grim, May tar - ry for a night,
And now, no long - er si - lent, My heart Thy praise will sing;

Thou, Lord, from death didst ran - som And keep me from the grave.
But joy the heart will glad - den When dawns the morn - ing light.
O Lord, my God, for - ev - er My thanks to Thee I bring. A-MEN.

Music copyright by John Ribble.

GOD: HIS PRESENCE

Our God, to Whom We Turn

128

O GOTT, DU FROMMER GOTT: 6. 7. 6. 7. 6. 6. 6. 6.
Melody by Ahasuerus Fritzsch, 1679
Har. by Johann Sebastian Bach (1685-1750)

Edward Grubb, 1925

1. Our God, to whom we turn When weary with il-lu-sion,
2. Thou art Thy-self the Truth; Though we, who fain would find Thee,
3. All beau-ty speaks of Thee— The moun-tains and the riv-ers,
4. Wher-ev-er good-ness lurks We catch Thy tones ap-peal-ing;
5. Thou hid-den fount of love, Of peace, and truth, and beau-ty,

Whose stars se-rene-ly burn A-bove this earth's con-fu-sion,
Have tried, with thoughts un-couth, In fee-ble words to bind Thee,
The line of lift-ed sea, Where spread-ing moon-light quiv-ers,
Where man for jus-tice works Thou art Thy-self re-veal-ing;
In-spire us from a-bove With joy and strength for du-ty;

Thine is the might-y plan, The stead-fast or-der sure,
It is be-cause Thou art We're driv-en to the quest;
The deep-toned or-gan blast That rolls through arch-es dim—
The blood of man, for man On friend-ship's al-tar spilt,
May Thy fresh light a-rise With-in each cloud-ed heart,

In which the world be-gan, En-dures, and shall en-dure.
Till truth from false-hood part, Our souls can find no rest.
Hints of the mu-sic vast Of Thy e-ter-nal hymn.
Be-trays the mys-tic plan On which Thy house is built.
And give us o-pen eyes To see Thee as Thou art. A-MEN.

Words used by permission of the author's heirs.

[117]

GOD: HIS PRESENCE

129   O Lord, My Inmost Heart and Thought

From Psalm 139
The Psalter, 1912

WALSALL: C. M.
Ascribed to Henry Purcell (1658-1695)
In Anchors' *A Choice Collection*, c. 1721

1. O Lord, my in-most heart and thought Thy search-ing eye doth see;
2. Each spo-ken word, each si-lent thought, Thou, Lord, dost un-der-stand;
3. If I the wings of morn-ing take To some re-mot-est land,
4. From Thee, O Lord, I can-not hide, Though dark-ness cov-er me;
5. Search me, O God, and know my heart, Try me, my thoughts to know;

Wher-e'er I rest, wher-e'er I go, My ways are known to Thee.
Be-fore me and be-hind art Thou, Re-strain-ing by Thy hand.
Still I shall be up-held by Thee And guid-ed by Thy hand.
The dark-ness and the light of day Are both a-like to Thee.
O lead me, if in sin I stray, In paths of life to go. A-MEN.

GOD: HIS PRESENCE

130   How Sweet the Name of Jesus Sounds

John Newton, 1779
Stanza 4, line 1, alt.

ST. PETER: C. M.
Alexander R. Reinagle, c. 1830

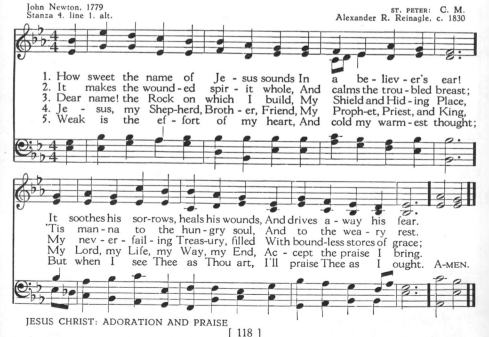

1. How sweet the name of Je-sus sounds In a be-liev-er's ear!
2. It makes the wound-ed spir-it whole, And calms the trou-bled breast;
3. Dear name! the Rock on which I build, My Shield and Hid-ing Place,
4. Je-sus, my Shep-herd, Broth-er, Friend, My Proph-et, Priest, and King,
5. Weak is the ef-fort of my heart, And cold my warm-est thought;

It soothes his sor-rows, heals his wounds, And drives a-way his fear.
'Tis man-na to the hun-gry soul, And to the wea-ry rest.
My nev-er-fail-ing Treas-ury, filled With bound-less stores of grace;
My Lord, my Life, my Way, my End, Ac-cept the praise I bring.
But when I see Thee as Thou art, I'll praise Thee as I ought. A-MEN.

JESUS CHRIST: ADORATION AND PRAISE

[118]

Come, Christians, Join to Sing

131

MADRID: 6. 6. 6. 6. D.
Source unknown
Har. by David Evans, 1927

Christian Henry Bateman, 1843; alt.

1. Come, Chris-tians, join to sing Al - le - lu - ia! A - men!
2. Come, lift your hearts on high; Al - le - lu - ia! A - men!
3. Praise yet our Christ a - gain; Al - le - lu - ia! A - men!

Loud praise to Christ our King; Al - le - lu - ia! A - men!
Let prais - es fill the sky; Al - le - lu - ia! A - men!
Life shall not end the strain; Al - le - lu - ia! A - men!

Let all, with heart and voice, Be - fore His throne re - joice;
He is our Guide and Friend; To us He'll con - de - scend;
On heav - en's bliss - ful shore His good - ness we'll a - dore,

Praise is His gra-cious choice: Al - le - lu - ia! A - men!
His love shall nev - er end: Al - le - lu - ia! A - men!
Sing - ing for - ev - er-more, "Al - le - lu - ia! A - men!" A-men.

Music from *The Church Hymnary*, Revised Edition. Used by permission of Oxford University Press.

JESUS CHRIST: ADORATION AND PRAISE

132 All Hail the Power of Jesus' Name!

Edward Perronet, 1779, 1780; alt.
Stanza 4, John Rippon, 1787

(FIRST TUNE)

CORONATION: C. M.
Oliver Holden, 1793

1. All hail the power of Je - sus' name! Let an - gels pros - trate fall;
2. Ye cho - sen seed of Is - rael's race, Ye ran-somed from the Fall,
3. Let ev - ery kin - dred, ev - ery tribe, On this ter - res - trial ball,
4. O that with yon - der sa - cred throng We at His feet may fall!

Bring forth the roy - al di - a - dem, And crown Him Lord of all;
Hail Him who saves you by His grace, And crown Him Lord of all;
To Him all maj - es - ty as - cribe, And crown Him Lord of all;
We'll join the ev - er - last - ing song, And crown Him Lord of all;

Bring forth the roy - al di - a - dem, And crown Him Lord of all!
Hail Him who saves you by His grace, And crown Him Lord of all!
To Him all maj - es - ty as - cribe, And crown Him Lord of all!
We'll join the ev - er - last - ing song, And crown Him Lord of all! A-MEN.

(SECOND TUNE)

Edward Perronet, 1779, 1780; alt.

MILES' LANE: C. M.
William Shrubsole, 1785

1. All hail the power of Je - sus' name! Let an - gels pros - trate fall;

Bring forth the roy - al di - a - dem, And crown Him,

JESUS CHRIST: ADORATION AND PRAISE

[120]

All Hail the Power of Jesus' Name!

crown Him, crown Him, crown Him Lord of all! A-MEN.

Look, Ye Saints, the Sight Is Glorious 133

CORONAE: 8. 7. 8. 7. 4. 7.

Thomas Kelly, 1809

William H. Monk, 1871

1. Look, ye saints, the sight is glo-rious; See the Man of Sor-rows now;
2. Crown the Sav-iour! An-gels, crown Him! Rich the tro-phies Je-sus brings;
3. Sin - ners in de - ri-sion crowned Him, Mock-ing thus the Sav-iour's claim;
4. Hark! those bursts of ac - cla - ma - tion! Hark! those loud tri - um-phant chords!

From the fight re-turned vic - to - rious, Ev - ery knee to Him shall bow:
In the seat of power en-throne Him, While the vault of heav - en rings:
Saints and an - gels crowd a - round Him, Own His ti - tle, praise His name:
Je - sus takes the high - est sta-tion; O what joy the sight af-fords!

Crown Him! Crown Him! Crowns be - come the Vic - tor's brow.
Crown Him! Crown Him! Crown the Sav-iour King of Kings.
Crown Him! Crown Him! Spread a - broad the Vic - tor's fame!
Crown Him! Crown Him King of Kings, and Lord of Lords. A-MEN.

JESUS CHRIST: ADORATION AND PRAISE

134   O Could I Speak the Matchless Worth

ARIEL: 8. 8. 6. 8. 8. 6.
Wolfgang A. Mozart (1756-1791)
Arr. by Lowell Mason, 1836

Samuel Medley, 1789

1. O could I speak the match - less worth,
2. I'd sing the pre - cious blood He spilt,
3. I'd sing the char - ac - ters He bears,
4. Soon, the de - light - ful day will come

O could I sound the glo - ries forth Which in my Sav - iour shine!
My ran - som from the dread - ful guilt Of sin, and wrath di - vine;
And all the forms of love He wears, Ex - alt - ed on His throne:
When my dear Lord will bring me home, And I shall see His face;

I'd sing His glo - rious right-eous-ness, And mag - ni - fy the won-drous grace
I'd sing His glo - rious right-eous-ness, In which all-per - fect, heaven-ly dress
In loft-iest songs of sweet-est praise, I would to ev - er - last - ing days
Then with my Sav-iour, Broth-er, Friend, A blest e - ter - ni - ty I'll spend,

Which made sal - va - tion mine, Which made sal - va - tion mine.
My soul shall ev - er shine, My soul shall ev - er shine.
Make all His glo - ries known, Make all His glo - ries known.
Tri - um-phant in His grace, Tri - um-phant in His grace. A - MEN.

JESUS CHRIST: ADORATION AND PRAISE

[122]

Fairest Lord Jesus

135

(FIRST TUNE)

German, 17th century
Translator unknown

CRUSADER'S HYMN: 5. 6. 8. 5. 5. 8.
Silesian folk song
In *Schlesische Volkslieder*, Leipzig, 1842

1. Fair-est Lord Je-sus, Rul-er of all na-ture, O Thou of God and man the Son,
2. Fair are the mead-ows, Fair-er still the wood-lands, Robed in the bloom-ing garb of spring:
3. Fair is the sun-shine, Fair-er still the moon-light, And all the twink-ling, star-ry host:

Thee will I cher-ish, Thee will I hon-or, Thou, my soul's Glo-ry, Joy, and Crown.
Je-sus is fair-er, Je-sus is pur-er, Who makes the woe-ful heart to sing.
Je-sus shines bright-er, Je-sus shines pur-er, Than all the an-gels heaven can boast. A-MEN.

Trans. by Joseph A. Seiss, 1873

Optional Stanza

5. 5. 7. 5. 5. 8.

Beautiful Saviour, Lord of the nations,
Son of God and Son of Man!
Glory and honor, praise, adoration,
Now and forevermore be Thine!

Fairest Lord Jesus

135

(SECOND TUNE)

German, 17th century
Translator unknown

SCHÖNSTER HERR JESU: 5. 6. 8. 5. 5. 8.
Münster Gesangbuch, 1677

1. Fair - est Lord Je-sus, Rul-er of all na-ture, O Thou of God and man the Son,
2. Fair are the mead-ows, Fair-er still the wood-lands, Robed in the bloom-ing garb of spring:
3. Fair is the sun-shine, Fair-er still the moon-light, And all the twink-ling, star-ry host:

Thee will I cher-ish, Thee will I hon-or, Thou, my soul's Glo-ry, Joy, and Crown.
Je - sus is fair-er, Je-sus is pur-er, Who makes the woe-ful heart to sing.
Je - sus shines bright-er, Je-sus shines pur-er, Than all the an-gels heaven can boast. A-MEN.

JESUS CHRIST: ADORATION AND PRAISE

[123]

136 Christ Is the World's Redeemer

Columba (521-597)
Trans. by Duncan Macgregor (1854-1923)

MOVILLE: 7. 6. 7. 6. D.
Traditional Irish melody
Arr. for the *Church Hymnal*

1. Christ is the world's re - deem - er, The lov - er of the pure,
2. Christ hath our host sur - round - ed With clouds of mar - tyrs bright,
3. Down in the realm of dark - ness He lay a cap - tive bound,
4. All glo - ry to the Fa - ther, The un - be - got - ten One;

The fount of heaven-ly wis - dom, Our trust and hope se - cure;
Who wave their palms in tri - umph, And fire us for the fight.
But at the hour ap - point - ed He rose, a vic - tor crowned;
All hon - or be to Je - sus, His sole - be - got - ten Son;

The ar - mor of His sol - diers, The Lord of earth and sky;
Christ the red cross as - cend - ed To save a world un - done,
And now, to heaven as - cend - ed, He sits up - on the throne,
And to the Ho - ly Spir - it— The per - fect Trin - i - ty.

Our health while we are liv - ing, Our life when we shall die.
And, suf - fering for the sin - ful, Our full re-demp - tion won.
In glo - ri - ous do - min - ion, His Fa - ther's and His own.
Let all the worlds give an - swer, "A - men—so let it be." A-MEN.

Music copyright by the Association for Promoting Christian Knowledge. Used by permission.
JESUS CHRIST: ADORATION AND PRAISE

Blessing and Honor and Glory and Power 137

Horatius Bonar (1808-1889)

O QUANTA QUALIA: 10. 10. 10. 10.
La Feillée's *Méthode du plain-chant,* 1808

1. Bless - ing and hon - or and glo - ry and power,
2. Sound - eth the heaven of the heavens with His name;
3. Ev - er as - cend - eth the song and the joy;
4. Give we the glo - ry and praise to the Lamb;

Wis - dom and rich - es and strength ev - er - more
Ring - eth the earth with His glo - ry and fame;
Ev - er de - scend - eth the love from on high;
Take we the robe and the harp and the palm;

Give ye to Him who our bat - tle hath won,
O - cean and moun - tain, stream, for - est, and flower
Bless - ing and hon - or and glo - ry and praise—
Sing we the song of the Lamb that was slain,

Whose are the King - dom, the crown, and the throne.
Ech - o His prais - es and tell of His power.
This is the theme of the hymns that we raise.
Dy - ing in weak - ness, but ris - ing to reign. A - MEN.

JESUS CHRIST: ADORATION AND PRAISE

138 Light of the World, We Hail Thee

John S. B. Monsell, 1863

SALVE DOMINE: 7. 6. 7. 6. D.
Lawrence W. Watson, 1909

1. Light of the world, we hail Thee, Flush-ing the east-ern skies;
2. Light of the world, Thy beau-ty Steals in-to ev-ery heart,
3. Light of the world, be-fore Thee Our spir-its pros-trate fall;
4. Light of the world, il-lu-mine This dark-ened earth of Thine,

Nev-er shall dark-ness veil Thee A-gain from hu-man eyes;
And glo-ri-fies with du-ty Life's poor-est, hum-blest part;
We wor-ship, we a-dore Thee, Thou Light, the Life of all;
Till ev-ery-thing that's hu-man Be filled with what's di-vine;

Too long, a-las, with-hold-en, Now spread from shore to shore;
Thou rob-est in Thy splen-dor The sim-ple ways of men,
With Thee is no for-get-ting Of all Thy hand hath made;
Till ev-ery tongue and na-tion, From sin's do-min-ion free,

Thy light, so glad and gold-en, Shall set on earth no more.
And help-est them to ren-der Light back to Thee a-gain.
Thy ris-ing hath no set-ting, Thy sun-shine hath no shade.
Rise in the new cre-a-tion Which springs from love and Thee. A-MEN.

Music used by permission of G. R. D. Watson.
JESUS CHRIST: ADORATION AND PRAISE

Blessed Assurance, Jesus Is Mine!

ASSURANCE: 9. 10. 9. 9. with Refrain

Fanny Crosby, 1873

Phoebe P. Knapp, 1873

1. Bless-ed as-sur-ance, Je-sus is mine! O what a fore-taste of glo-ry di-
2. Per-fect sub-mis-sion, per-fect de-light, Vi-sions of rap-ture now burst on my
3. Per-fect sub-mis-sion, all is at rest, I in my Sav-iour am hap-py and

vine! Heir of sal-va-tion, pur-chase of God, Born of His
sight; An-gels de-scend-ing, bring from a-bove Ech-oes of
blest, Watch-ing and wait-ing, look-ing a-bove, Filled with His

REFRAIN

Spir-it, washed in His blood. This is my sto-ry, this is my
mer-cy, whis-pers of love.
good-ness, lost in His love.

song, Prais-ing my Sav-iour all the day long; This is my

sto-ry, this is my song, Prais-ing my Sav-iour all the day long. A-MEN.

JESUS CHRIST: ADORATION AND PRAISE

140 Rejoice, the Lord Is King

Charles Wesley, 1746

DARWALL'S 148TH: 6. 6. 6. 6. 8. 8.
John Darwall, 1770

1. Re - joice, the Lord is King: Your Lord and King a - dore!
2. His King - dom can - not fail, He rules o'er earth and heaven;
3. He all His foes shall quell, Shall all our sins de - stroy,

Re - joice, give thanks, and sing, And tri - umph
The keys of death and hell Are to our
And ev - ery bos - om swell With pure se -

ev - er - more: Lift up your heart, lift up your voice!
Je - sus given: Lift up your heart, lift up your voice!
raph - ic joy: Lift up your heart, lift up your voice!

Re - joice, a - gain I say, re - joice!
Re - joice, a - gain I say, re - joice!
Re - joice, a - gain I say, re - joice! A - MEN.

JESUS CHRIST: ADORATION AND PRAISE

O for a Thousand Tongues to Sing 141

Charles Wesley, 1739; alt.

AZMON: C. M.
Carl G. Gläser, 1828
Arr. by Lowell Mason. 1839

1. O for a thou-sand tongues to sing My dear Re-deem-er's praise,
2. Je-sus, the name that charms our fears, That bids our sor-rows cease;
3. He breaks the power of reign-ing sin, He sets the pris-oner free;
4. My gra-cious Mas-ter and my God, As-sist me to pro-claim,

The glo-ries of my God and King, The tri-umphs of His grace!
'Tis mu-sic in the sin-ner's ears, 'Tis life, and health, and peace.
His blood can make the sin-ful clean, His blood a-vailed for me.
To spread through all the earth a-broad, The hon-ors of Thy name. A-MEN.

Alternative tune, "Richmond," Hymn 436.

Majestic Sweetness Sits Enthroned 142

Samuel Stennett, 1787

ORTONVILLE: C. M.
Thomas Hastings, 1837

1. Ma-jes-tic sweet-ness sits en-throned Up-on the Sav-iour's brow; His head with ra-diant
2. No mor-tal can with Him com-pare A-mong the sons of men; Fair-er is He than
3. To Him I owe my life and breath, And all the joys I have; He makes me tri-umph
4. To heaven, the place of His a-bode, He brings my wea-ry feet; Shows me the glo-ries
5. Since from His boun-ty I re-ceive Such proofs of love di-vine, Had I a thou-sand

glo-ries crowned, His lips with grace o'er-flow, His lips with grace o'er-flow.
all the fair That fill the heaven-ly train, That fill the heaven-ly train.
o-ver death, And saves me from the grave, And saves me from the grave.
of my God, And makes my joys com-plete, And makes my joys com-plete.
hearts to give, Lord, they should all be Thine, Lord, they should all be Thine. A-MEN.

JESUS CHRIST: ADORATION AND PRAISE

[129]

143 At the Name of Jesus

Caroline Maria Noel, 1870
Stanza 5 alt.

KING'S WESTON: 6. 5. 6. 5. D.
R. Vaughan Williams, 1925
Four-part arr. for this book, 1953

1. At the name of Je - sus Ev - ery knee shall bow,
2. Hum - bled for a sea - son, To re - ceive a name
3. Bore it up tri - umph - ant, With its hu - man light,
4. In your hearts en - throne Him; There let Him sub - due
5. Broth - ers, this Lord Je - sus Shall re - turn a - gain,

Ev - ery tongue con - fess Him King of Glo - ry now;
From the lips of sin - ners, Un - to whom He came,
Through all ranks of crea - tures, To the cen - tral height,
All that is not ho - ly, All that is not true:
With His Fa - ther's glo - ry O'er the earth to - reign;

'Tis the Fa - ther's pleas - ure We should call Him Lord,
Faith - ful - ly He bore it Spot - less to the last,
To the throne of God - head, To the Fa - ther's breast;
Crown Him as your Cap - tain In temp - ta - tion's hour;
For all wreaths of em - pire Meet up - on His brow,

Who from the be - gin - ning Was the migh - ty Word.
Brought it back vic - to - rious, When from death He passed;
Filled it with the glo - ry Of that per - fect rest.
Let His will en - fold you In its light and power.
And our hearts con - fess Him King of Glo - ry now. A - MEN.

Music, in four-part arrangement, used by permission of Oxford University Press.

JESUS CHRIST: ADORATION AND PRAISE

John Calvin, 1545
Trans. by Elizabeth L. Smith, 1868; alt.

TOULON: 10. 10. 10. 10.
Genevan Psalter, 1551

1. I greet Thee, who my sure Re-deem-er art,
2. Thou art the King of mer-cy and of grace,
3. Thou art the life, by which a-lone we live,
4. Thou hast the true and per-fect gen-tle-ness,
5. Our hope is in no oth-er save in Thee;

My on-ly Trust and Sav-iour of my heart,
Reign-ing om-nip-o-tent in ev-ery place:
And all our sub-stance and our strength re-ceive;
No harsh-ness hast Thou and no bit-ter-ness:
Our faith is built up-on Thy prom-ise free;

Who pain didst un-der-go for my poor sake;
So come, O King, and our whole be-ing sway;
Sus-tain us by Thy faith and by Thy power,
O grant to us the grace we find in Thee,
Lord, give us peace, and make us calm and sure,

I pray Thee from our hearts all cares to take.
Shine on us with the light of Thy pure day.
And give us strength in ev-ery try-ing hour.
That we may dwell in per-fect u-ni-ty.
That in Thy strength we ev-er-more en-dure. A-MEN.

JESUS CHRIST: ADORATION AND PRAISE

145 O Light, Whose Beams Illumine All

Edward H. Plumptre, 1864

ST. PETERSBURG: 8. 8. 8. 8. 8. 8.
Dimitri S. Bortniansky, 1825

1. O Light, whose beams il - lu - mine all From twi - light
2. O Way, through whom our souls draw near To yon e -
3. O Truth, be - fore whose shrine we bow, Thou price - less
4. O Life, the Well that ev - er flows To slake the

dawn to per - fect day, Shine Thou be - fore the shad - ows fall
ter - nal home of peace, Where per - fect love shall cast out fear,
Pearl for all who seek, To Thee our ear - liest strength we vow,
thirst of those that faint, Thy power to bless what ser - aph knows?

That lead our wan-dering feet a - stray; At morn and eve Thy
And earth's vain toil and wan - dering cease: In strength or weak - ness
Thy love will bless the pure and meek; When dreams or mists be -
Thy joy su - preme what words can paint? In earth's last hour of

ra - diance pour, That youth may love, and age a - dore.
may we see Our heaven-ward path, O Lord, through Thee.
guile our sight, Turn Thou our dark - ness in - to light.
fleet - ing breath Be Thou our Con - queror o - ver death. A - MEN.

JESUS CHRIST: ADORATION AND PRAISE

Hail to the Lord's Anointed

146

James Montgomery, 1822

ROCKPORT: 7. 6. 7. 6. D.
T. Tertius Noble, 1938

1. Hail to the Lord's A - noint - ed, Great Da - vid's great-er Son!
2. Kings shall fall down be - fore Him, And gold and in - cense bring;
3. He shall come down like show - ers Up - on the fruit - ful earth,
4. O'er ev - ery foe vic - to - rious, He on His throne shall rest,

Hail, in the time ap - point - ed, His reign on earth be - gun!
All na - tions shall a - dore Him, His praise all peo - ple sing;
And love, joy, hope, like flow - ers, Spring in His path to birth;
From age to age more glo - rious, All bless - ing and all blest;

He comes to break op - pres - sion, To set the cap - tive free,
For He shall have do - min - ion O'er riv - er, sea, and shore,
Be - fore Him on the moun - tains Shall peace, the her - ald, go;
The tide of time shall nev - er His cov - e - nant re - move;

To take a - way trans - gres - sion, And rule in e - qui - ty.
Far as the ea - gle's pin - ion Or dove's light wing can soar.
And right-eous - ness in foun-tains From hill to val - ley flow.
His name shall stand for - ev - er; That name to us is Love. A-MEN.

Music copyright, 1941, by Eden Publishing House. Used by permission.
Alternative tunes, "Webb," Hymn 99, and "Tours," Hymn 186.

[133]

JESUS CHRIST: HIS ADVENT

147 O Come, O Come, Emmanuel

Latin, c. 12th century
Stanzas 1, 2, trans. by John Mason Neale, 1851, 1853
Stanza 3 trans. by Henry Sloane Coffin, 1916

VENI EMMANUEL: 8. 8. 8. 8. 8. 8.
Plain song (Mode I), 13th century
Arr. for *The Hymnal Noted*, 1854

1. O come, O come, Em - man - u - el, And ran - som cap - tive
2. O come, Thou Day-spring, come and cheer Our spir - its by Thine
3. O come, De - sire of na - tions, bind All peo - ples in one

Is - ra - el, That mourns in lone - ly ex - ile here
ad - vent here; Dis - perse the gloom - y clouds of night,
heart and mind; Bid en - vy, strife, and dis - cord cease;

Un - til the Son of God ap - pear. Re - joice! Re - joice! Em -
And death's dark shad - ows put to flight. Re - joice! Re - joice! Em -
Fill the whole world with heav - en's peace. Re - joice! Re - joice! Em -

man - u - el Shall come to thee, O Is - ra - el!
man - u - el Shall come to thee, O Is - ra - el!
man - u - el Shall come to thee, O Is - ra - el! A - MEN.

Stanza 3 from *Hymns of the Kingdom of God*, Coffin and Vernon, copyright, 1910, 1916. Used by permission of Harper & Brothers, publishers.

JESUS CHRIST: HIS ADVENT

[134]

Let All Mortal Flesh Keep Silence

148

From the Liturgy of St. James
Trans. by Gerard Moultrie, 1864

PICARDY: 8. 7. 8. 7. 8. 7.
Traditional French melody

In unison

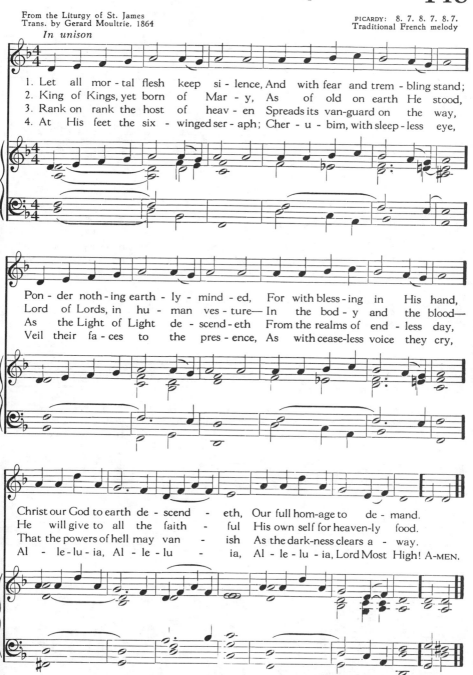

1. Let all mor-tal flesh keep si-lence, And with fear and trem-bling stand;
2. King of Kings, yet born of Mar-y, As of old on earth He stood,
3. Rank on rank the host of heav-en Spreads its van-guard on the way,
4. At His feet the six-winged ser-aph; Cher-u-bim, with sleep-less eye,

Pon-der noth-ing earth-ly-mind-ed, For with bless-ing in His hand,
Lord of Lords, in hu-man ves-ture— In the bod-y and the blood—
As the Light of Light de-scend-eth From the realms of end-less day,
Veil their fa-ces to the pres-ence, As with cease-less voice they cry,

Christ our God to earth de-scend-eth, Our full hom-age to de-mand.
He will give to all the faith-ful His own self for heaven-ly food.
That the powers of hell may van-ish As the dark-ness clears a-way.
Al-le-lu-ia, Al-le-lu-ia, Al-le-lu-ia, Lord Most High! A-MEN.

JESUS CHRIST: HIS ADVENT

[135]

149 Watchman, Tell Us of the Night

ST. GEORGE'S, WINDSOR: 7. 7. 7. 7. D.
John Bowring, 1825
George J. Elvey, 1859

1. Watch-man, tell us of the night, What its signs of prom-ise are:
2. Watch-man, tell us of the night; High - er yet that star as-cends:
3. Watch-man, tell us of the night, For the morn-ing seems to dawn:

Trav - eler, o'er yon moun-tain's height, See that glo - ry - beam-ing star!
Trav - eler, bless - ed - ness and light, Peace and truth, its course por - tends.
Trav - eler, dark-ness takes its flight; Doubt and ter - ror are with-drawn.

Watch - man, doth its beau-teous ray Aught of joy or hope fore - tell?
Watch - man, will its beams a - lone Gild the spot that gave them birth?
Watch - man, let thy wan-derings cease; Hie thee to thy qui - et home.

Trav-eler, yes; it brings the day, Prom-ised day of Is - ra - el.
Trav-eler, a - ges are its own, And it bursts o'er all the earth!
Trav-eler, lo, the Prince of Peace, Lo, the Son of God, is come! A - MEN.

Alternative tune, "Aberystwyth," Hymn 216.
JESUS CHRIST: HIS ADVENT

[136]

Hark, What a Sound

Frederick William Henry Myers (1843-1901)

WELWYN: 11. 10. 11. 10.
Alfred Scott-Gatty, 1902

1. Hark, what a sound, and too di - vine for hear - ing,
2. Sure - ly He com - eth, and a thou-sand voi - ces
3. So e - ven I, and with a pang more thrill - ing,
4. Yea, through life, death, through sor - row and through sin - ning

Stirs on the earth and trem - bles in the air!
Shout to the saints and to the deaf are dumb;
So e - ven I, and with a hope more sweet,
He shall suf - fice me, for He hath suf - ficed;

Is it the thun - der of the Lord's ap - pear - ing?
Sure - ly He com - eth, and the earth re - joi - ces,
Yearn for the sign, O Christ, of Thy ful - fill - ing,
Christ is the end, for Christ was the be - gin - ning,

Is it the mu - sic of His peo - ple's prayer?
Glad in His com - ing who hath sworn, "I come."
Faint for the flam - ing of Thine ad - vent feet.
Christ the be - gin - ning, for the end is Christ. A - MEN.

Music used by permission of Mrs. Denis Hyde and the Abbot of Downside.

JESUS CHRIST: HIS ADVENT

151 Come, Thou Long-expected Jesus

(FIRST TUNE)

Charles Wesley, 1744

HYFRYDOL: 8. 7. 8. 7. D.
Rowland Hugh Prichard, 1855

1. Come, Thou long - ex - pect - ed Je - sus, Born to set Thy peo - ple free;
2. Born Thy peo - ple to de - liv - er, Born a child and yet a King,

From our fears and sins re - lease us; Let us find our rest in Thee.
Born to reign in us for - ev - er, Now Thy gra - cious King-dom bring.

Is - rael's Strength and Con - so - la - tion, Hope of all the earth Thou art;
By Thine own e - ter - nal Spir - it Rule in all our hearts a - lone;

Dear De - sire of ev - ery na - tion, Joy of ev - ery long-ing heart.
By Thine all - suf - fi - cient mer - it Raise us to Thy glo-rious throne. A-MEN.

JESUS CHRIST: HIS ADVENT

[138]

Come, Thou Long-expected Jesus
(SECOND TUNE)

151

Charles Wesley, 1744

STUTTGART: 8. 7. 8. 7.
Arr. from *Psalmodia Sacra*, Gotha, 1715

1. Come, Thou long-ex-pect-ed Je-sus, Born to set Thy peo-ple free;
2. Is-rael's Strength and Con-so-la-tion, Hope of all the earth Thou art;
3. Born Thy peo-ple to de-liv-er, Born a child and yet a King,
4. By Thine own e-ter-nal Spir-it Rule in all our hearts a-lone;

From our fears and sins re-lease us; Let us find our rest in Thee.
Dear De-sire of ev-ery na-tion, Joy of ev-ery long-ing heart.
Born to reign in us for-ev-er, Now Thy gra-cious King-dom bring.
By Thine all-suf-fi-cient mer-it Raise us to Thy glo-rious throne. A-MEN.

Lift Up Your Heads, Ye Mighty Gates

152

From Psalm 24
George Weissel, 1642
Trans. by Catherine Winkworth, 1855

TRURO: L. M.
T. Williams' *Psalmodia Evangelica*, 1789

1. Lift up your heads, ye might-y gates, Be-hold, the King of Glo-ry waits;
2. Fling wide the por-tals of your heart; Make it a tem-ple, set a-part
3. Re-deem-er, come! I o-pen wide My heart to Thee; here, Lord, a-bide.

The King of Kings is draw-ing near; The Sav-iour of the world is here!
From earth-ly use for heav-en's em-ploy, A-dorned with prayer, and love, and joy.
Let me Thy in-ner pres-ence feel; Thy grace and love in me re-veal. A-MEN.

For higher key, see Hymn 481.

JESUS CHRIST: HIS ADVENT

153 The Race That Long in Darkness Pined

John Morison
Scottish Paraphrases, 1781

COVENANTERS: C. M.
Traditional melody
Arr. by A. L. Jacob, 1938

In unison

1. The race that long in dark-ness pined Have seen a glo-rious light;
2. To hail Thy rise, Thou bet-ter Sun! The gath-ering na-tions come,
3. To us a Child of hope is born, To us a Son is given;
4. His name shall be the Prince of Peace, For ev-er-more a-dored,
5. His power in-creas-ing still shall spread, His reign no end shall know;

The peo-ple dwell in day who dwelt In death's sur-round-ing night.
Joy-ous, as when the reap-ers bear The har-vest treas-ures home.
Him shall the tribes of earth o-bey, Him all the hosts of heaven.
The Won-der-ful, the Coun-sel-or, The great and might-y Lord.
Jus-tice shall guard His throne a-bove, And peace a-bound be-low. A-MEN.

Music used by permission of the arranger.
Alternative tune, "Dunfermline," Hymn 95.

JESUS CHRIST: HIS ADVENT

154 Silent Night! Holy Night!

Joseph Mohr, 1818

STILLE NACHT: Irregular
Ascribed to Franz Grüber, 1818

1. Si - lent night! ho - ly night! All is calm, all is bright, Round yon
2. Si - lent night! ho - ly night! Shep-herds quake at the sight, Glo - ries
3. Si - lent night! ho - ly night! Son of God, love's pure Light Ra - diant
4. Si - lent night! ho - ly night! Won-drous Star, lend thy light; With the

Vir - gin Moth-er and Child! Ho - ly In - fant, so ten - der and mild,
stream from heav-en a - far, Heaven-ly hosts sing: "Al - le - lu - ia;
beams from Thy ho-ly face, With the dawn of re - deem - ing grace,
an - gels let us sing, Al - le - lu - ia to our King;

JESUS CHRIST: HIS BIRTH

Silent Night! Holy Night!

Sleep in heav-en-ly peace, Sleep in heav-en-ly peace.
Christ the Sav-iour is born, Christ the Sav-iour is born.
Je - sus, Lord, at Thy birth, Je - sus, Lord, at Thy birth.
Christ the Sav-iour is born, Christ the Sav-iour is born. A-MEN.

There's a Song in the Air! 155

CHRISTMAS SONG: 6. 6. 6. 6. 12. 12.

Josiah G. Holland, 1872

Karl P. Harrington, 1904

1. There's a song in the air! There's a star in the sky! There's a moth-er's deep
2. There's a tu-mult of joy O'er the won-der - ful birth, For the Vir-gin's sweet
3. In the light of that star Lie the a - ges im-pearled; And that song from a-
4. We re-joice in the light, And we ech - o the song That comes down through the

prayer And a ba - by's low cry! And the star rains its fire while the
boy Is the Lord of the earth. Ay! the star rains its fire while the
far Has swept o - ver the world. Ev - ery hearth is a - flame, and the
night From the heav - en - ly throng. Ay! we shout to the love - ly e-

beau - ti - ful sing, For the man-ger of Beth - le - hem cra-dles a King!
beau - ti - ful sing, For the man-ger of Beth - le - hem cra-dles a King!
beau - ti - ful sing In the homes of the na-tions that Je - sus is King!
van - gel they bring, And we greet in His cra - dle our Sav-iour and King! A - MEN.

Words used by permission of Charles Scribner's Sons. Music copyright by Karl P. Harrington: renewal, 1933. Used by permission.

JESUS CHRIST: HIS BIRTH

156 The First Noel

Old English carol

THE FIRST NOEL: Irregular, with Refrain
Traditional melody
In Sandys' *Christmas Carols*, 1833

1. The first No - el the an - gel did say Was to cer - tain poor
2. They look - ed up and saw a star Shin-ing in the
3. And by the light of that same star, Three Wise Men
4. This star drew nigh to the north-west; O'er Beth - le -
5. Then en - tered in those Wise Men three, Fell rev - erent -
6. Then let us all with one ac - cord Sing prais - es

shep-herds in fields as they lay; In fields where they lay a - keep-ing their
east be - yond them far, And to the earth it gave great
came from coun - try far; To seek for a king was their in -
hem it took its rest; And there it did both stop and
ly up - on their knee, And of - fered there in His pres -
to our heav - en - ly Lord, That hath made heaven and earth of

sheep, On a cold win - ter's night that was so deep.
light, And so it con - tin - ued both day and night.
tent, And to fol - low the star wher - ev - er it went. No - el, No -
stay, Right o - ver the place where Je - sus lay.
ence, Their gold, and myrrh, and frank - in - cense.
nought, And with His blood man - kind hath bought.

REFRAIN

el, No - el, No - el, Born is the King of Is - ra - el. A - MEN.

JESUS CHRIST: HIS BIRTH

The First Noel

156

ALTERNATIVE REFRAIN

Arr. by Healey Willan, 1926

No - el, No - el, No - el, No - el,

Born is the King of Is - ra - el.

This refrain may be used for choir and organ throughout, or with one or more stanzas, the congregation singing the other refrain in unison.
Music used by permission of the composer and Oxford University Press, Inc.

Away in a Manger

157

Anon. Stanzas 1, 2, c. 1884
Stanza 3, c. 1892

MUELLER: 11. 11. 11. 11.
James R. Murray, 1887

1. A - way in a man - ger, no crib for His bed, The lit - tle Lord
2. The cat - tle are low - ing, the poor Ba - by wakes, But lit - tle Lord
3. Be near me, Lord Je - sus; I ask Thee to stay Close by me for -

Je - sus laid down His sweet head. The stars in the sky looked
Je - sus, no cry - ing He makes. I love Thee, Lord Je - sus, look
ev - er and love me, I pray. Bless all the dear chil - dren in

down where He lay, The lit - tle Lord Je - sus, a - sleep on the hay.
down from the sky, And stay by my side un - til morn - ing is nigh.
Thy ten - der care, And fit us for heav - en to live with Thee there. A - MEN.

JESUS CHRIST: HIS BIRTH

158 Angels We Have Heard on High

Anon.
Alt. by Earl Marlatt, 1937

GLORIA: 7. 7. 7. 7. with Refrain
French carol melody, Arr. by Edward Shippen Barnes, 1937

1. An - gels we have heard on high, Sing - ing sweet - ly through the night,
2. Shep-herds, why this ju - bi - lee? Why these songs of hap - py cheer?
3. Come to Beth - le - hem and see Him whose birth the an - gels sing;
4. See Him in a man - ger laid Whom the an - gels praise a - bove;

And the moun - tains in re - ply Ech - o - ing their brave de - light.
What great bright - ness did you see? What glad ti - dings did you hear?
Come, a - dore on bend - ed knee Christ, the Lord, the new - born King.
Mar - y, Jos - eph, lend your aid, While we raise our hearts in love.

REF.

Glo - - - - - - - - - - - - ri - a

in ex - cel - sis De - o, Glo - - - - - - - - -

- - - - - - - ri - a in ex - cel - sis De - o. A-MEN.

Words and music copyright, 1937. From *The New Church Hymnal*. Used by permission of Fleming H. Revell Company.

JESUS CHRIST: HIS BIRTH

[144]

What Child Is This

159

GREENSLEEVES: 8. 7. 8. 7. with Refrain
English melody
Probably 16th century

William C. Dix (1837-1898)

1. What Child is this, who, laid to rest, On Mar-y's lap is sleep-ing?
2. Why lies He in such mean es-tate Where ox and ass are feed-ing?
3. So bring Him in-cense, gold, and myrrh, Come, peas-ant, king, to own Him;

Whom an-gels greet with an-thems sweet, While shep-herds watch are keep-ing?
Good Chris-tian, fear: for sin-ners here The si-lent Word is plead-ing.
The King of Kings sal-va-tion brings, Let lov-ing hearts en-throne Him.

REFRAIN

This, this is Christ the King, Whom shep-herds guard and an-gels sing:

Haste, haste to bring Him laud, The Babe, the Son of Mar-y. A-MEN.

JESUS CHRIST: HIS BIRTH

[145]

160 It Came Upon the Midnight Clear

Edmund H. Sears, 1849

CAROL: C. M. D.
Richard Storrs Willis, 1850

1. It came up-on the mid-night clear, That glo-rious song of old, From an-gels bend-ing near the earth, To touch their harps of gold: "Peace on the earth, good will to men, From heaven's all-gra-cious King": The world in sol-emn still-ness lay, To hear the an-gels sing.

2. Still through the clo-ven skies they come, With peace-ful wings un-furled, And still their heaven-ly mu-sic floats O'er all the wea-ry world: A-bove its sad and low-ly plains They bend on hov-ering wing, And ev-er o'er its Ba-bel sounds The bless-ed an-gels sing.

3. And ye, be-neath life's crush-ing load, Whose forms are bend-ing low, Who toil a-long the climb-ing way With pain-ful steps and slow, Look now! for glad and gold-en hours Come swift-ly on the wing: O rest be-side the wea-ry road, And hear the an-gels sing.

4. For lo, the days are has-tening on, By proph-et bards fore-told, When with the ev-er-cir-cling years Comes round the age of gold; When peace shall o-ver all the earth Its an-cient splen-dors fling, And the whole world give back the song Which now the an-gels sing. A-MEN.

JESUS CHRIST: HIS BIRTH

Joy to the World!

161

From Psalm 98
Isaac Watts, 1719

ANTIOCH: C. M.
Arr. from Georg Friedrich Handel, 1742

1. Joy to the world! the Lord is come: Let earth re-
2. Joy to the world! the Saviour reigns: Let men their
3. No more let sins and sorrows grow, Nor thorns in-
4. He rules the world with truth and grace, And makes the

ceive her King; Let every heart prepare Him room,
songs employ; While fields and floods, rocks, hills, and plains
fest the ground; He comes to make His blessings flow
na-tions prove The glo-ries of His right-eous-ness,

And heaven and na-ture sing, And heaven and na-ture
Re-peat the sound-ing joy, Re-peat the sound-ing
Far as the curse is found, Far as the curse is
And won-ders of His love, And won-ders of His

And heaven and na-ture sing,

And

sing, And heaven, and heaven and na-ture sing.
joy, Re-peat, re-peat the sound-ing joy.
found, Far as, far as the curse is found.
love, And won-ders, won-ders of His love. A-MEN.

heaven and na-ture sing,

JESUS CHRIST: HIS BIRTH

[147]

162 Lo, How a Rose E'er Blooming

German. 15th or 16th century
Trans. by Theodore Baker. 1894

ES IST EIN ROS': 7. 6. 7. 6. 6. 7. 6.
Traditional melody
Har. by Michael Praetorius, 1609; alt.

In unison

1. Lo, how a rose e'er bloom - ing From ten - der stem hath sprung,
2. I - sa - iah 'twas fore - told it, The rose I have in mind,

Of Jes - se's lin - eage com - ing, As men of old have sung.
With Mar - y we be - hold it, The Vir - gin Moth - er kind.

It came a flower - et bright, A - mid the cold of
To show God's love a - right She bore to men a

win - ter When half spent was the night.
Sav - iour, When half spent was the night. A - MEN.

JESUS CHRIST: HIS BIRTH

Hark, the Herald Angels Sing

163

MENDELSSOHN: 7. 7. 7. 7. D. with Refrain
Felix Mendelssohn, 1840
Arr. by William H. Cummings, 1856

Charles Wesley, 1739

1. Hark, the her - ald an - gels sing, "Glo - ry to the new - born King;
2. Christ, by high - est heaven a - dored; Christ, the Ev - er - last - ing Lord!
3. Hail, the heaven-born Prince of Peace! Hail, the Sun of Right-eous-ness!

Peace on earth, and mer - cy mild, God and sin - ners rec - on - ciled!"
Late in time be - hold Him come To the earth from heav - en's home;
Light and life to all He brings, Risen with heal - ing in His wings.

Joy - ful, all ye na - tions, rise, Join the tri - umph of the skies;
Veiled in flesh the God - head see; Hail th' in - car - nate De - i - ty,
Mild He lays His glo - ry by, Born that man no more may die,

With th' an-gel - ic host pro - claim, "Christ is born in Beth - le - hem!"
Pleased as man with men to dwell, Je - sus, our Em - man - u - el.
Born to raise the sons of earth, Born to give them sec - ond birth.

REFRAIN

Hark, the her - ald an - gels sing, "Glo - ry to the new-born King." A-MEN.

164   Infant Holy, Infant Lowly

From the Polish
Para. by Edith M. G. Reed (1885-1933)

W ZLOBIE LEZY: 4. 4. 7. 4. 4. 7. 4. 4. 4. 4. 7.
Polish carol
Har. by David Hugh Jones, 1953

1. In - fant ho - ly, In - fant low - ly, For His bed a cat - tle stall;
2. Flocks were sleep - ing; Shep - herds keep-ing Vig - il till the morn-ing new

Ox - en low - ing, Lit - tle know - ing Christ the Babe is Lord of all.
Saw the glo - ry, Heard the sto - ry, Ti - dings of a gos - pel true.

Swift are wing - ing An - gels sing - ing, No - els ring - ing,
Thus re - joic - ing, Free from sor - row, Prais - es voic - ing

Tid - ings bring - ing: Christ the Babe is Lord of all.
Greet the mor - row: Christ the Babe was born for you. A - MEN.

Words from *Kingsway Carol Book*. Used by permission of the publishers. Evans Brothers Limited. Music copyright, 1955, by John Ribble.

JESUS CHRIST: HIS BIRTH

Good Christian Men, Rejoice

IN DULCI JUBILO: 6. 6. 7. 9. 7. 8. 5. 5.
German melody, 14th century

Medieval Latin
Para. by John Mason Neale, 1853

Har. in *Christmas Carols Old and New*, 1871; alt., 1953

1. Good Chris - tian men, re - joice With heart, and soul, and voice;
2. Good Chris - tian men, re - joice With heart, and soul, and voice;
3. Good Chris - tian men, re - joice With heart, and soul, and voice;

Give ye heed to what we say: News! news! Je - sus Christ is born to-day:
Now ye hear of end - less bliss; Joy! joy! Je - sus Christ was born for this!
Now ye need not fear the grave: Peace! peace! Je - sus Christ was born to save!

Ox and ass be - fore Him bow, And He is in the man - ger now.
He has oped the heaven - ly door, And man is bless - ed ev - er - more.
Calls you one and calls you all, To gain His ev - er - last - ing hall.

Christ is born to - day! Christ is born to - day!
Christ was born for this! Christ was born for this!
Christ was born to save! Christ was born to save! A - MEN.

JESUS CHRIST: HIS BIRTH

166 God Rest You Merry, Gentlemen

GOD REST YOU MERRY: Irregular, with Refrain
English melody, 18th century
Har. in *Christmas Carols Old and New*, 1871

English carol, 18th century

1. God rest you mer - ry, gen - tle-men, Let noth - ing you dis - may,
2. From God our heaven - ly Fa - ther A bless - ed an - gel came;
3. "Fear not, then," said the an - gel, "Let noth - ing you af - fright,
4. Now to the Lord sing prais - es, All you with - in this place,

Re - mem - ber Christ our Sav - iour Was born on Christ-mas Day;
And un - to cer - tain shep - herds Brought ti - dings of the same;
This day is born a Sav - iour Of a pure Vir - gin bright,
And with true love and broth-er-hood Each oth - er now em - brace;

To save us all from Sa - tan's power When we were gone a - stray.
How that in Beth - le - hem was born The Son of God by name.
To free all those who trust in Him From Sa - tan's power and might."
This ho - ly tide of Christ - mas All oth - ers doth de - face.

REFRAIN

O ti - dings of com - fort and joy, Com - fort and joy;

O ti - dings of com - fort and joy. A - MEN.

JESUS CHRIST: HIS BIRTH

Gentle Mary Laid Her Child

167

TEMPUS ADEST FLORIDUM: 7. 6. 7. 6. D.
Spring carol, c. 14th century
Arr. by Ernest C. MacMillan, 1930

Joseph Simpson Cook, 1919

1. Gen - tle Mar - y laid her Child Low - ly in a man - ger;
2. An - gels sang a - bout His birth, Wise Men sought and found Him;
3. Gen - tle Mar - y laid her Child Low - ly in a man - ger;

There He lay, the Un - de - filed, To the world a stran - ger.
Heav - en's star shone bright - ly forth Glo - ry all a - round Him.
He is still the Un - de - filed, But no more a stran - ger.

Such a Babe in such a place, Can He be the Sav - iour?
Shep - herds saw the won - drous sight, Heard the an - gels sing - ing;
Son of God of hum - ble birth, Beau - ti - ful the sto - ry;

Ask the saved of all the race Who have found His fa - vor.
All the plains were lit that night, All the hills were ring - ing.
Praise His name in all the earth, Hail! the King of Glo - ry! A - MEN.

Words used by permission of Alta Lind Cook. Music used by permission of Ernest C. MacMillan.

JESUS CHRIST: HIS BIRTH

168   Angels, from the Realms of Glory

James Montgomery, 1816, 1825

REGENT SQUARE: 8. 7. 8. 7. 8. 7.
Henry Smart, 1867

1. An - gels, from the realms of glo - ry, Wing your flight o'er
2. Shep - herds, in the fields a - bid - ing, Watch - ing o'er your
3. Sa - ges, leave your con - tem - pla - tions, Bright - er vi - sions
4. Saints, be - fore the al - tar bend - ing, Watch - ing long in

all the earth; Ye who sang cre - a - tion's sto - ry
flocks by night, God with man is now re - sid - ing,
beam a - far; Seek the great De - sire of na - tions;
hope and fear, Sud - den - ly the Lord, de - scend - ing,

Now pro - claim Mes - si - ah's birth: Come and wor - ship,
Yon - der shines the in - fant Light: Come and wor - ship,
Ye have seen His na - tal star: Come and wor - ship,
In His tem - ple shall ap - pear: Come and wor - ship,

come and wor - ship, Wor - ship Christ, the new - born King!
come and wor - ship, Wor - ship Christ, the new - born King!
come and wor - ship, Wor - ship Christ, the new - born King!
come and wor - ship, Wor - ship Christ, the new - born King! A-MEN.

JESUS CHRIST: HIS BIRTH

[154]

While Shepherds Watched Their Flocks by Night 169

Nahum Tate, 1700

CHRISTMAS: C. M.
Arr. from Georg Friedrich Handel, 1728

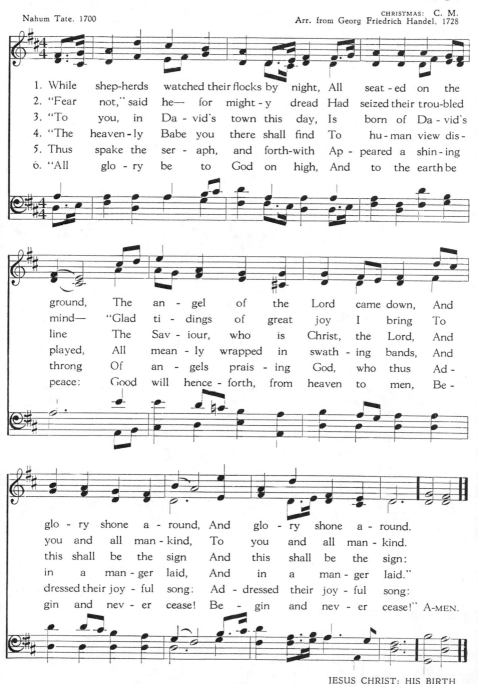

1. While shep-herds watched their flocks by night, All seat-ed on the
2. "Fear not," said he— for might-y dread Had seized their trou-bled
3. "To you, in Da - vid's town this day, Is born of Da - vid's
4. "The heaven-ly Babe you there shall find To hu-man view dis-
5. Thus spake the ser - aph, and forth-with Ap - peared a shin-ing
6. "All glo - ry be to God on high, And to the earth be

ground, The an - gel of the Lord came down, And
mind— "Glad ti - dings of great joy I bring To
line The Sav - iour, who is Christ, the Lord, And
played, All mean - ly wrapped in swath - ing bands, And
throng Of an - gels prais - ing God, who thus Ad -
peace: Good will hence - forth, from heaven to men, Be -

glo - ry shone a - round, And glo - ry shone a - round.
you and all man - kind, To you and all man - kind.
this shall be the sign And this shall be the sign:
in a man - ger laid, And in a man - ger laid."
dressed their joy - ful song: Ad - dressed their joy - ful song:
gin and nev - er cease! Be - gin and nev - er cease!" A-MEN.

JESUS CHRIST: HIS BIRTH

[155]

170   O Come, All Ye Faithful

Latin, 18th century
Trans. by Frederick Oakeley, 1841; alt.

ADESTE FIDELES: 6. 6. 10. 5. 6. with Refrain
J. F. Wade's *Cantus Diversi*, 1751

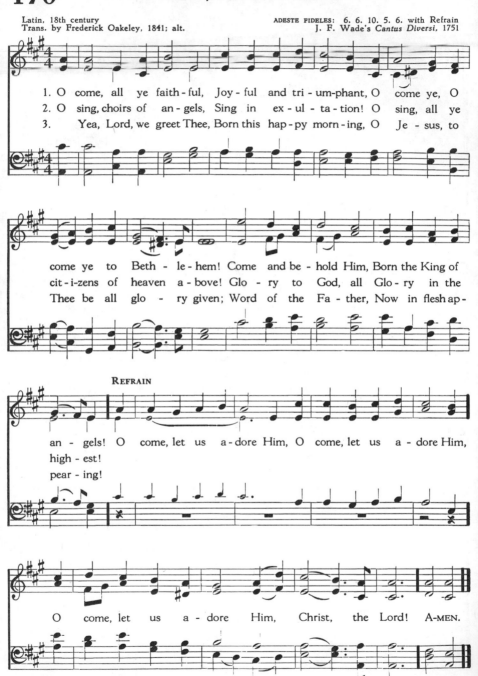

1. O come, all ye faith-ful, Joy-ful and tri-um-phant, O come ye, O
2. O sing, choirs of an-gels, Sing in ex-ul-ta-tion! O sing, all ye
3.   Yea, Lord, we greet Thee, Born this hap-py morn-ing, O Je-sus, to

come ye to Beth-le-hem! Come and be-hold Him, Born the King of
cit-i-zens of heaven a-bove! Glo-ry to God, all Glo-ry in the
Thee be all glo-ry given; Word of the Fa-ther, Now in flesh ap-

REFRAIN

an-gels! O come, let us a-dore Him, O come, let us a-dore Him,
high-est!
pear-ing!

O come, let us a-dore Him, Christ, the Lord! A-MEN.

JESUS CHRIST: HIS BIRTH

O Little Town of Bethlehem

Phillips Brooks, 1868

ST. LOUIS: 8. 6. 8. 6. 7. 6. 8. 6.
Lewis H. Redner, 1868

1. O lit - tle town of Beth - le - hem, How still we see thee lie;
2. For Christ is born of Mar - y; And gath - ered all a - bove,
3. How si - lent - ly, how si - lent - ly The won - drous gift is given!
4. O ho - ly Child of Beth - le - hem, De - scend to us, we pray;

A - bove thy deep and dream-less sleep The si - lent stars go by.
While mor - tals sleep, the an - gels keep Their watch of won-dering love.
So God im - parts to hu - man hearts The bless - ings of His heaven.
Cast out our sin, and en - ter in, Be born in us to - day.

Yet in thy dark streets shin - eth The ev - er - last - ing Light;
O morn - ing stars, to - geth - er Pro - claim the ho - ly birth;
No ear may hear His com - ing, But in this world of sin,
We hear the Christ - mas an - gels The great glad ti - dings tell;

The hopes and fears of all the years Are met in thee to - night.
And prais - es sing to God the King, And peace to men on earth.
Where meek souls will re - ceive Him, still The dear Christ en - ters in.
O come to us, a - bide with us, Our Lord Em - man - u - el. A - MEN.

JESUS CHRIST: HIS BIRTH

172 All My Heart This Night Rejoices

Paul Gerhardt, 1653
Trans. by Catherine Winkworth, 1858

EBELING (BONN): 8. 3. 3. 6. D.
Johann Georg Ebeling, 1666

1. All my heart this night re - joi - ces, As I hear, Far and near,
2. Hark! a voice from yon - der man - ger, Soft and sweet, Doth en - treat,
3. Come, then, let us has - ten yon - der; Here let all, Great and small,

Sweet-est an - gel voi - ces; "Christ is born," their choirs are sing - ing,
"Flee from woe and dan - ger; Breth - ren, come; from all that grieves you
Kneel in awe and won - der, Love Him who with love is yearn - ing;

Till the air, Ev - ery-where, Now with joy is ring - ing.
You are freed; All you need I will sure - ly give you."
Hail the Star That from far Bright with hope is burn - ing. A - MEN.

173 Ah, Dearest Jesus, Holy Child

Martin Luther, 1535
Trans. by Catherine Winkworth, 1855

VOM HIMMEL HOCH: L. M.
Geistliche Lieder, Leipzig, 1539

1. Ah, dear-est Je - sus, ho - ly Child, Make Thee a bed, soft, un - de - filed
2. My heart for ver - y joy doth leap, My lips no more can si - lence keep;
3. Glo - ry to God in high-est heaven, Who un - to man His Son hath given,

JESUS CHRIST: HIS BIRTH

[158]

Ah, Dearest Jesus, Holy Child

With-in my heart, that it may be A qui-et cham-ber kept for Thee.
I, too, must sing with joy-ful tongue, That sweet-est an-cient cra-dle song.
While an-gels sing with ten-der mirth, A glad new year to all the earth. A-MEN.

As with Gladness Men of Old   174

DIX: 7. 7. 7. 7. 7. 7.

William C. Dix, 1860

Abridged from chorale by Conrad Kocher, 1838

1. As with glad-ness men of old Did the guid-ing star be-hold;
2. As with joy-ful steps they sped To that low-ly man-ger bed,
3. As they of-fered gifts most rare At that man-ger rude and bare;
4. Ho-ly Je-sus, ev-ery day Keep us in the nar-row way;

As with joy they hailed its light, Lead-ing on-ward, beam-ing bright;
There to bend the knee be-fore Him whom heaven and earth a-dore;
So may we with ho-ly joy, Pure, and free from sin's al-loy,
And, when earth-ly things are past, Bring our ran-somed souls at last

So, most gra-cious Lord, may we Ev-er-more be led to Thee.
So may we with will-ing feet Ev-er seek Thy mer-cy seat.
All our cost-liest treas-ures bring, Christ, to Thee, our heaven-ly King.
Where they need no star to guide, Where no clouds Thy glo-ry hide. A-MEN.

For lower key, see Hymn 2.

JESUS CHRIST: HIS EPIPHANY

175 Brightest and Best of the Sons of the Morning

Reginald Heber, 1811

MORNING STAR: 11. 10. 11. 10.
James P. Harding, 1892

1. Bright - est and best of the sons of the morn - ing,
2. Cold on His cra - dle the dew - drops are shin - ing;
3. Shall we not yield Him, in cost - ly de - vo - tion,
4. Vain - ly we of - fer each am - ple ob - la - tion,

Dawn on our dark - ness and lend us Thine aid;
Low lies His head with the beasts of the stall:
O - dors of E - dom and of - ferings di - vine,
Vain - ly with gifts would His fa - vor se - cure;

Star of the East, the ho - ri - zon a - dorn - ing,
An - gels a - dore Him in slum - ber re - clin - ing,
Gems of the moun - tain and pearls of the o - cean,
Rich - er by far is the heart's ad - o - ra - tion,

Guide where our in - fant Re - deem - er is laid.
Mak - er and Mon - arch and Sav - iour of all!
Myrrh from the for - est, or gold from the mine?
Dear - er to God are the prayers of the poor. A - MEN.

JESUS CHRIST: HIS EPIPHANY

We Three Kings of Orient Are

John H. Hopkins, Jr., 1857; alt.

KINGS OF ORIENT: 8. 8. 8. 6. with Refrain
John H. Hopkins, Jr., 1857; alt.

1. We three kings of O - ri - ent are; Bear - ing gifts we trav-erse a - far,
2. Born a king on Beth - le - hem's plain, Gold I bring to crown Him a - gain,
3. Frank - in - cense to of - fer have I; In - cense owns a De - i - ty nigh;
4. Myrrh is mine: its bit - ter per - fume Breathes a life of gath-er-ing gloom;
5. Glo - rious now be - hold Him a - rise, King and God and Sac - ri - fice;

Field and foun - tain, moor and moun-tain, Fol - low-ing yon - der star.
King for - ev - er, ceas - ing nev - er O - ver us all to reign.
Prayer and prais - ing all men rais - ing, Wor - ship Him, God on high.
Sor - rowing, sigh - ing, bleed-ing, dy - ing, Sealed in the stone-cold tomb.
Al - le - lu - ia, Al - le - lu - ia! Sounds through the earth and skies.

REFRAIN

O star of won-der, star of night, Star with roy - al beau-ty bright,

West-ward lead-ing, still pro-ceed-ing, Guide us to thy per-fect Light. A-MEN.

JESUS CHRIST: HIS EPIPHANY

177   O Sing a Song of Bethlehem

Louis F. Benson, 1899

KINGSFOLD: C. M. D.
Arr. from a traditional English melody, 1906
Copyright version

1. O sing a song of Beth-le-hem, Of shep-herds watch-ing there,
2. O sing a song of Naz-a-reth, Of sun-ny days of joy,
3. O sing a song of Gal-i-lee, Of lake and woods and hill,
4. O sing a song of Cal-va-ry, Its glo-ry and dis-may;

And of the news that came to them From an-gels in the air:
O sing of fra-grant flow-ers' breath, And of the sin-less Boy:
Of Him who walked up-on the sea And bade its waves be still:
Of Him who hung up-on the tree, And took our sins a-way:

The light that shone on Beth-le-hem Fills all the world to-day;
For now the flowers of Naz-a-reth In ev-ery heart may grow;
For though, like waves on Gal-i-lee, Dark seas of trou-ble roll,
For He who died on Cal-va-ry Is ris-en from the grave,

Of Je-sus' birth and peace on earth The an-gels sing al-way.
Now spreads the fame of His dear name On all the winds that blow.
When faith has heard the Mas-ter's word, Falls peace up-on the soul.
And Christ, our Lord, by heaven a-dored, Is might-y now to save. A-MEN.

Music from *The Church Hymnary*, Revised Edition. Used by permission of Oxford University Press.

JESUS CHRIST: HIS LIFE AND MINISTRY

O Master Workman of the Race

178

Jay T. Stocking. 1912

AMESBURY: C. M. D.
Uzziah C. Burnap. 1895

1. O Mas-ter Work-man of the race, Thou Man of Gal-i-lee,
2. O Car-pen-ter of Naz-a-reth, Build-er of life di-vine,
3. O Thou who dost the vi-sion send And giv-est each his task,

Who with the eyes of ear-ly youth E-ter-nal things didst see,
Who shap-est man to God's own law, Thy-self the fair de-sign,
And with the task suf-fi-cient strength, Show us Thy will, we ask;

We thank Thee for Thy boy-hood faith That shone Thy whole life through;
Build us a tower of Christ-like height, That we the land may view,
Give us a con-science bold and good, Give us a pur-pose true,

"Did ye not know it is my work, My Fa-ther's work to do?"
And see, like Thee, our no-blest work, Our Fa-ther's work to do.
That it may be our high-est joy Our Fa-ther's work to do. A-MEN.

Words from *The Pilgrim Hymnal.* Copyright by The Pilgrim Press. Used by permission.

JESUS CHRIST: HIS LIFE AND MINISTRY

[163]

179 Thine Arm, O Lord, in Days of Old

ST. MATTHEW: C. M. D.
William Croft
Supplement to the New Version, 1708

Edward H. Plumptre, 1864

1. Thine arm, O Lord, in days of old Was strong to heal and save;
2. And lo, Thy touch brought life and health, Gave speech, and strength, and sight;
3. Be Thou our great De-liv-erer still, Thou Lord of life and death;

It tri-umphed o'er dis-ease and death, O'er dark-ness and the grave.
And youth re-newed and fren-zy calmed Owned Thee, the Lord of light.
Re-store and quick-en, soothe and bless With Thine al-might-y breath.

To Thee they went, the blind, the dumb, The pal-sied and the lame,
And now, O Lord, be near to bless, Al-might-y as of yore,
To hands that work and eyes that see, Give wis-dom's heaven-ly lore,

The lep-er with his taint-ed life, The sick with fe-vered frame.
In crowd-ed street, by rest-less couch, As by Gen-nes-aret's shore.
That whole and sick, and weak and strong, May praise Thee ev-er-more. A-MEN.

JESUS CHRIST: HIS LIFE AND MINISTRY

What Grace, O Lord, and Beauty Shone 180

Edward Denny, 1839

THIS ENDRIS NYGHT: C. M.
English carol, 15th century
Arr. by R. Vaughan Williams, 1906

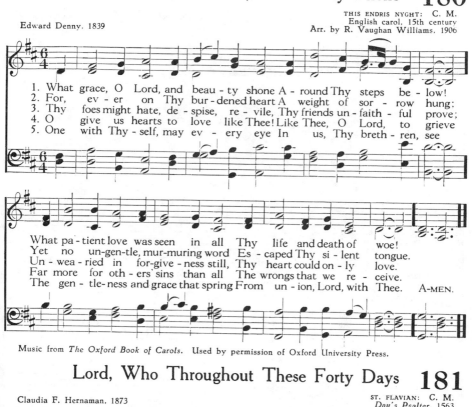

1. What grace, O Lord, and beau - ty shone A - round Thy steps be - low!
2. For, ev - er on Thy bur - dened heart A weight of sor - row hung;
3. Thy foes might hate, de - spise, re - vile, Thy friends un - faith - ful prove;
4. O give us hearts to love like Thee! Like Thee, O Lord, to grieve
5. One with Thy - self, may ev - ery eye In us, Thy breth - ren, see

What pa - tient love was seen in all Thy life and death of woe!
Yet no un - gen - tle, mur - muring word Es - caped Thy si - lent tongue.
Un - wea - ried in for - give - ness still, Thy heart could on - ly love.
Far more for oth - ers' sins than all The wrongs that we re - ceive.
The gen - tle - ness and grace that spring From un - ion, Lord, with Thee. A-MEN.

Music from *The Oxford Book of Carols.* Used by permission of Oxford University Press.

Lord, Who Throughout These Forty Days 181

Claudia F. Hernaman, 1873

ST. FLAVIAN: C. M.
Day's Psalter, 1563

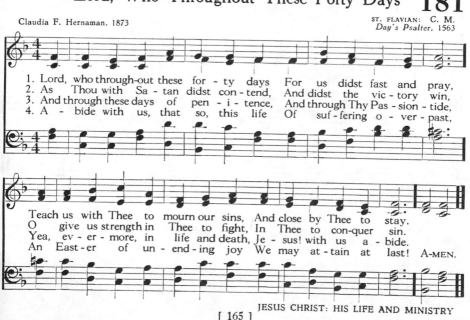

1. Lord, who through - out these for - ty days For us didst fast and pray,
2. As Thou with Sa - tan didst con - tend, And didst the vic - tory win,
3. And through these days of pen - i - tence, And through Thy Pas - sion - tide,
4. A - bide with us, that so, this life Of suf - fering o - ver - past,

Teach us with Thee to mourn our sins, And close by Thee to stay.
O give us strength in Thee to fight, In Thee to con - quer sin.
Yea, ev - er - more, in life and death, Je - sus! with us a - bide.
An East - er of un - end - ing joy We may at - tain at last! A-MEN.

JESUS CHRIST: HIS LIFE AND MINISTRY

182 O Wondrous Type, O Vision Fair

Latin, 15th century
Trans. by John Mason Neale, 1854

DEO GRACIAS: L. M.
"The Agincourt Song," 1415

In unison

1. O won - drous type, O vi - sion fair
2. With shin - ing face and bright ar - ray,
3. And faith - ful hearts are raised on high
4. O Fa - ther, with th'e - ter - nal Son,

Of glo - ry that the Church shall share,
Christ deigns to man - i - fest to - day
By this great vi - sion's mys - ter - y;
And Ho - ly Spir - it, ev - er One,

Which Christ up - on the moun - tain shows
What glo - ry shall be theirs a - bove
For which in joy - ful strains we raise
Vouch - safe to bring us by Thy grace

Where bright - er than the sun He glows.
Who joy in God with per - fect love.
The voice of prayer, the hymn of praise.
To see Thy glo - ry face to face. A - MEN.

JESUS CHRIST: HIS LIFE AND MINISTRY

We Would See Jesus; Lo! His Star Is Shining 183

J. Edgar Park, 1913

CUSHMAN: 11. 10. 11. 10.
Herbert B. Turner, 1905

1. We would see Je - sus; lo! His star is shin - ing
2. We would see Je - sus, Mar - y's Son most ho - ly,
3. We would see Je - sus, on the moun - tain teach - ing,
4. We would see Je - sus, in His work of heal - ing,
5. We would see Je - sus; in the ear - ly morn - ing

A - bove the sta - ble while the an - gels sing;
Light of the vil - lage life from day to day;
With all the lis - tening peo - ple gath - ered round;
At e - ven - tide be - fore the sun was set;
Still as of old He call - eth, "Fol - low Me";

There in a man - ger on the hay re - clin - ing,
Shin - ing re - vealed through ev - ery task most low - ly,
While birds and flowers and sky a - bove are preach - ing,
Di - vine and hu - man, in His deep re - veal - ing,
Let us a - rise, all mean - er serv - ice scorn - ing:

Haste, let us lay our gifts be - fore the King.
The Christ of God, the Life, the Truth, the Way.
The bless - ed - ness which sim - ple trust has found.
Of God and man in lov - ing serv - ice met.
Lord, we are Thine, we give our - selves to Thee! A - MEN.

Words from *New Worship and Song.* Copyright by The Pilgrim Press. Used by permission. Music copyright, 1905, by Herbert B. Turner. Used by permission.

JESUS CHRIST: HIS LIFE AND MINISTRY

184 Thou Didst Leave Thy Throne

MARGARET: Irregular

Emily E. S. Elliott, 1864; alt.

Timothy R. Matthews, 1876

1. Thou didst leave Thy throne and Thy king - ly crown When Thou cam - est to earth for me; But in Beth - le-hem's home there was found no room For Thy ho - ly na - tiv - i - ty. O come to my heart, Lord Je - sus: There is room in my heart for Thee!

2. Heav - en's arch - es rang when the an - gels sang, Pro - claim-ing Thy roy - al de - gree; But in low - ly birth didst Thou come to earth, And in great hu - mil - i - ty. O come to my heart, Lord Je - sus: There is room in my heart for Thee!

3. The fox - es found rest, and the birds their nest In the shade of the for - est tree; But Thy couch was the sod, O Thou Son of God, In the des - erts of Gal - i - lee. O come to my heart, Lord Je - sus: There is room in my heart for Thee!

4. Thou cam - est, O Lord, with the liv - ing Word That should set Thy peo - ple free; But with mock - ing scorn and with crown of thorn They bore Thee to Cal - va - ry. O come to my heart, Lord Je - sus: There is room in my heart for Thee!

5. When the heavens shall ring, and the an - gels sing At Thy com - ing to vic - to - ry, Let Thy voice call me home, say - ing, "Yet there is room, There is room at My side for thee." And my heart shall re-joice, Lord Je - sus: There is room in my heart for Thee! A-men.

Music used by permission of Novello & Co., Ltd.

JESUS CHRIST: HIS LIFE AND MINISTRY

Hosanna, Loud Hosanna

ELLACOMBE: 7. 6. 7. 6. D.
Gesangbuch der Herzogl. Wirtembergischen
Katholischen Hofkapelle, 1784

Jennette Threlfall, 1873

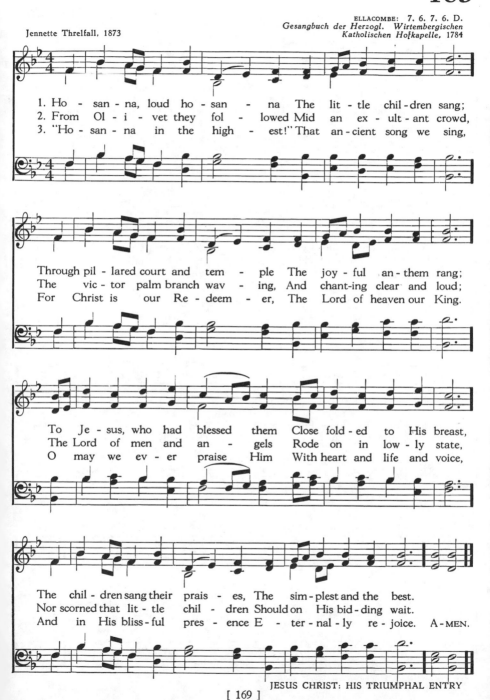

1. Ho - san - na, loud ho - san - na The lit - tle chil - dren sang;
2. From Ol - i - vet they fol - lowed Mid an ex - ult - ant crowd,
3. "Ho - san - na in the high - est!" That an - cient song we sing,

Through pil - lared court and tem - ple The joy - ful an - them rang;
The vic - tor palm branch wav - ing, And chant - ing clear and loud;
For Christ is our Re - deem - er, The Lord of heaven our King.

To Je - sus, who had blessed them Close fold - ed to His breast,
The Lord of men and an - gels Rode on in low - ly state,
O may we ev - er praise Him With heart and life and voice,

The chil - dren sang their prais - es, The sim - plest and the best.
Nor scorned that lit - tle chil - dren Should on His bid - ding wait.
And in His bliss - ful pres - ence E - ter - nal - ly re - joice. A - MEN.

JESUS CHRIST: HIS TRIUMPHAL ENTRY

186 When, His Salvation Bringing

John King, 1830

TOURS: 7. 6. 7. 6. D.
Berthold Tours, 1872

1. When, His sal - va - tion bring - ing, To Zi - on Je - sus came,
2. And since the Lord re - tain - eth His love for chil - dren still,
3. For should we fail pro - claim - ing Our great Re - deem - er's praise,

The chil - dren all stood sing - ing Ho - san - na to His name;
Though now as King He reign - eth On Zi - on's heaven - ly hill,
The stones, our si - lence sham - ing, Would their ho - san - nas raise.

Nor did their zeal of - fend Him, But, as He rode a - long,
We'll flock a - round His ban - ner Who sits up - on His throne,
But shall we on - ly ren - der The trib - ute of our words?

He let them still at - tend Him, And smiled to hear their song.
And cry a - loud, "Ho - san - na To Da - vid's roy - al Son!"
No; while our hearts are ten - der, They, too, shall be the Lord's. A - MEN.

JESUS CHRIST: HIS TRIUMPHAL ENTRY

All Glory, Laud, and Honor

187

Theodulph of Orleans, c. 820
Trans. by John Mason Neale, 1854

ST. THEODULPH: 7. 6. 7. 6. D.
Melchior Teschner, c. 1615

1. All glo - ry, laud, and hon - or To Thee, Re - deem - er, King,
2. Thou art the King of Is - rael, Thou Da - vid's roy - al Son,
3. Thou didst ac - cept their prais - es; Ac - cept the prayers we bring,

To whom the lips of chil - dren Made sweet ho - san - nas ring!
Who in the Lord's name com - est, The King and bless - ed One!
Who in all good de - light - est, Thou good and gra - cious King!

The peo - ple of the He - brews With palms be - fore Thee went;
To Thee, be - fore Thy Pas - sion, They sang their hymns of praise;
All glo - ry, laud, and hon - or To Thee, Re - deem - er, King,

Our praise and prayer and an - thems Be - fore Thee we pre - sent.
To Thee, now high ex - alt - ed, Our mel - o - dy we raise.
To whom the lips of chil - dren Made sweet ho - san - nas ring! A-MEN.

JESUS CHRIST: HIS TRIUMPHAL ENTRY

[171]

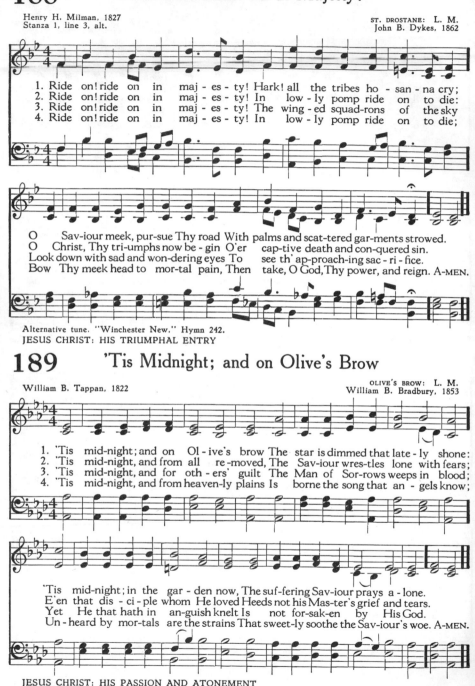

188 Ride On! Ride On in Majesty!

Henry H. Milman, 1827
Stanza 1, line 3, alt.

ST. DROSTANE: L. M.
John B. Dykes, 1862

1. Ride on! ride on in maj - es - ty! Hark! all the tribes ho - san - na cry;
2. Ride on! ride on in maj - es - ty! In low - ly pomp ride on to die:
3. Ride on! ride on in maj - es - ty! The wing - ed squad-rons of the sky
4. Ride on! ride on in maj - es - ty! In low - ly pomp ride on to die;

O Sav-iour meek, pur-sue Thy road With palms and scat-tered gar-ments strowed.
O Christ, Thy tri-umphs now be - gin O'er cap-tive death and con-quered sin.
Look down with sad and won-dering eyes To see th' ap-proach-ing sac - ri - fice.
Bow Thy meek head to mor-tal pain, Then take, O God, Thy power, and reign. A-MEN.

Alternative tune. "Winchester New." Hymn 242.
JESUS CHRIST: HIS TRIUMPHAL ENTRY

189 'Tis Midnight; and on Olive's Brow

William B. Tappan, 1822

OLIVE'S BROW: L. M.
William B. Bradbury, 1853

1. 'Tis mid-night; and on Ol - ive's brow The star is dimmed that late - ly shone:
2. 'Tis mid-night, and from all re - moved, The Sav-iour wres-tles lone with fears;
3. 'Tis mid-night, and for oth - ers' guilt The Man of Sor-rows weeps in blood;
4. 'Tis mid-night, and from heaven-ly plains Is borne the song that an - gels know;

'Tis mid-night; in the gar - den now, The suf-fering Sav-iour prays a - lone.
E'en that dis - ci - ple whom He loved Heeds not his Mas-ter's grief and tears.
Yet He that hath in an-guish knelt Is not for-sak-en by His God.
Un - heard by mor-tals are the strains That sweet-ly soothe the Sav-iour's woe. A-MEN.

JESUS CHRIST: HIS PASSION AND ATONEMENT

[172]

Beneath the Cross of Jesus

Elizabeth C. Clephane. 1872

ST. CHRISTOPHER: 7. 6. 8. 6. 8. 6. 8. 6.
Frederick C. Maker, 1881

1. Be - neath the cross of Je - sus I fain would take my stand—
2. Up - on the cross of Je - sus Mine eye at times can see
3. I take, O cross, thy shad - ow For my a - bid - ing place:

The shad - ow of a might - y Rock With - in a wea - ry land;
The ver - y dy - ing form of One Who suf - fered there for me:
I ask no oth - er sun - shine than The sun - shine of His face;

A home with - in the wil - der - ness, A rest up - on the way,
And from my strick-en heart with tears Two won - ders I con - fess—
Con - tent to let the world go by, To know no gain nor loss:

From the burn-ing of the noon-tide heat, And the bur - den of the day.
The won-ders of re - deem-ing love And my un-worth-i - ness.
My sin - ful self my on - ly shame, My glo - ry all, the cross. A-MEN.

Music copyright by The Psalms & Hymns Trust. Used by permission.

JESUS CHRIST: HIS PASSION AND ATONEMENT

191 Ah, Holy Jesus, How Hast Thou Offended

Johann Heermann, c. 1630
Trans. by Robert Bridges, 1899

HERZLIEBSTER JESU: 11. 11. 11. 5.
Johann Crüger, 1640

1. Ah, ho-ly Je-sus, how hast Thou of-fend-ed,
2. Who was the guilt-y? Who brought this up-on Thee?
3. For me, kind Je-sus, was Thy in-car-na-tion,
4. There-fore, kind Je-sus, since I can-not pay Thee,

That man to judge Thee hath in hate pre-tend-ed? By foes de-
A-las, my trea-son, Je-sus, hath un-done Thee! 'Twas I, Lord
Thy mor-tal sor-row, and Thy life's ob-la-tion; Thy death of
I do a-dore Thee, and will ev-er pray Thee, Think on Thy

rid-ed, by Thine own re-ject-ed, O most af-flict-ed!
Je-sus, I it was de-nied Thee: I cru-ci-fied Thee.
an-guish and Thy bit-ter pas-sion, For my sal-va-tion.
pit-y and Thy love un-swerv-ing, Not my de-serv-ing. A-MEN.

Words from *The Yattendon Hymnal*, edited by Robert Bridges and H. Ellis Wooldridge. Used by permission of the Clarendon Press, Oxford. Music used by permission of The Church Pension Fund.

192 O Come and Mourn with Me Awhile

ST. CROSS: L. M.
John B. Dykes, 1861

Frederick W. Faber, 1849; alt.

1. O come and mourn with me a-while; O come ye to the Sav-iour's side;
2. Seven times He spake, seven words of love; And all three hours His si-lence cried
3. O break, O break, hard heart of mine! Thy weak self-love and guilt-y pride
4. A bro-ken heart, a fount of tears, Ask, and they will not be de-nied;
5. O love of God! O sin of man! In this dread act your strength is tried,

JESUS CHRIST: HIS PASSION AND ATONEMENT

[174]

O Come and Mourn with Me Awhile

O come, to-geth-er let us mourn: Je-sus, our Lord, is cru-ci-fied!
For mer-cy on the souls of men: Je-sus, our Lord, is cru-ci-fied!
His Pi-late and His Ju-das were: Je-sus, our Lord, is cru-ci-fied!
A bro-ken heart love's cra-dle is: Je-sus, our Lord, is cru-ci-fied!
And vic-to-ry re-mains with love: Je-sus, our Lord, is cru-ci-fied! A-MEN.

Go to Dark Gethsemane 193

REDHEAD, NO. 76: 7. 7. 7. 7. 7. 7.

James Montgomery, 1820, 1825
Richard Redhead, 1853

1. Go to dark Geth-sem-a-ne, Ye that feel the tempt-er's power;
2. Fol-low to the judg-ment hall; View the Lord of life ar-raigned.
3. Cal-vary's mourn-ful moun-tain climb; There, a-dor-ing at His feet,
4. Ear-ly has-ten to the tomb Where they laid His breath-less clay:

Your Re-deem-er's con-flict see; Watch with Him one bit-ter hour;
O the worm-wood and the gall! O the pangs His soul sus-tained!
Mark that mir-a-cle of time, God's own sac-ri-fice com-plete:
All is sol-i-tude and gloom; Who hath tak-en Him a-way?

Turn not from His griefs a-way; Learn of Je-sus Christ to pray.
Shun not suf-fering, shame, or loss; Learn of Him to bear the cross.
"It is fin-ished!"—hear Him cry; Learn of Je-sus Christ to die.
Christ is risen! He meets our eyes. Sav-iour, teach us so to rise. A-MEN.

JESUS CHRIST: HIS PASSION AND ATONEMENT

194 O Sacred Head, Now Wounded

Ascribed to Bernard of Clairvaux (1091-1153)
Trans. into German by Paul Gerhardt, 1656
Trans. from the German by James W. Alexander, 1830

PASSION CHORALE: 7. 6. 7. 6. D.
Hans Leo Hassler, 1601
Har. by Johann Sebastian Bach, 1729

1. O sa - cred Head, now wound - ed, With grief and shame weighed down;
2. What Thou, my Lord, hast suf - fered Was all for sin - ners' gain:
3. What lan - guage shall I bor - row To thank Thee, dear - est Friend,

Now scorn-ful - ly sur - round - ed With thorns, Thine on - ly crown;
Mine, mine was the trans-gres - sion, But Thine the dead - ly pain.
For this Thy dy - ing sor - row, Thy pit - y with - out end?

O sa - cred Head, what glo - ry, What bliss till now was Thine!
Lo, here I fall, my Sav - iour! 'Tis I de - serve Thy place;
O make me Thine for - ev - er; And should I faint - ing be,

Yet, though de-spised and go - ry, I joy to call Thee mine.
Look on me with Thy fa - vor, Vouch-safe to me Thy grace.
Lord, let me nev - er, nev - er Out - live my love to Thee. A - MEN.

JESUS CHRIST: HIS PASSION AND ATONEMENT

[176]

In the Cross of Christ I Glory

195

John Bowring, 1849

RATHBUN: 8. 7. 8. 7.
Ithamar Conkey, 1849

1. In the cross of Christ I glo - ry, Tower-ing o'er the wrecks of 'time;
2. When the woes of life o'er - take me, Hopes de -ceive, and fears an-noy,
3. When the sun of bliss is beam-ing Light and love up - on my way,
4. Bane and bless-ing, pain and pleas-ure, By the cross are sanc - ti-fied;

All the light of sa - cred sto - ry Gath-ers round its head sub-lime.
Nev - er shall the cross for - sake me: Lo! it glows with peace and joy.
From the cross the ra - diance stream-ing Adds more lus - ter to the day.
Peace is there that knows no meas-ure, Joys that through all time a - bide. A-MEN.

Cross of Jesus, Cross of Sorrow

196

William J. S. Simpson, 1886

CROSS OF JESUS: 8. 7. 8. 7.
John Stainer, 1887

1. Cross of Je - sus, cross of sor - row, Where the blood of Christ was shed,
2. Here the King of all the a - ges, Throned in light ere worlds could be,
3. O mys - te - rious con - de - scend-ing! O a - ban - don-ment sub - lime!
4. Ev - er-more for hu - man fail - ure By His pas - sion we can plead;

Per - fect man on thee did suf - fer, Per - fect God on thee has bled!
Robed in mor - tal flesh is dy - ing, Cru - ci - fied by sin for me.
Ver - y God Him-self is bear - ing All the suf - fer - ings of time!
God has borne all mor - tal an - guish, Sure - ly He will know our need. A-MEN.

Words used by permission of Novello & Co., Ltd.

JESUS CHRIST: HIS PASSION AND ATONEMENT

[177]

197 Throned Upon the Awful Tree

ARFON: 7. 7. 7. 7. 7. 7.
Welsh hymn melody
Har. by Hugh Davies

John Ellerton, 1875

1. Throned up - on the aw - ful tree, King of grief, I watch with Thee.
2. Si - lent through those three dread hours, Wres-tling with the e - vil powers,
3. Hark, that cry that peals a - loud Up-ward through the whelm-ing cloud!
4. Lord, should fear and an-guish roll Dark-ly o'er my sin - ful soul,

Dark - ness veils Thine an-guished face: None its lines of woe can trace:
Left a - lone with hu - man sin, Gloom a - round Thee and with - in,
Thou, the Fa-ther's on - ly Son, Thou, His own a - noint - ed One,
Thou, who once wast thus be - reft That Thine own might ne'er be left,

None can tell what pangs un-known Hold Thee si - lent and a - lone—
Till th' ap-point-ed time is nigh, Till the Lamb of God may die.
Thou dost ask Him—can it be?— 'Why hast Thou for - sak - en Me?'
Teach me by that bit - ter cry In the gloom to know Thee nigh. A-MEN.

198 When I Survey the Wondrous Cross

HAMBURG: L. M.
Lowell Mason, 1824

Isaac Watts, 1707

1. When I sur-vey the won - drous cross On which the Prince of Glo - ry died,
2. For - bid it, Lord, that I should boast, Save in the death of Christ my God:
3. See, from His head, His hands, His feet, Sor - row and love flow min - gled down:
4. Were the whole realm of na - ture mine, That were a pres - ent far too small;

JESUS CHRIST: HIS PASSION AND ATONEMENT
[178]

When I Survey the Wondrous Cross

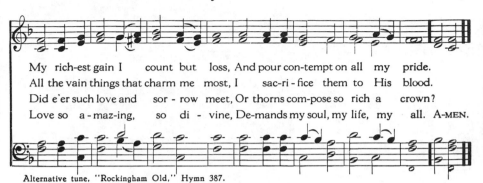

My rich-est gain I count but loss, And pour con-tempt on all my pride.
All the vain things that charm me most, I sac-ri-fice them to His blood.
Did e'er such love and sor-row meet, Or thorns com-pose so rich a crown?
Love so a-maz-ing, so di-vine, De-mands my soul, my life, my all. A-MEN.

Alternative tune, "Rockingham Old," Hymn 387.

Alas! and Did My Saviour Bleed   199

Isaac Watts, 1707

MARTYRDOM (AVON): C. M.
Hugh Wilson, 1825

1. A - las! and did my Sav-iour bleed, And did my Sov-ereign die!
2. Was it for sins that I have done He suf-fered on the tree?
3. Well might the sun in dark-ness hide, And shut his glo-ries in,
4. Thus might I hide my blush-ing face While His dear cross ap-pears;
5. But drops of grief can ne'er re-pay The debt of love I owe;

Would He de-vote that sa-cred head For sin-ners such as I!
A - maz-ing pit-y! grace un-known! And love be-yond de-gree!
When God, the might-y Mak-er, died For man the crea-ture's sin.
Dis-solve my heart in thank-ful-ness, And melt mine eyes to tears.
Here, Lord, I give my-self a-way; 'Tis all that I can do. A-MEN.

JESUS CHRIST: HIS PASSION AND ATONEMENT

200 O Jesus, We Adore Thee

Arthur T. Russell, 1851

MEIRIONYDD: 7. 6. 7. 6. D.
Ascribed to William Lloyd, 1840

1. O Je - sus, we a - dore Thee, Up - on the cross, our King!
2. Yet doth the world dis - dain Thee, Still pass - ing by the cross;
3. O glo - rious King, we bless Thee, No long - er pass Thee by;

We bow our hearts be - fore Thee, Thy gra - cious name we sing.
Lord, may our hearts re - tain Thee; All else we count but loss.
O Je - sus, we con - fess Thee The Son en - throned on high.

That name hath brought sal - va - tion, That name in life our stay,
Ah, Lord, our sins ar - raigned Thee, And nailed Thee to the tree:
Lord, grant to us re - mis - sion; Life through Thy death re - store;

Our peace, our con - so - la - tion, When life shall fade a - way.
Our pride, our Lord, dis - dained Thee; Yet deign our Hope to be.
Yea, grant us the fru - i - tion Of life for - ev - er - more. A-MEN.

JESUS CHRIST: HIS PASSION AND ATONEMENT

[180]

Were You There When They Crucified My Lord? 201

WERE YOU THERE: Irregular
Negro melody

Negro spiritual

1. Were you there when they cru-ci-fied my Lord? Were you
2. Were you there when they nailed Him to the tree? Were you
3. Were you there when they laid Him in the tomb? Were you

there when they cru-ci-fied my Lord?
there when they nailed Him to the tree? Oh!.............
there when they laid Him in the tomb?

Some-times it caus-es me to trem-ble, trem-ble, trem-ble.

Were you there when they cru-ci-fied my Lord?
Were you there when they nailed Him to the tree?
Were you there when they laid Him in the tomb? A-men.

JESUS CHRIST: HIS PASSION AND ATONEMENT

[181]

202

There Is a Green Hill Far Away

Cecil Frances Alexander, 1848

MEDITATION: C. M.
John H. Gower, 1890

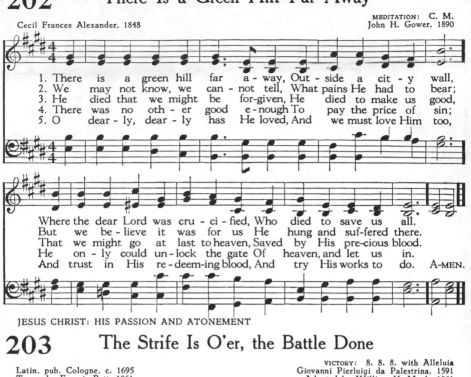

1. There is a green hill far a-way, Out-side a cit-y wall,
2. We may not know, we can-not tell, What pains He had to bear,
3. He died that we might be for-given, He died to make us good,
4. There was no oth-er good e-nough To pay the price of sin;
5. O dear-ly, dear-ly has He loved, And we must love Him too,

Where the dear Lord was cru-ci-fied, Who died to save us all.
But we be-lieve it was for us He hung and suf-fered there.
That we might go at last to heaven, Saved by His pre-cious blood.
He on-ly could un-lock the gate Of heaven, and let us in.
And trust in His re-deem-ing blood, And try His works to do. A-MEN.

JESUS CHRIST: HIS PASSION AND ATONEMENT

203

The Strife Is O'er, the Battle Done

Latin, pub. Cologne, c. 1695
Trans. by Francis Pott, 1861

VICTORY: 8. 8. 8. with Alleluia
Giovanni Pierluigi da Palestrina, 1591
Adapted by William H. Monk, 1861

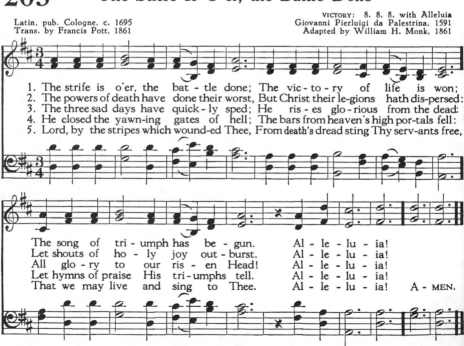

1. The strife is o'er, the bat-tle done; The vic-to-ry of life is won;
2. The powers of death have done their worst, But Christ their le-gions hath dis-persed:
3. The three sad days have quick-ly sped; He ris-es glo-rious from the dead:
4. He closed the yawn-ing gates of hell; The bars from heaven's high por-tals fell:
5. Lord, by the stripes which wound-ed Thee, From death's dread sting Thy serv-ants free,

The song of tri-umph has be-gun. Al-le-lu-ia!
Let shouts of ho-ly joy out-burst. Al-le-lu-ia!
All glo-ry to our ris-en Head! Al-le-lu-ia!
Let hymns of praise His tri-umphs tell. Al-le-lu-ia!
That we may live and sing to Thee. Al-le-lu-ia! A-MEN.

JESUS CHRIST: HIS RESURRECTION

[182]

Jesus Christ Is Risen Today

Stanzas 1 to 3 based on the Latin, 14th century
Stanza 4, Charles Wesley, 1740

EASTER HYMN: 7. 7. 7. 7. with Alleluias
Lyra Davidica, 1708

1. Je - sus Christ is risen to - day, Al - - le - lu - ia!
2. Hymns of praise then let us sing, Al - - le - lu - ia!
3. But the pains which He en - dured, Al - - le - lu - ia!
4. Sing we to our God a - bove, Al - - le - lu - ia!

Our tri - um - phant ho - ly day, Al - - le - lu - ia!
Un - to Christ, our heaven-ly King, Al - - le - lu - ia!
Our sal - va - tion have pro - cured; Al - - le - lu - ia!
Praise e - ter - nal as His love; Al - - le - lu - ia!

Who did once, up - on the cross, Al - - le - lu - ia!
Who en - dured the cross and grave, Al - - le - lu - ia!
Now a - bove the sky He's King, Al - - le - lu - ia!
Praise Him, all ye heaven - ly host, Al - - le - lu - ia!

Suf - fer to re - deem our loss. Al - - le - lu - ia!
Sin - ners to re - deem and save. Al - - le - lu - ia!
Where the an - gels ev - er sing. Al - - le - lu - ia!
Fa - ther, Son, and Ho - ly Ghost. Al - - le - lu - ia! A - MEN.

Alternative tune, "Llanfair," Hymn 4.

JESUS CHRIST: HIS RESURRECTION

205 Come, Ye Faithful, Raise the Strain

John of Damascus. 8th century
Trans. by John Mason Neale. 1859

ST. KEVIN: 7. 6. 7. 6. D.
Arthur S. Sullivan. 1872; alt.

1. Come, ye faith-ful, raise the strain Of tri - um - phant glad - ness:
2. 'Tis the spring of souls to - day: Christ hath burst His pris - on,

God hath brought His peo - ple forth In - to joy from sad - ness.
And from three days' sleep in death As a sun hath ris - en;

Now re - joice, Je - ru - sa - lem, And with true af - fec - tion
All the win - ter of our sins, Long and dark, is fly - ing

Wel - come in un - wea - ried strains Je - sus' res - ur - rec - tion.
From His light, to whom we give Laud and praise un - dy - ing. A - MEN.

JESUS CHRIST: HIS RESURRECTION

[184]

O Sons and Daughters, Let Us Sing! 206

Jean Tisserand, d. 1494
Trans. by John Mason Neale, 1852

O FILII ET FILIAE: 8. 8. 8. with Alleluias
French melody, 15th century

Al - le - lu - ia! Al - le - lu - ia! Al - le - lu - ia! Al -

le - lu - ia! 1. O sons and daugh - ters, let us sing!
2. That East - er morn, at break of day,
3. An an - gel clad in white they see,
4. How blest are they who have not seen,
5. On this most ho - ly day of days,

The King of heaven, the glo - rious King, O'er death to - day rose
The faith - ful wom - en went their way To seek the tomb where
Who sat, and spake un - to the three, "Your Lord doth go to
And yet whose faith hath con - stant been; For they e - ter - nal
Our hearts and voi - ces, Lord, we raise To Thee, in ju - bi -

tri - umph - ing. Al - le - lu - ia! Al - le - lu - ia!
Je - sus lay. Al - le - lu - ia! Al - le - lu - ia!
Gal - i - lee." Al - le - lu - ia! Al - le - lu - ia!
life shall win. Al - le - lu - ia! Al - le - lu - ia!
lee and praise. Al - le - lu - ia! Al - le - lu - ia! A - MEN.

JESUS CHRIST: HIS RESURRECTION

207 "Welcome, Happy Morning!"

Venantius Fortunatus (530-609)
Trans. by John Ellerton, 1868

FORTUNATUS: 11. 11. 11. 11. with Refrain
Arthur S. Sullivan, 1872

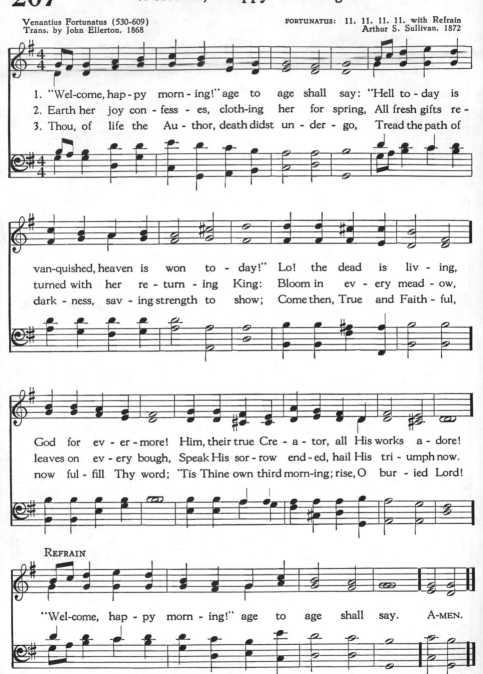

1. "Wel-come, hap-py morn-ing!" age to age shall say: "Hell to - day is van-quished, heaven is won to - day!" Lo! the dead is liv - ing, God for ev - er-more! Him, their true Cre - a - tor, all His works a - dore!

2. Earth her joy con - fess - es, cloth-ing her for spring, All fresh gifts re - turned with her re - turn - ing King: Bloom in ev - ery mead - ow, leaves on ev - ery bough, Speak His sor - row end - ed, hail His tri - umph now.

3. Thou, of life the Au - thor, death didst un - der - go, Tread the path of dark - ness, sav - ing strength to show; Come then, True and Faith - ful, now ful - fill Thy word; 'Tis Thine own third morn-ing; rise, O bur - ied Lord!

REFRAIN

"Wel-come, hap - py morn - ing!" age to age shall say. A-MEN.

JESUS CHRIST: HIS RESURRECTION

The Day of Resurrection!

208

John of Damascus, 8th century
Trans. by John Mason Neale, 1862; alt.

LANCASHIRE: 7. 6. 7. 6. D.
Henry Smart, c. 1835

1. The day of res-ur-rec-tion! Earth, tell it out a-broad;
2. Our hearts be pure from e-vil, That we may see a-right
3. Now let the heavens be joy-ful, Let earth her song be-gin;

The Pass-o-ver of glad-ness, The Pass-o-ver of God.
The Lord in rays e-ter-nal Of res-ur-rec-tion light;
Let the round world keep tri-umph, And all that is there-in;

From death to life e-ter-nal, From this world to the sky,
And, lis-tening to His ac-cents, May hear, so calm and plain,
Let all things seen and un-seen Their notes of glad-ness blend,

Our Christ hath brought us o-ver With hymns of vic-to-ry.
His own "All hail!" and, hear-ing, May raise the vic-tor strain.
For Christ the Lord hath ris-en, Our Joy that hath no end. A-MEN.

Alternative tune, "Llangloffan," Hymn 231.

JESUS CHRIST: HIS RESURRECTION

[187]

209 Thine Is the Glory

Edmond Budry, 1884
Trans. by R. Birch Hoyle, 1923

JUDAS MACCABEUS: 5. 5. 6. 5. 6. 5. 6. 5. with Refrain
Georg Friedrich Handel, 1747

1. Thine is the glo - ry, Ris - en, con-quering Son; End - less is the
2. Lo! Je - sus meets us, Ris - en from the tomb, Lov - ing - ly He
3. No more we doubt Thee, Glo - rious Prince of life! Life is nought with-

vic - tory Thou o'er death hast won. An - gels in bright rai - ment
greets us, Scat - ters fear and gloom; Let His Church with glad - ness
out Thee; Aid us in our strife; Make us more than con-querors,

Rolled the stone a - way, Kept the fold - ed grave-clothes
Hymns of tri - umph sing, For her Lord now liv - eth;
Through Thy death - less love; Bring us safe through Jor - dan

REFRAIN

Where Thy bod - y lay. Thine is the glo - ry, Ris - en, con-quering Son;
Death hath lost its sting.
To Thy home a - bove.

End - less is the vic - tory Thou o'er death hast won. A-MEN.

Words from *Cantate Domino.* Copyright by World's Student Christian Federation. Used by permission.
JESUS CHRIST: HIS RESURRECTION   [188]

Hail, Thou Once Despised Jesus

John Bakewell. 1757: alt.

PLEADING SAVIOUR: 8. 7. 8. 7. D.
Christian Lyre, 1830

1. Hail, Thou once de - spis - ed Je - sus, Crowned in mock - er - y a King!
2. Je - sus, hail! en-throned in glo - ry, There for - ev - er to a - bide;
3. Wor - ship, hon - or, power, and bless - ing Thou art wor - thy to re - ceive;

Thou didst suf - fer to re - lease us; Thou didst free sal - va - tion bring.
All the heaven-ly hosts a - dore Thee, Seat - ed at Thy Fa-ther's side:
Loud - est prais - es, with - out ceas - ing, Meet it is for us to give.

Hail, Thou ag - o - niz - ing Sav - iour, Bear - er of our sin and shame!
There for sin - ners Thou art plead - ing; There Thou dost our place pre - pare:
Help, ye bright an - gel - ic spir - its, Bring your sweet-est, no - blest lays;

By Thy mer - its we find fa - vor; Life is giv - en through Thy name.
Ev - er for us in - ter - ced - ing, Till in glo - ry we ap - pear.
Help to sing our Sav-iour's mer - its; Help to chant Im - man-uel's praise. A-MEN.

Music used by permission of Oxford University Press.
Alternative tune, "Autumn," Hymn 10.

[189]

JESUS CHRIST: HIS ASCENSION

211 The Head That Once Was Crowned with Thorns

ST. MAGNUS: C. M.
Jeremiah Clark, 1709

Thomas Kelly, 1820

1. The Head that once was crowned with thorns Is crowned with glo - ry now;
2. The high - est place that heaven af - fords Is His, is His by right,
3. The Joy of all who dwell a - bove, The Joy of all be - low
4. To them the cross, with all its shame, With all its grace, is given;
5. They suf - fer with their Lord be - low, They reign with Him a - bove;

A roy - al di - a - dem a - dorns The might - y Vic - tor's brow.
The King of Kings, and Lord of Lords, And heaven's e - ter - nal Light:
To whom He man - i - fests His love, And grants His name to know.
Their name an ev - er - last - ing name, Their joy the joy of heaven.
Their prof - it and their joy to know The won - der of His love. A - MEN.

MELODY IN THE TENOR

ST. MAGNUS: C. M.
Jeremiah Clark, 1709
Arr. by Healey Willan, 1930

Thomas Kelly, 1820

1. The Head that once was crowned with thorns Is crowned with glo - ry now;
2. The high - est place that heaven af - fords Is His, is His by right,
3. The Joy of all who dwell a - bove, The Joy of all be - low
4. To them the cross, with all its shame, With all its grace, is given;
5. They suf - fer with their Lord be - low, They reign with Him a - bove;

A roy - al di - a - dem a - dorns The might - y Vic - tor's brow.
The King of Kings, and Lord of Lords, And heaven's e - ter - nal Light:
To whom He man - i - fests His love, And grants His name to know.
Their name an ev - er - last - ing name, Their joy the joy of heaven.
Their prof - it and their joy to know The won - der of His love. A - MEN.

Music used by permission of British American Music Company, sole U. S. A. agents for Western Music Company, Ltd.
This alternative version may be used for one or more stanzas, the congregation singing the melody.
JESUS CHRIST: HIS ASCENSION   [190]

The Lord Ascendeth Up on High

Arthur T. Russell (1806-1874)

ASCENDIT DEUS: 8. 8. 7. D.
Johann Gottfried Schicht (1753-1823)

1. The Lord as-cend-eth up on high, The Lord hath tri-umphed glo-rious-ly, In power and might ex-cell-ing; The grave and hell are cap-tive led, Lo! He re-turns, our glo-rious Head, To His e-ter-nal dwell-ing.

2. The heavens with joy re-ceive their Lord, By saints, by an-gel hosts a-dored; O day of ex-ul-ta-tion! O earth, a-dore thy glo-rious King! His ris-ing, His as-cen-sion sing With grate-ful ad-o-ra-tion!

3. Our great High Priest hath gone be-fore, Now on His Church His grace to pour, And still His love He giv-eth; O may our hearts to Him as-cend; May all with-in us up-ward tend To Him who ev-er liv-eth! A-MEN.

JESUS CHRIST: HIS ASCENSION

213 Crown Him with Many Crowns

Matthew Bridges, 1851

DIADEMATA: S. M. D.
George J. Elvey, 1868

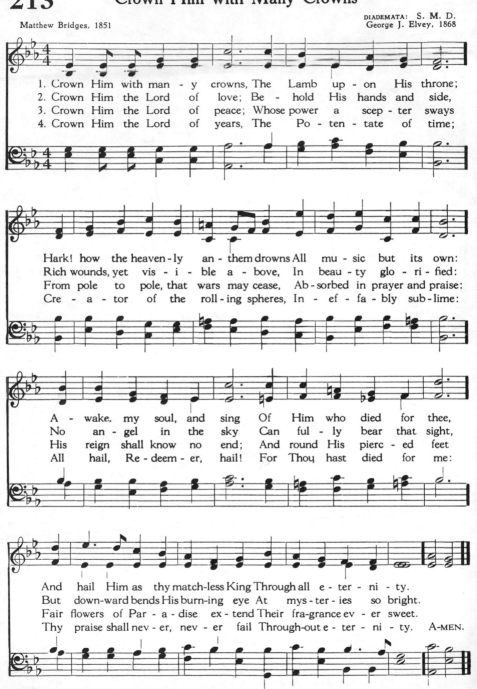

1. Crown Him with man - y crowns, The Lamb up - on His throne;
2. Crown Him the Lord of love; Be - hold His hands and side,
3. Crown Him the Lord of peace; Whose power a scep - ter sways
4. Crown Him the Lord of years, The Po - ten - tate of time;

Hark! how the heaven - ly an - them drowns All mu - sic but its own:
Rich wounds, yet vis - i - ble a - bove, In beau - ty glo - ri - fied:
From pole to pole, that wars may cease, Ab - sorbed in prayer and praise:
Cre - a - tor of the roll - ing spheres, In - ef - fa - bly sub - lime:

A - wake, my soul, and sing Of Him who died for thee,
No an - gel in the sky Can ful - ly bear that sight,
His reign shall know no end; And round His pierc - ed feet
All hail, Re - deem - er, hail! For Thou hast died for me:

And hail Him as thy match-less King Through all e - ter - ni - ty.
But down-ward bends His burn-ing eye At mys - ter - ies so bright.
Fair flowers of Par - a - dise ex - tend Their fra-grance ev - er sweet.
Thy praise shall nev - er, nev - er fail Through-out e - ter - ni - ty. A-MEN.

JESUS CHRIST: HIS ASCENSION

O Holy Saviour, Friend Unseen

214

Charlotte Elliott, 1834, 1836

FLEMMING: 8. 8. 8. 6.
Friedrich F. Flemming, 1811

1. O Ho-ly Sav-iour, Friend un - seen, The faint, the weak on Thee may lean,
2. Blest with this fel-low-ship di - vine, Take what Thou wilt, I'll ne'er re - pine,
3. Though faith and hope may long be tried, I ask not, need not aught be - side;
4. Blest is my lot, what-e'er be - fall; What can dis-turb me, who ap - pall,

Help me, through-out life's vary - ing scene, By faith to cling to Thee.
E'en as the branch-es to the vine, My soul would cling to Thee.
How safe, how calm, how sat - is - fied, The souls that cling to Thee!
While as my Strength, my Rock, my All, Sav-iour, I cling to Thee? A-MEN.

Jesus, Thou Joy of Loving Hearts

215

Attributed to Bernard of Clairvaux, c. 1150
Trans. and arr. by Ray Palmer, 1858

QUEBEC: L. M.
Henry Baker, 1854

1. Je - sus, Thou Joy of lov-ing hearts, Thou Fount of life, Thou Light of men,
2. Thy truth un-changed hath ev - er stood; Thou sav - est those that on Thee call;
3. We taste Thee, O Thou liv-ing Bread, And long to feast up - on Thee still;
4. Our rest-less spir - its yearn for Thee, Wher-e'er our change-ful lot is cast,
5. O Je - sus, ev - er with us stay, Make all our mo-ments calm and bright;

From the best bliss that earth im-parts We turn un - filled to Thee a - gain.
To them that seek Thee Thou art good, To them that find Thee All in all.
We drink of Thee, the Foun-tain-head, And thirst our souls from Thee to fill.
Glad when Thy gra-cious smile we see, Blest when our faith can hold Thee fast.
Chase the dark night of sin a - way, Shed o'er the world Thy ho - ly light. A-MEN.

Music copyright by W. Garrett Horder. Used by permission.

JESUS CHRIST: HIS PRESENCE

216 Jesus, Lover of My Soul

(FIRST TUNE)

Charles Wesley, 1740

ABERYSTWYTH: 7. 7. 7. 7. D.
Joseph Parry, 1879

1. Je - sus, Lov - er of my soul, Let me to Thy bos - om fly,
2. Oth - er ref - uge have I none; Hangs my help - less soul on Thee;
3. Thou, O Christ, art all I want; More than all in Thee I find:
4. Plen - teous grace with Thee is found, Grace to cov - er all my sin;

While the near - er wa - ters roll, While the tem - pest still is high:
Leave, ah! leave me not a - lone, Still sup - port and com - fort me.
Raise the fall - en, cheer the faint, Heal the sick, and lead the blind.
Let the heal - ing streams a - bound; Make and keep me pure with - in.

Hide me, O my Sav - iour, hide, Till the storm of life is past;
All my trust on Thee is stayed, All my help from Thee I bring;
Just and ho - ly is Thy name; I am all un - right - eous - ness;
Thou of life the Foun - tain art, Free - ly let me take of Thee;

Safe in - to the ha - ven guide; O re - ceive my soul at last!
Cov - er my de - fense-less head With the shad - ow of Thy wing.
False and full of sin I am, Thou art full of truth and grace.
Spring Thou up with - in my heart, Rise to all e - ter - ni - ty. A-MEN.

JESUS CHRIST: HIS PRESENCE

Jesus, Lover of My Soul

(SECOND TUNE)

Charles Wesley. 1740

MARTYN: 7. 7. 7. 7. D.
Simeon B. Marsh, 1834

1. Je - sus, Lov - er of my soul, Let me to Thy bos - om fly,
2. Oth - er ref - uge have I none; Hangs my help - less soul on Thee;
3. Thou, O Christ, art all I want; More than all in Thee I find:
4. Plen-teous grace with Thee is found, Grace to cov - er all my sin;

While the near - er wa - ters roll, While the tem - pest still is high:
Leave, ah! leave me not a - lone, Still sup-port and com - fort me.
Raise the fall - en, cheer the faint, Heal the sick, and lead the blind.
Let the heal - ing streams a - bound; Make and keep me pure with - in.

Hide me, O my Sav - iour, hide, Till the storm of life is past;
All my trust on Thee is stayed, All my help from Thee I bring;
Just and ho - ly is Thy name; I am all un - right - eous - ness;
Thou of life the Foun - tain art, Free - ly let me take of Thee;

Safe in - to the ha - ven guide; O re-ceive my soul at last!
Cov - er my de-fense-less head With the shad - ow of Thy wing.
False and full of sin I am, Thou art full of truth and grace.
Spring Thou up with-in my heart, Rise to all e - ter - ni - ty. A-MEN.

JESUS CHRIST: HIS PRESENCE

217 O Son of Man, Our Hero Strong and Tender

Frank Fletcher, c. 1924

CHARTERHOUSE: 11. 10. 11. 10.
David Evans, 1927

In unison

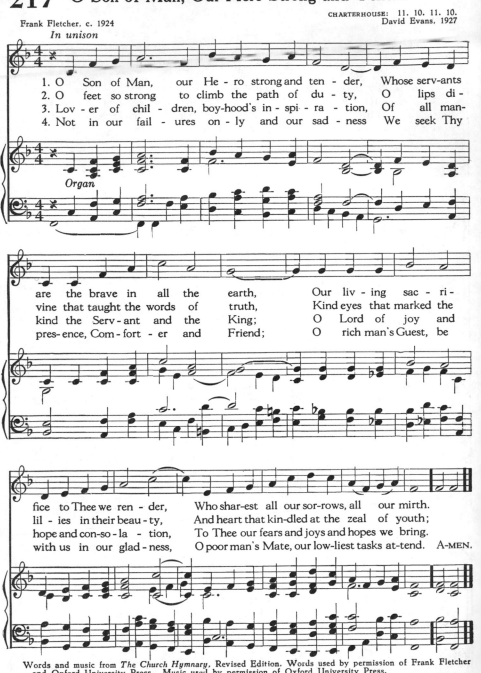

1. O Son of Man, our He - ro strong and ten - der, Whose serv-ants
2. O feet so strong to climb the path of du - ty, O lips di -
3. Lov - er of chil - dren, boy-hood's in - spi - ra - tion, Of all man-
4. Not in our fail - ures on - ly and our sad - ness We seek Thy

Organ

are the brave in all the earth, Our liv - ing sac - ri -
vine that taught the words of truth, Kind eyes that marked the
kind the Serv - ant and the King; O Lord of joy and
pres - ence, Com - fort - er and Friend; O rich man's Guest, be

fice to Thee we ren - der, Who shar-est all our sor-rows, all our mirth.
lil - ies in their beau - ty, And heart that kin-dled at the zeal of youth;
hope and con - so - la - tion, To Thee our fears and joys and hopes we bring.
with us in our glad - ness, O poor man's Mate, our low-liest tasks at-tend. A-MEN.

Words and music from *The Church Hymnary*, Revised Edition. Words used by permission of Frank Fletcher and Oxford University Press. Music used by permission of Oxford University Press.

JESUS CHRIST: HIS PRESENCE

[196]

Since Jesus Is My Friend

218

Paul Gerhardt, 1656
Trans. by Catherine Winkworth, 1855

GREENWOOD: S. M.
Joseph E. Sweetser, 1849

1. Since Je - sus is my Friend, And I to Him be - long,
2. He whis - pers in my breast Sweet words of ho - ly cheer;
3. My heart for glad - ness springs; It can - not more be sad;
4. The Sun that lights mine eyes Is Christ, the Lord I love;

It mat-ters not what foes in - tend, How - ev - er fierce and strong.
How they who seek in God their rest Shall ev - er find Him near.
For ver - y joy it laughs and sings, Sees nought but sun - shine glad.
I sing for joy of that which lies Stored up for me a - bove. A-MEN.

O Thou, in All Thy Might So Far

219

Frederick Lucian Hosmer, 1876

KILMARNOCK: C. M.
Neil Dougall (1776-1862)

1. O Thou, in all Thy might so far, In all Thy love so near,
2. What heart can com - pre - hend Thy name, Or, search - ing, find Thee out,
3. Yet though I know Thee but in part, I ask not, Lord, for more;
4. And dear - er than all things I know Is child - like faith to me,

Be - yond the range of sun and star, And yet be - side us here:
Who art with - in, a quick-ening Flame, A Pres - ence round a - bout.
E - nough for me to know Thou art, To love Thee and a - dore.
That makes the dark - est way I go An o - pen path to Thee. A-MEN.

Alternative tune, "St. Agnes," Hymn 239.

JESUS CHRIST: HIS PRESENCE

220   I've Found a Friend, O Such a Friend!

James G. Small, 1863

CONSTANCE: 8. 7. 8. 7. D.
Arthur S. Sullivan, 1875

1. I've found a Friend, O such a Friend! He loved me ere I knew Him;
2. I've found a Friend, O such a Friend! He bled, He died to save me;
3. I've found a Friend, O such a Friend! So kind and true and ten-der,

He drew me with the cords of love, And thus He bound me to Him;
And not a-lone the gift of life, But His own self He gave me!
So wise a Coun-sel-or and Guide, So might-y a De-fend-er!

And round my heart still close-ly twine Those ties which nought can sev-er,
Nought that I have mine own I call, I'll hold it for the Giv-er,
From Him who loves me now so well What power my soul can sev-er?

For I am His, and He is mine, For-ev-er and for-ev-er.
My heart, my strength, my life, my all Are His, and His for-ev-er.
Shall life or death, shall earth or hell? No! I am His for-ev-er. A-MEN.

JESUS CHRIST: HIS PRESENCE

Thou Art the Way: to Thee Alone 221

George W. Doane. 1824

ST. JAMES: C. M.
Raphael Courteville. 1697

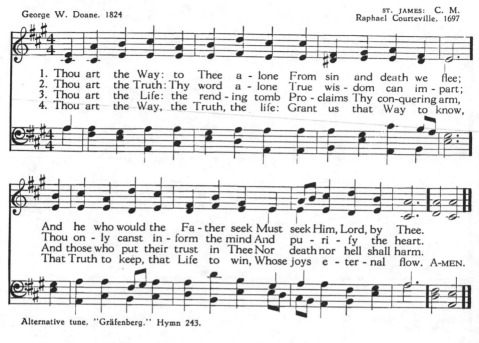

1. Thou art the Way: to Thee a - lone From sin and death we flee;
2. Thou art the Truth: Thy word a - lone True wis - dom can im - part;
3. Thou art the Life: the rend - ing tomb Pro - claims Thy con-quering arm,
4. Thou art the Way, the Truth, the life: Grant us that Way to know,

And he who would the Fa - ther seek Must seek Him, Lord, by Thee.
Thou on - ly canst in - form the mind And pu - ri - fy the heart.
And those who put their trust in Thee Nor death nor hell shall harm.
That Truth to keep, that Life to win, Whose joys e - ter - nal flow. A-MEN.

Alternative tune, "Gräfenberg." Hymn 243.

Jesus, Stand Among Us 222

William Pennefather, c. 1855

BEMERTON (CASWALL): 6. 5. 6. 5.
Friedrich Filitz, 1847

1. Je - sus, stand a - mong us In Thy ris - en power;
2. Breathe the Ho - ly Spir - it In - to ev - ery heart;
3. Thus with quick-ened foot - steps We pur - sue our way,

Let this time of wor - ship Be a hal - lowed hour.
Bid the fears and sor - rows From each soul de - part.
Watch-ing for the dawn - ing Of e - ter - nal day. A-MEN.

JESUS CHRIST: HIS PRESENCE

223

Jesus Merciful

T. C. Chao, 1931
Trans. by Frank W. Price, 1952

HUBBARD: 5. 5. 5. 5.
Chinese folk tune
Arr. by Bliss Wiant, 1936; alt., 1953

1. Je - sus mer - ci - ful, Je - sus pit - y - ing,
2. Je - sus val - or - ous, Je - sus wise and good,
3. Je - sus, Broth - er Man, Je - sus, Friend who knows,
4. Je - sus, ho - ly Lord, Je - sus, Mas - ter true,

Melt my ston - y heart, Com - fort to me bring.
Save me by Thy blood, Feed me with Thy food.
Shar - ing all my load, Bear - ing all my woes.
Re - in - spire me now, Thy great work to do. A-MEN.

Translation copyright, 1953, by Frank W. Price. Used by permission. Music from *Hymns of Universal Praise*. Used by permission.

224 I Know Not How that Bethlehem's Babe

Harry Webb Farrington, 1910

EXETER: C. M.
Henry Lowell Mason, 1923

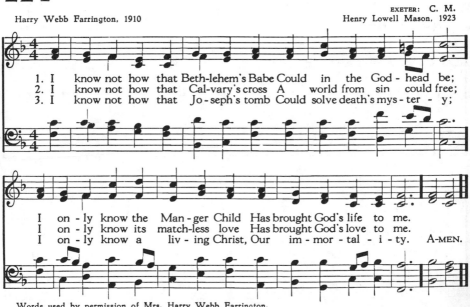

1. I know not how that Beth-lehem's Babe Could in the God - head be;
2. I know not how that Cal-vary's cross A world from sin could free;
3. I know not how that Jo-seph's tomb Could solve death's mys - ter - y;

I on - ly know the Man - ger Child Has brought God's life to me.
I on - ly know its match-less love Has brought God's love to me.
I on - ly know a liv - ing Christ, Our im - mor - tal - i - ty. A-MEN.

Words used by permission of Mrs. Harry Webb Farrington.
JESUS CHRIST: HIS PRESENCE

Jesus, Kneel Beside Me

225

Allen Eastman Cross, 1907

EUDOXIA: 6. 5. 6. 5.
Sabine Baring-Gould (1834-1924)

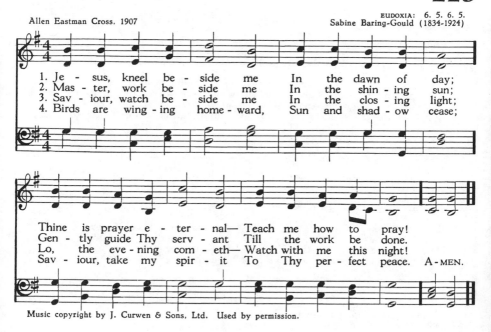

1. Je - sus, kneel be - side me In the dawn of day;
2. Mas - ter, work be - side me In the shin - ing sun;
3. Sav - iour, watch be - side me In the clos - ing light;
4. Birds are wing - ing home - ward, Sun and shad - ow cease;

Thine is prayer e - ter - nal— Teach me how to pray!
Gen - tly guide Thy serv - ant Till the work be done.
Lo, the eve - ning com - eth— Watch with me this night!
Sav - iour, take my spir - it To Thy per - fect peace. A - MEN.

Music copyright by J. Curwen & Sons, Ltd. Used by permission.

Blest Are the Pure in Heart

226

Stanzas 1, 3, John Keble, 1819; alt.
Stanzas 2, 4, Mitre Hymn Book, 1836; alt.

FRANCONIA: S. M.
Johann B. König, 1738
Arr. by William H. Havergal, 1840

1. Blest are the pure in heart, For they shall see our God;
2. The Lord, who left the heavens Our life and peace to bring,
3. He to the low - ly soul Doth still Him - self im - part;
4. Lord, we Thy pres - ence seek; May ours this bless - ing be;

The se - cret of the Lord is theirs; Their soul is Christ's a - bode.
To dwell in low - li - ness with men Their pat-tern and their King;
And for His dwell - ing and His throne Choos - eth the pure in heart.
Give us a pure and low - ly heart, A tem-ple meet for Thee. A - MEN.

JESUS CHRIST: HIS PRESENCE

227 We Bear the Strain of Earthly Care

AZMON: C. M.
Carl G. Gläser, 1828
Arr. by Lowell Mason, 1839

Ozora Stearns Davis, 1909

1. We bear the strain of earth-ly care, But bear it not a-lone;
2. Through din of mar-ket, whirl of wheels, And thrust of driv-ing trade,
3. The com-mon hopes that make us men Were His in Gal-i-lee;
4. Our broth-er-hood still rests in Him, The Broth-er of us all,

Be-side us walks our Broth-er Christ And makes our task His own.
We fol-low where the Mas-ter leads, Se-rene and un-a-fraid.
The tasks He gives are those He gave Be-side the rest-less sea.
And o'er the cen-turies still we hear The Mas-ter's win-some call. A-MEN.

Words used by permission of Elizabeth Davis Burford.
Alternative tune, "Walsall," Hymn 129.

228 Strong Son of God, Immortal Love

ST. CRISPIN: L. M.
George J. Elvey, 1862

Alfred Tennyson, 1850

1. Strong Son of God, im-mor-tal Love, Whom we, that have not seen Thy face,
2. Thou seem-est hu-man and di-vine, The high-est, ho-liest man-hood, Thou.
3. Our lit-tle sys-tems have their day; They have their day and cease to be;
4. Let knowl-edge grow from more to more, But more of rev-er-ence in us dwell;

By faith, and faith a-lone, em-brace, Be-liev-ing where we can-not prove;
Our wills are ours, we know not how; Our wills are ours, to make them Thine.
They are but bro-ken lights of Thee, And Thou, O Lord, art more than they.
That mind and soul, ac-cord-ing well, May make one mu-sic as be-fore. A-MEN.

Alternative tune, "Quebec," Hymn 215.

JESUS CHRIST: HIS PRESENCE   [202]

Immortal Love, Forever Full

John Greenleaf Whittier, 1866

SERENITY: C. M.
Arr. from William V. Wallace, 1856

1. Im - mor - tal Love, for - ev - er full, For - ev - er flow-ing free,
2. We may not climb the heaven-ly steeps To bring the Lord Christ down;
3. But warm, sweet, ten - der, e - ven yet A pres - ent help is He;
4. The heal - ing of His seam-less dress Is by our beds of pain;
5. O Lord and Mas - ter of us all, What-e'er our name or sign,

For - ev - er shared, for - ev - er whole, A nev - er - ebb-ing sea!
In vain we search the low - est deeps, For Him no depths can drown.
And faith has still its Ol - i - vet, And love its Gal - i - lee.
We touch Him in life's throng and press, And we are whole a - gain.
We own Thy sway, we hear Thy call, We test our lives by Thine. A-MEN.

Words used by permission of Houghton Mifflin Company, authorized publishers.

JESUS CHRIST: HIS PRESENCE

The Lord Will Come and Not Be Slow

From Psalms 82; 85; 86
John Milton, 1648

OLD 107TH: C. M.
Scottish Psalter, 1635
Based on Genevan Psalter

1. The Lord will come and not be slow, His foot-steps can - not err;
2. Truth from the earth, like to a flower, Shall bud and blos - som then;
3. Rise, God, judge Thou the earth in might, This wick - ed earth re - dress;
4. For great Thou art, and won-ders great By Thy strong hand are done.

Be - fore Him right-eous-ness shall go, His roy - al har - bin - ger.
And jus - tice, from her heaven-ly bower, Look down on mor - tal men.
For Thou art He who shall by right The na - tions all pos - sess.
Thou in Thy ev - er - last - ing seat Re - main-est God a - lone. A-MEN.

JESUS CHRIST: HIS COMING IN GLORY

231 Rejoice, Rejoice, Believers

Laurentius Laurenti. 1700
Trans. by Sarah B. Findlater. 1854

LLANGLOFFAN: 7. 6. 7. 6. D.
Welsh hymn melody
D. Evans' *Hymnau a Thonau,* 1865

1. Re - joice, re - joice, be - liev - ers, And let your lights ap - pear;
2. See that your lamps are burn - ing; Re - plen - ish them with oil;
3. Our Hope and Ex - pec - ta - tion, O Je - sus, now ap - pear!

The eve - ning is ad - vanc - ing, And dark - er night is near:
And wait for your sal - va - tion, The end of earth - ly toil.
A - rise, Thou Sun so longed for, O'er this be - night - ed sphere!

The Bride-groom is a - ris - ing, And soon He draw - eth nigh;
The watch - ers on the moun - tain Pro - claim the Bride-groom near,
With hearts and hands up - lift - ed, We plead, O Lord, to see

Up, pray, and watch, and wres - tle: At mid-night comes the cry.
Go meet Him as He com - eth, With al - le - lu - ias clear.
The day of earth's re - demp - tion That brings us un - to Thee. A - MEN.

Words used by permission of Thomas Nelson & Sons, Ltd.
Alternative tune, "Lancashire," Hymn 208.

JESUS CHRIST: HIS COMING IN GLORY [204]

The King Shall Come When Morning Dawns 232

Based on the Greek
Trans. by John Brownlie, 1907

ST. STEPHEN: C. M.
William Jones, 1789

1. The King shall come when morn-ing dawns, And light tri - um-phant breaks;
2. Not as of old a lit - tle child To bear, and fight, and die,
3. O bright-er than the ris - ing morn When He, vic - to - rious, rose,
4. O bright-er than that glo - rious morn Shall this fair morn - ing be,
5. The King shall come when morn-ing dawns, And light and beau - ty brings:

When beau - ty gilds the east - ern hills, And life to joy a - wakes.
But crowned with glo - ry like the sun That lights the morn - ing sky.
And left the lone-some place of death, De - spite the rage of foes—
When Christ, our King, in beau - ty comes, And we His face shall see!
Hail, Christ the Lord! Thy peo - ple pray, Come quick-ly, King of Kings. A-MEN.

Words from *Hymns of the Russian Church.* Used by permission of Oxford University Press.

Come, Lord, and Tarry Not 233

Horatius Bonar, 1846

ST. BRIDE: S. M.
Samuel Howard, 1762

1. Come, Lord, and tar - ry not; Bring the long - looked-for day;
2. Come, for Thy saints still wait; Dai - ly as - cends their sigh:
3. Come, for cre - a - tion groans, Im - pa - tient of Thy stay,
4. Come, and make all things new; Build up this ru - ined earth;
5. Come, and be - gin Thy reign Of ev - er - last - ing peace;

O why these years of wait - ing here, These a - ges of de - lay?
The Spir - it and the Bride say, "Come": Dost Thou not hear the cry?
Worn out with these long years of ill, These a - ges of de - lay.
Re - store our fad - ed Par - a - dise, Cre - a-tion's sec - ond birth.
Come, take the King-dom to Thy - self, Great King of Right-eous-ness. A-MEN.

For alternative arrangement, see Hymn 308. [205] JESUS CHRIST: HIS COMING IN GLORY

Lo! He Comes, with Clouds Descending

John Cennick, 1752. and
Charles Wesley, 1758; alt.

HOLYWOOD: 8. 7. 8. 7. 8. 7.
J. F. Wade's *Cantus Diversi*, 1751

1. Lo! He comes, with clouds de-scend-ing, Once for our sal - va - tion slain;
2. Ev - ery eye shall now be - hold Him, Robed in dread-ful maj - es - ty;
3. Yea, A - men! let all a - dore Thee, High on Thine e - ter - nal throne;

Thou-sand thou-sand saints at - tend-ing Swell the tri - umph of His train:
Those who set at nought and sold Him, Pierced, and nailed Him to the tree,
Sav - iour, take the power and glo - ry; Claim the King-dom for Thine own:

Al - le - lu - ia, al - le - lu - ia! Christ the Lord re - turns to reign.
Deep-ly wail-ing, deep-ly wail-ing, Shall the true Mes-si - ah see.
Al - le - lu - ia, al - le - lu - ia! Thou shalt reign, and Thou a - lone. A-MEN.

JESUS CHRIST: HIS COMING IN GLORY

235 Breathe on Me, Breath of God

Edwin Hatch, 1886

TRENTHAM: S. M.
Robert Jackson, 1894

1. Breathe on me, Breath of God, Fill me with life a - new, That I may
2. Breathe on me, Breath of God, Un - til my heart is pure, Un - til with
3. Breathe on me, Breath of God, Till I am whol - ly Thine, Un - til this
4. Breathe on me, Breath of God, So shall I nev - er die, But live with

THE HOLY SPIRIT

[206]

Breathe on Me, Breath of God

love what Thou dost love, And do what Thou wouldst do.
Thee I will one will, To do and to en - dure.
earth - ly part of me Glows with Thy fire di - vine.
Thee the per - fect life Of Thine e - ter - ni - ty. A - MEN.

Music used by permission of Mrs. Ethel Taylor.
Alternative tune, "St. Bride," Hymn 233.

Spirit of God, Descend Upon My Heart 236

MORECAMBE: 10. 10. 10. 10.
Attributed to George Croly, 1866
Frederick C. Atkinson, 1870

1. Spir - it of God, de - scend up - on my heart; Wean it from earth; through
2. I ask no dream, no proph-et ec - sta-sies, No sud - den rend - ing
3. Hast Thou not bid us love Thee, God and King? All, all Thine own, soul,
4. Teach me to feel that Thou art al - ways nigh; Teach me the strug-gles
5. Teach me to love Thee as Thine an - gels love, One ho - ly pas - sion

all its puls - es move; Stoop to my weak-ness, might - y as Thou art,
of the veil of clay, No an - gel vis - it - ant, no o-pening skies;
heart, and strength, and mind; I see Thy cross—there teach my heart to cling:
of the soul to bear, To check the ris - ing doubt, the reb - el sigh:
fill - ing all my frame; The bap-tism of the heaven-de - scend-ed Dove,

And make me love Thee as I ought to love.
But take the dim - ness of my soul a - way.
O let me seek Thee, and O let me find!
Teach me the pa - tience of un - an - swered prayer.
My heart an al - tar, and Thy love the flame. A - MEN.

THE HOLY SPIRIT

[207]

237 Come, Holy Ghost, Our Souls Inspire

Latin, c. 9th century
Para. by John Cosin, 1627

VENI CREATOR: L. M.
Plain song (Mode VIII)
Mechlin version

In unison

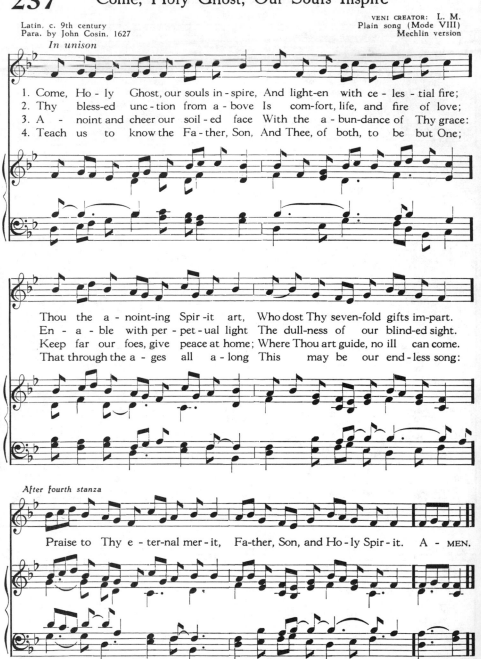

1. Come, Ho - ly Ghost, our souls in - spire, And light-en with ce - les - tial fire;
2. Thy bless-ed unc - tion from a - bove Is com-fort, life, and fire of love;
3. A - noint and cheer our soil - ed face With the a - bun-dance of Thy grace:
4. Teach us to know the Fa - ther, Son, And Thee, of both, to be but One;

Thou the a - noint-ing Spir - it art, Who dost Thy seven-fold gifts im-part.
En - a - ble with per - pet - ual light The dull-ness of our blind-ed sight.
Keep far our foes, give peace at home; Where Thou art guide, no ill can come.
That through the a - ges all a - long This may be our end - less song:

After fourth stanza

Praise to Thy e - ter-nal mer - it, Fa-ther, Son, and Ho - ly Spir - it. A - MEN.

Music from *The BBC Hymn Book*. Used by permission of Oxford University Press.

THE HOLY SPIRIT

[208]

Seal Us, O Holy Spirit

MEREDITH: 7. 7. 8. 7. with Refrain
Isaac H. Meredith, 1900
Har. by David Hugh Jones, 1953

Isaac H. Meredith, 1900

1. Seal us, O Ho - ly Spir - it, Grant us Thine im-press, we pray;
2. Seal us, O Ho - ly Spir - it, Help us Thy like-ness to show;
3. Seal us, O Ho - ly Spir - it, Make us Thine own from this hour;

We would be more like the Sav - iour, Stamped with His im - age to - day.
Then from our lives un - to oth - ers Streams of rich bless - ing shall flow.
May we be use - ful, dear Mas - ter, Seal us with wit - ness - ing power.

REFRAIN

Seal us, seal us, Seal us just now, we pray; Seal us, O

Ho - ly Spir - it, Seal us for serv - ice to - day. A - MEN.

Words and music copyright, 1900, 1928. Used by permission of Lorenz Publishing Company, owner.

THE HOLY SPIRIT

239

Come, Holy Spirit, Heavenly Dove

Isaac Watts, 1707

ST. AGNES: C. M.
John B. Dykes, 1866

1. Come, Ho - ly Spir - it, heaven-ly Dove, With all Thy quick-ening powers;
2. In vain we tune our for - mal songs, In vain we strive to rise;
3. Dear Lord, and shall we ev - er live At this poor dy - ing rate?
4. Come, Ho - ly Spir - it, heaven-ly Dove, With all Thy quick-ening powers;

Kin - dle a flame of sa - cred love In these cold hearts of ours.
Ho - san-nas lan-guish on our tongues, And our de - vo - tion dies.
Our love so faint, so cold to Thee, And Thine to us so great!
Come, shed a-broad a Sav - iour's love, And that shall kin - dle ours. A - MEN.

240

Holy Spirit, Truth Divine

Samuel Longfellow, 1864

MERCY: 7. 7. 7. 7.
Arr. from Louis M. Gottschalk, 1867

1. Ho - ly Spir - it, Truth di - vine, Dawn up - on this soul of mine;
2. Ho - ly Spir - it, Love di - vine, Glow with - in this heart of mine;
3. Ho - ly Spir - it, Power di - vine, Fill and nerve this will of mine;
4. Ho - ly Spir - it, Right di - vine, King with - in my con-science reign;

Word of God, and in - ward Light, Wake my spir - it, clear my sight.
Kin - dle ev - ery high de - sire; Per - ish self in Thy pure fire.
By Thee may I strong-ly live, Brave-ly bear, and no - bly strive.
Be my Law, and I shall be Firm - ly bound, for-ev - er free. A-MEN.

THE HOLY SPIRIT

[210]

Gracious Spirit, Dwell with Me

Thomas Toke Lynch, 1855

REDHEAD NO. 76: 7. 7. 7. 7. 7. 7.
Richard Redhead, 1853

1. Gra - cious Spir - it, dwell with me; I my - self would
2. Truth - ful Spir - it, dwell with me; I my - self would
3. Ho - ly Spir - it, dwell with me; I my - self would

gra - cious be; And with words that help and heal
truth - ful be; And with wis - dom kind and clear
ho - ly be; Sep - a - rate from sin, I would

Would Thy life in mine re - veal; And with ac - tions
Let Thy life in mine ap - pear; And with ac - tions
Choose and cher - ish all things good, And what - ev - er

bold and meek Would for Christ my Sav - iour speak.
broth - er - ly Speak my Lord's sin - cer - i - ty.
I can be Give to Him who gave me Thee! A - MEN.

THE HOLY SPIRIT

[211]

242

O Spirit of the Living God

James Montgomery, 1823

WINCHESTER NEW: L. M.
Musikalisches Handbuch, Hamburg, 1690

1. O Spir - it of the liv - ing God, In all Thy plen - i - tude of grace,
2. Give tongues of fire and hearts of love, To preach the rec - on - cil - ing word;
3. Be dark - ness, at Thy com - ing, light; Con - fu - sion, or - der in Thy path;
4. O Spir - it of the Lord, pre - pare All the round earth her God to meet;
5. Bap - tize the na - tions; far and nigh The tri - umphs of the cross re - cord;

Wher - e'er the foot of man hath trod, De - scend on our a - pos - tate race.
Give power and unc - tion from a - bove, When e'er the joy - ful sound is heard.
Souls with - out strength in - spire with might; Bid mer - cy tri - umph o - ver wrath.
Breathe Thou a - broad like morn - ing air, Till hearts of stone be - gin to beat.
The name of Je - sus glo - ri - fy, Till ev - ery kin - dred call Him Lord. A - MEN.

Alternative tune, "Melcombe," Hymn 45.

243

Spirit Divine, Attend Our Prayers

Andrew Reed, 1829

GRÄFENBERG: C. M.
Ascribed to Johann Crüger
Praxis Pietatis Melica, 1653

1. Spir - it di - vine, at - tend our prayers, And make this house Thy home;
2. Come as the light: to us re - veal Our emp - ti - ness and woe;
3. Come as the fire: and purge our hearts Like sac - ri - fi - cial flame;
4. Come as the dove: and spread Thy wings, The wings of peace - ful love;
5. Spir - it di - vine, at - tend our prayers; Make a lost world Thy home;

De - scend with all Thy gra - cious powers; O come, great Spir - it, come!
And lead us in those paths of life Where all the right - eous go.
Let our whole soul an of - fering be To our Re - deem - er's name.
And let Thy Church on earth be - come Blest as the Church a - bove.
De - scend with all Thy gra - cious powers; O come, great Spir - it, come! A - MEN.

Come, Thou Almighty King

244

ITALIAN HYMN: 6. 6. 4. 6. 6. 6. 4.
Felice de Giardini, 1769

Anon., c. 1757; alt.

1. Come, Thou Almighty King, Help us Thy name to sing, Help us to praise: Father, all-glorious, O'er all victorious, Come, and reign over us, Ancient of Days.

2. Come, Thou Incarnate Word, Gird on Thy mighty sword, Our prayer attend: Come, and Thy people bless, And give Thy word success; Spirit of holiness, On us descend.

3. Come, Holy Comforter, Thy sacred witness bear In this glad hour: Thou who almighty art, Now rule in every heart, And ne'er from us depart, Spirit of power.

4. To Thee, great One in Three, The highest praises be, Hence evermore! Thy sovereign majesty May we in glory see, And to eternity Love and adore. A-MEN.

THE HOLY TRINITY

[213]

245

O Trinity of Blessed Light

(FIRST TUNE)

Latin, c. 6th century
Trans. by John Mason Neale, 1852

PLAIN SONG: L. M.
Plain song from the *Sarum Antiphonal*
Har. by J. H. Arnold, 1925

In unison

1. O Trin - i - ty of bless - ed light, O U-
ni - ty of prince - ly might, The fier - y sun now
goes his way; Shed Thou with - in our hearts Thy ray.

2. To Thee our morn - ing song of praise, To Thee
our eve - ning prayer we raise; Thy glo - ry sup - pliant
we a - dore For - ev - er and for - ev - er - more.

3. All laud to God the Fa - ther be; All praise,
e - ter - nal Son, to Thee; All glo - ry, as is
ev - er meet, To God the ho - ly Par - a - clete. A - MEN.

Music from *Songs of Praise*, Enlarged Edition. Used by permission of Oxford University Press.

THE HOLY TRINITY

O Trinity of Blessed Light

245

(SECOND TUNE)

Latin, c. 6th century
Trans. by John Mason Neale, 1852

ADESTO SANCTA TRINITAS: L. M.
Chartres church melody
Har. by R. Vaughan Williams, 1906

1. O Trin - i - ty of bless - ed light, O U - ni-
2. To Thee our morn - ing song of praise, To Thee our
3. All laud to God the Fa - ther be; All praise, e-

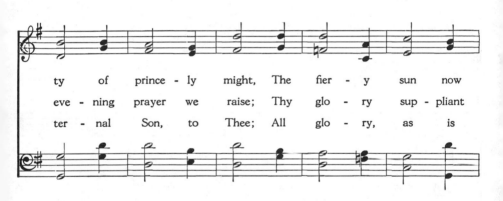

ty of prince - ly might, The fier - y sun now
eve - ning prayer we raise; Thy glo - ry sup - pliant
ter - nal Son, to Thee; All glo - ry, as is

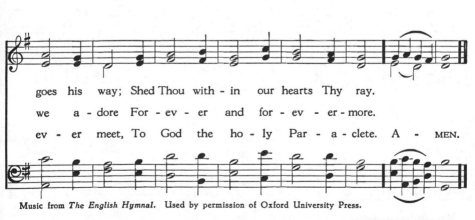

goes his way; Shed Thou with - in our hearts Thy ray.
we a - dore For - ev - er and for - ev - er - more.
ev - er meet, To God the ho - ly Par - a - clete. A - MEN.

Music from *The English Hymnal.* Used by permission of Oxford University Press.

THE HOLY TRINITY

246 Ancient of Days, Who Sittest Throned in Glory

William C. Doane, 1886, 1892

ANCIENT OF DAYS: 11. 10. 11. 10.
J. Albert Jeffery, 1886

1. An - cient of Days, who sit - test throned in glo - ry,
2. O Ho - ly Fa - ther, who hast led Thy chil - dren
3. O Ho - ly Je - sus, Prince of Peace and Sav - iour,
4. O Ho - ly Ghost, the Lord and the Life Giv - er,
5. O Tri - une God, with heart and voice a - dor - ing,

To Thee all knees are bent, all voi - ces pray;
In all the a - ges, with the fire and cloud,
To Thee we owe the peace that still pre - vails,
Thine is the quick - ening power that gives in - crease;
Praise we the good - ness that doth crown our days;

Thy love has blessed the wide world's won - drous sto - ry
Through seas dry - shod, through wea - ry wastes be - wil - dering;
Still - ing the rude wills of men's wild be - hav - ior,
From Thee have flowed, as from a pleas - ant riv - er,
Pray we that Thou wilt hear us, still im - plor - ing

With light and life since E - den's dawn - ing day.
To Thee, in rev - erent love, our hearts are bowed.
And calm - ing pas - sion's fierce and storm - y gales.
Our plen - ty, wealth, pros - per - i - ty, and peace.
Thy love and fa - vor, kept to us al - ways. A - MEN.

Alternative tune, "Donne Secours," Hymn 285.

THE HOLY TRINITY

O God of Light, Thy Word, a Lamp Unfailing 247

Sarah E. Taylor, 1952

CHARTERHOUSE: 11. 10. 11. 10.
David Evans, 1927

In unison

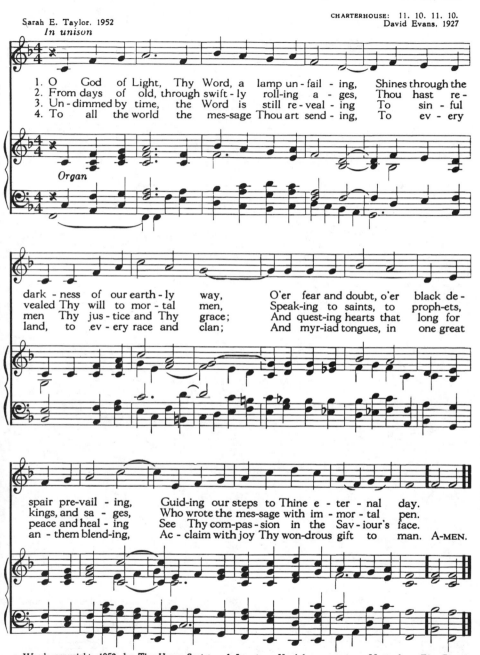

1. O God of Light, Thy Word, a lamp un-fail-ing, Shines through the
2. From days of old, through swift-ly roll-ing a-ges, Thou hast re-
3. Un-dimmed by time, the Word is still re-veal-ing To sin-ful
4. To all the world the mes-sage Thou art send-ing, To ev-ery

Organ

dark-ness of our earth-ly way, O'er fear and doubt, o'er black de-
vealed Thy will to mor-tal men, Speak-ing to saints, to proph-ets,
men Thy jus-tice and Thy grace; And quest-ing hearts that long for
land, to ev-ery race and clan; And myr-iad tongues, in one great

spair pre-vail-ing, Guid-ing our steps to Thine e-ter-nal day.
kings, and sa-ges, Who wrote the mes-sage with im-mor-tal pen.
peace and heal-ing, See Thy com-pas-sion in the Sav-iour's face.
an-them blend-ing, Ac-claim with joy Thy won-drous gift to man. A-MEN.

Words copyright, 1952, by The Hymn Society of America. Used by permission. Music from *The Church Hymnary*, Revised Edition. Used by permission of Oxford University Press.
Alternative tune, "Ancient of Days," opposite page.

THE HOLY SCRIPTURES

248 Book of Books, Our People's Strength

LIEBSTER JESU: 7. 8. 7. 8. 8. 8.
Johann Rudolph Ahle, 1664
Percy Dearmer, 1925
Arr. by Johann Sebastian Bach (1685-1750)

1. Book of books, our peo-ple's strength, States-man's, teach-er's, he-ro's treas - ure,
2. Thank we those who toiled in thought, Man - y di - verse scrolls com-plet - ing,
3. Praise we God, who hath in - spired Those whose wis-dom still di - rects us;

Bring - ing free - dom, spread-ing truth, Shed-ding light that none can meas - ure;
Po - ets, proph-ets, schol - ars, saints, Each his word from God re - peat - ing;
Praise Him for the Word made flesh, For the Spir - it who pro - tects us.

Wis - dom comes to those who know thee, All the best we have we owe thee.
Till they came, who told the sto - ry Of the Word, and showed His glo - ry.
Light of knowl-edge, ev - er burn-ing, Shed on us thy death-less learn - ing. A-MEN.

Words from *Songs of Praise*. Used by permission of Oxford University Press.

249 Father of Mercies, in Thy Word

BEATITUDO: C. M.
Anne Steele, 1760
John B. Dykes, 1875

1. Fa - ther of mer - cies, in Thy Word What end - less glo - ry shines;
2. Here the Re-deem - er's wel - come voice Spreads heaven-ly peace a - round;
3. O may these heaven-ly pa - ges be My ev - er dear de - light;
4. Di - vine In - struc - tor, gra - cious Lord, Be Thou for - ev - er near;

THE HOLY SCRIPTURES

Father of Mercies, in Thy Word

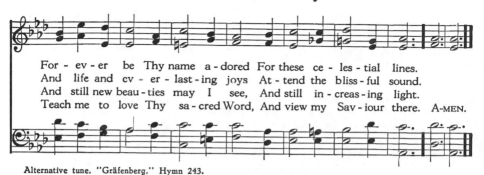

For - ev - er   be Thy name a - dored For these ce - les - tial   lines.
And   life and ev - er - last - ing joys At - tend the bliss - ful sound.
And   still new beau - ties may I   see, And still in - creas - ing light.
Teach me to love Thy   sa - cred Word, And view my Sav - iour there. A-MEN.

Alternative tune, "Gräfenberg," Hymn 243.

Break Thou the Bread of Life   250

Mary A. Lathbury, 1877; alt.

BREAD OF LIFE: 6. 4. 6. 4. D.
William F. Sherwin, 1877; alt.

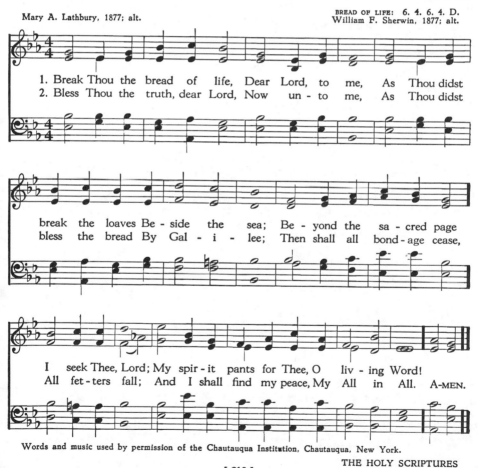

1. Break Thou the bread of   life, Dear Lord, to   me,   As   Thou didst
2. Bless Thou the   truth, dear Lord, Now un - to   me,   As   Thou didst

break the   loaves Be - side   the   sea; Be - yond the   sa - cred page
bless the   bread By Gal - i - lee; Then shall all   bond - age cease,

I   seek Thee, Lord; My spir - it pants for Thee, O   liv - ing Word!
All fet - ters fall; And I shall find my peace, My All   in All. A-MEN.

Words and music used by permission of the Chautauqua Institution, Chautauqua, New York.

THE HOLY SCRIPTURES

251 O Word of God Incarnate

(FIRST TUNE)

MUNICH: 7. 6. 7. 6. D.
Neuvermehrtes Meiningisches Gesangbuch, 1693
Har. by Felix Mendelssohn, 1847

William Walsham How, 1867

1. O Word of God In - car - nate, O Wis - dom from on high,
2. The Church from her dear Mas - ter Re - ceived the gift di - vine.
3. It float - eth like a ban - ner Be - fore God's host un - furled;
4. O make Thy Church, dear Sav - iour, A lamp of pur - est gold,

O Truth un-changed, un - chang - ing, O Light of our dark sky,
And still that light she lift - eth O'er all the earth to shine.
It shin - eth like a bea - con A - bove the dark - ling world.
To bear be - fore the na - tions Thy true light, as of old.

We praise Thee for the ra - diance That from the hal - lowed page,
It is the gold - en cas - ket, Where gems of truth are stored;
It is the chart and com - pass That o'er life's surg - ing sea,
O teach Thy wan-dering pil - grims By this their path to trace,

A lan - tern to our foot-steps, Shines on from age to age.
It is the heaven-drawn pic-ture Of Christ, the liv - ing Word.
'Mid mists and rocks and quick-sands, Still guides, O Christ, to Thee.
Till, clouds and dark - ness end - ed, They see Thee face to face. A - MEN.

O Word of God Incarnate

251

(SECOND TUNE)

CHENIES: 7. 6. 7. 6. D.
Timothy R. Matthews, 1855

Music used by permission of Novello & Co., Ltd.
For words, see opposite page.

Lord, Thy Word Abideth

252

Henry W. Baker, 1861; alt.

ST. CYPRIAN: 6. 6. 6. 6.
Richard R. Chope, 1862

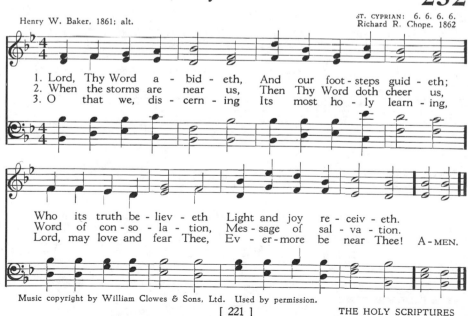

1. Lord, Thy Word a - bid - eth, And our foot - steps guid - eth;
2. When the storms are near us, Then Thy Word doth cheer us,
3. O that we, dis - cern - ing Its most ho - ly learn - ing,

Who its truth be - liev - eth Light and joy re - ceiv - eth.
Word of con - so - la - tion, Mes - sage of sal - va - tion.
Lord, may love and fear Thee, Ev - er - more be near Thee! A - MEN.

Music copyright by William Clowes & Sons, Ltd. Used by permission.

[221]

THE HOLY SCRIPTURES

253 How I Love Thy Law, O Lord!

From Psalm 119
The Psalter, 1912; alt., 1950

SPANISH HYMN: 7. 7. 7. 7. with Refrain
Source unknown
Har. by David Evans, 1927

1. How I love Thy law, O Lord! Dai - ly joy its truths af - ford;
2. Thy com-mand-ments in my heart Tru - est wis - dom can im - part;
3. While my heart Thy word o - beys, I am kept from e - vil ways;

In its con-stant light I go, Wise to con - quer ev - ery foe.
To my eyes Thy pre-cepts show Wis - dom more than sa - ges know.
From Thy law, with Thee to guide, May I nev - er turn a - side.

REFRAIN

Sweet - er are Thy words to me Than all oth - er good can be;

Safe I walk, Thy truth my light, Hat - ing false-hood, lov - ing right. A-MEN.

Music from *The Church Hymnary*, Revised Edition. Used by permission of Oxford University Press.

THE HOLY SCRIPTURES

Lamp of Our Feet, Whereby We Trace 254

Bernard Barton, 1826

LAMBETH: C. M.
Wilhelm A. F. Schulthes, 1871

1. Lamp of our feet, where - by we trace Our path when wont to stray;
2. Bread of our souls, where - on we feed, True man - na from on high;
3. Pil - lar of fire, through watch - es dark, Or ra - diant cloud by day;
4. Word of the ev - er - liv - ing God, Will of His glo - rious Son:
5. Lord, grant that we a - right may learn The wis - dom it im - parts,

Stream from the fount of heaven - ly grace, Brook by the trav-eler's way.
Our guide and chart, where-in we read Of realms be - yond the sky;
When waves would whelm our toss-ing bark, Our an-chor and our stay;
With - out thee how could earth be trod, Or heaven it - self be won?
And to its heaven-ly teach - ing turn With sim - ple, child-like hearts. A - MEN.

O Come, My People, to My Law 255

From Psalm 78
The Psalter, 1912

HEBER (Kingsley): C. M.
George Kingsley, 1838

1. O come, my peo - ple, to my law At - ten-tive-ly give ear;
2. My mouth shall speak in par - a - bles Of hid - den truths of old,
3. We will not from their chil - dren hide Je - ho - vah's wor - thy praise,
4. A tes - ti - mo - ny and a law The Lord our God de - creed,
5. He willed that each suc - ceed - ing race His deeds might learn and know,
6. Let chil - dren learn God's right-eous ways And on Him stay their heart,

With will - ing heart and teach - a - ble The words of wis - dom hear.
Which, hand - ed down from age to age, To us our fa - thers told.
But tell the great-ness of His strength, His won-drous works and ways.
And bade our fa - thers teach their sons, That they His ways might heed.
That chil-dren's chil - dren to their sons Might all these won-ders show.
That they may not for - get His works, Nor from His ways de - part. A - MEN.

[223]

THE HOLY SCRIPTURES

256 O Lord of Life, to Thee We Lift

FOREST GREEN: C. M. D.
Traditional English melody
Arr. by R. Vaughan Williams, 1906

Washington Gladden, 1897

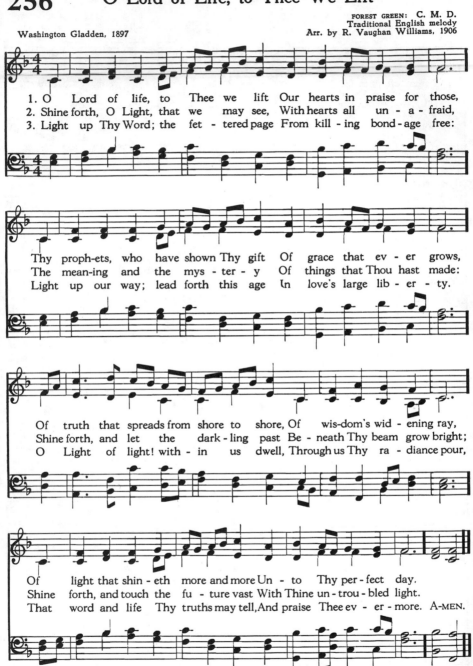

1. O Lord of life, to Thee we lift Our hearts in praise for those,
2. Shine forth, O Light, that we may see, With hearts all un - a - fraid,
3. Light up Thy Word; the fet - tered page From kill - ing bond - age free:

Thy proph-ets, who have shown Thy gift Of grace that ev - er grows,
The mean-ing and the mys - ter - y Of things that Thou hast made:
Light up our way; lead forth this age In love's large lib - er - ty.

Of truth that spreads from shore to shore, Of wis-dom's wid - ening ray,
Shine forth, and let the dark - ling past Be - neath Thy beam grow bright;
O Light of light! with - in us dwell, Through us Thy ra - diance pour,

Of light that shin - eth more and more Un - to Thy per - fect day.
Shine forth, and touch the fu - ture vast With Thine un - trou - bled light.
That word and life Thy truths may tell, And praise Thee ev - er - more. A-MEN.

Music from *The English Hymnal.* Used by permission of Oxford University Press.
THE HOLY SCRIPTURES

[224]

Most Perfect Is the Law of God 257

From Psalm 19
The Psalter, 1912

GLASGOW: C. M.
Moore's *Psalm Singer's Pocket Companion*, 1756

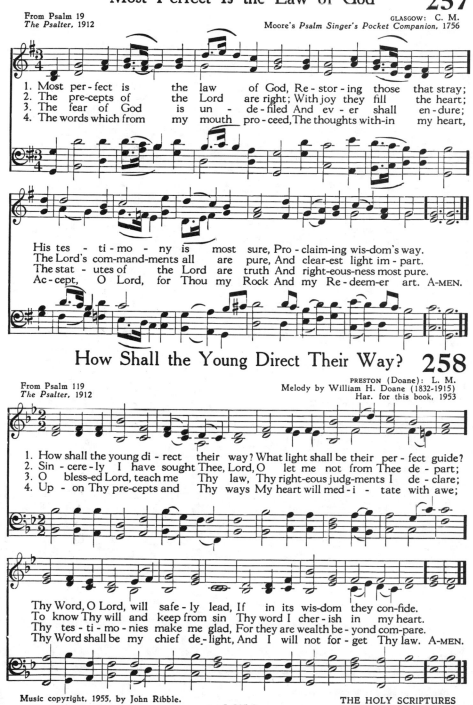

1. Most per-fect is the law of God, Re-stor-ing those that stray;
2. The pre-cepts of the Lord are right; With joy they fill the heart;
3. The fear of God is un-de-filed And ev-er shall en-dure;
4. The words which from my mouth pro-ceed, The thoughts with-in my heart,

His tes-ti-mo-ny is most sure, Pro-claim-ing wis-dom's way.
The Lord's com-mand-ments all are pure, And clear-est light im-part.
The stat-utes of the Lord are truth And right-eous-ness most pure.
Ac-cept, O Lord, for Thou my Rock And my Re-deem-er art. A-MEN.

How Shall the Young Direct Their Way? 258

From Psalm 119
The Psalter, 1912

PRESTON (Doane): L. M.
Melody by William H. Doane (1832-1915)
Har. for this book, 1953

1. How shall the young di-rect their way? What light shall be their per-fect guide?
2. Sin-cere-ly I have sought Thee, Lord, O let me not from Thee de-part;
3. O bless-ed Lord, teach me Thy law, Thy right-eous judg-ments I de-clare;
4. Up-on Thy pre-cepts and Thy ways My heart will med-i-tate with awe;

Thy Word, O Lord, will safe-ly lead, If in its wis-dom they con-fide.
To know Thy will and keep from sin Thy word I cher-ish in my heart.
Thy tes-ti-mo-nies make me glad, For they are wealth be-yond com-pare.
Thy Word shall be my chief de-light, And I will not for-get Thy law. A-MEN.

Music copyright, 1955, by John Ribble.

[225]

THE HOLY SCRIPTURES

259 The Heavens Declare Thy Glory, Lord

From Psalm 19
Isaac Watts, 1719

UXBRIDGE: L. M.
Lowell Mason, 1830

1. The heavens de-clare Thy glo - ry, Lord; In ev - ery star Thy wis - dom shines;
2. The roll - ing sun, the chang-ing light, And nights and days, Thy power con-fess;
3. Sun, moon, and stars con-vey Thy praise Round the whole earth, and nev-er stand;
4. Nor shall Thy spread-ing gos - pel rest Till through the world Thy truth has run;

But when our eyes be - hold Thy Word, We read Thy name in fair - er lines.
But the blest Vol-ume Thou hast writ Re-veals Thy jus-tice and Thy grace.
So when Thy truth be - gan its race, It touched and glanced on ev-ery land.
Till Christ has all the na - tions blest That see the light, or feel the sun. A-MEN.

260 The Spirit Breathes Upon the Word

William Cowper, 1799

BELMONT: C. M.
Arr. from William Gardiner's *Sacred Melodies*, 1812

1. The Spir - it breathes up - on the Word, And brings the truth to sight;
2. A glo - ry gilds the sa - cred page, Ma - jes - tic, like the sun:
3. The Hand that gave it still sup-plies The gra - cious light and heat:
4. Let ev - er - last - ing thanks be Thine For such a bright dis - play,
5. My soul re - joi - ces to pur-sue The steps of Him I love,

Pre-cepts and prom-is - es af - ford A sanc - ti - fy - ing light.
It gives a light to ev - ery age; It gives, but bor - rows none.
His truths up - on the na - tions rise; They rise, but nev - er set.
As makes a world of dark-ness shine With beams of heaven-ly day.
Till glo - ry break up - on my view In bright-er worlds a - bove. A-MEN.

Alternative tune, "Gräfenberg," Hymn 243.

THE HOLY SCRIPTURES

Come to the Saviour Now

John M. Wigner, 1871

INVITATION: 6. 6. 6. 6. D.
Frederick C. Maker, 1881

1. Come to the Sav - iour now, He gent - ly call - eth thee;
2. Come to the Sav - iour now, Ye who have wan - dered far;
3. Come to the Sav - iour, all, What - e'er your bur - dens be;

In true re - pent - ance bow, Be - fore Him bend the knee;
Re - new your sol - emn vow, For His by right you are;
Hear now His lov - ing call, "Cast all your care on Me."

He wait - eth to be - stow Sal - va - tion, peace, and love,
Come, like poor wan - dering sheep Re - turn - ing to His fold;
Come, and for ev - ery grief In Je - sus you will find

True joy on earth be - low, A home in heaven a - bove.
His arm will safe - ly keep, His love will ne'er grow cold.
A sure and safe re - lief, A lov - ing Friend and kind. A-MEN.

Music copyright by The Psalms & Hymns Trust. Used by permission.

LIFE IN CHRIST: THE CALL OF CHRIST

262 Thy Life Was Given for Me

Frances Ridley Havergal. 1858
Recast in *Church Hymns*, 1871

SACRIFICE: 6. 6. 6. 6. 6. 6.
Philip P. Bliss (1838-1876)

1 Thy life was given for me; Thy blood, O Lord, was shed,
2. Long years were spent for me In wea - ri - ness and woe,
3. And Thou hast brought to me, Down from Thy home a - bove,
4. O let my life be given, My years for Thee be spent,

That I might ran - somed be, And quick - ened from the dead:
That through e - ter - ni - ty Thy glo - ry I might know:
Sal - va - tion full and free, Thy par - don and Thy love:
World fet - ters all be riven, And joy with suf - fering blent!

Thy life was given for me; What have I given for Thee?
Long years were spent for me; Have I spent one for Thee?
Great gifts Thou brought-est me; What have I brought to Thee?
Thou gavest Thy - self for me; I give my - self to Thee. A - MEN.

263 Hark, My Soul, It Is the Lord!

William Cowper, 1768

ST. BEES: 7. 7. 7. 7.
John B. Dykes, 1862

1. Hark, my soul, it is the Lord! 'Tis thy Sav - iour, hear His word;
2. "I de - liv - ered thee when bound, And, when bleed-ing, healed thy wound,
3. "Can a wom - an's ten - der care Cease to - ward the child she bare?
4. "Mine is an un-chang-ing love, High - er than the heights a - bove,
5. Lord, it is my chief com-plaint That my love is weak and faint;

LIFE IN CHRIST: THE CALL OF CHRIST

[228]

Hark, My Soul, It Is the Lord!

Je - sus speaks, and speaks to thee, "Say, poor sin - ner, lovest thou Me?
Sought thee wan-dering, set thee right, Turned thy dark-ness in - to light.
Yes, she may for-get - ful be, Yet will I re - mem - ber thee.
Deep - er than the depths be-neath, Free and faith - ful, strong as death."
Yet I love Thee, and a - dore: O for grace to love Thee more! A-MEN.

Art Thou Weary, Art Thou Languid 264

(FIRST TUNE)

John Mason Neale, 1862; alt.

STEPHANOS: 8. 5. 8. 3.
Henry W. Baker, 1868

1. Art thou wea - ry, art thou lan - guid, Art thou sore dis - tressed?
2. Hath He marks to lead me to Him, If He be my Guide?
3. Is there di - a - dem, as Mon - arch, That His brow a - dorns?
4. If I find Him, if I fol - low, What His guer - don here?
5. If I still hold close - ly to Him, What hath He at last?
6. Find - ing, fol-lowing, keep - ing, strug-gling, Is He sure to bless?

"Come to Me," saith One, "and, com - ing, Be at rest."
"In His feet and hands are wound prints, And His side."
"Yea, a crown, in ver - y sure - ty, But of thorns."
"Man - y a sor - row, man - y a la - bor, Man - y a tear."
"Sor - row van-quished, la - bor end - ed, Jor - dan passed."
"Saints, a - pos - tles, proph - ets, mar - tyrs, An - swer, 'Yes.'" A - MEN.

(SECOND TUNE)

BULLINGER: 8. 5. 8. 3.
Ethelbert W. Bullinger, 1874

[229] LIFE IN CHRIST: THE CALL OF CHRIST

265   Sing Them Over Again to Me

WONDERFUL WORDS: 8. 6. 8. 6. 6. 6. with Refrain
Philip P. Bliss (1838-1876)
Har. for this book, 1953

Philip P. Bliss (1838-1876)

1. Sing them o - ver a - gain to me, Won - der - ful words of
2. Christ, the bless - ed One, gives to all Won - der - ful words of
3. Sweet - ly ech - o the gos - pel call, Won - der - ful words of

life; Let me more of their beau - ty see, Won - der - ful words of
life; Sin - ner, list to the lov - ing call, Won - der - ful words of
life; Of - fer par - don and peace to all, Won - der - ful words of

life. Words of life and beau - ty Teach me faith and du - ty:
life. All so free - ly giv - en, Woo - ing us to heav - en:
life. Je - sus, on - ly Sav - iour, Sanc - ti - fy for - ev - er:

REFRAIN

Beau - ti - ful words, won - der - ful words, Won - der - ful words of life,

Beau - ti - ful words, won - der - ful words, Won - der - ful words of life.   A - MEN.

Music copyright, 1955, by John Ribble.
LIFE IN CHRIST: THE CALL OF CHRIST

O Jesus, Thou Art Standing

266

ST. HILDA (ST. EDITH): 7. 6. 7. 6. D.
Justin H. Knecht, 1799
Edward Husband, 1871

William Walsham How, 1867

1. O Je - sus, Thou art stand - ing Out - side the fast-closed door,
2. O Je - sus, Thou art knock - ing; And lo, that hand is scarred,
3. O Je - sus, Thou art plead - ing In ac - cents meek and low,

In low - ly pa - tience wait - ing To pass the thresh - old o'er:
And thorns Thy brow en - cir - cle, And tears Thy face have marred:
"I died for you, My chil - dren, And will ye treat Me so?"

Shame on us, Chris - tian broth - ers, His name and sign who bear,
O love that pass - eth knowl - edge, So pa - tient - ly to wait!
O Lord, with shame and sor - row We o - pen now the door;

O shame, thrice shame up - on us, To keep Him stand - ing there!
O sin that hath no e - qual, So fast to bar the gate!
Dear Sav - iour, en - ter, en - ter, And leave us nev - er - more! A-MEN.

LIFE IN CHRIST: THE CALL OF CHRIST

[231]

267 Jesus Is Tenderly Calling Thee Home

JESUS IS CALLING: 10. 8. 10. 7. with Refrain
George C. Stebbins (1846-1945)
Har. for this book, 1954

Fanny Crosby (1820-1915)

1. Je - sus is ten - der - ly call - ing thee home—Call - ing to - day,
2. Je - sus is call - ing the wea - ry to rest— Call - ing to - day,
3. Je - sus is wait - ing— O come to Him now— Wait - ing to - day,
4. Je - sus is plead - ing; O list to His voice: Hear Him to - day,

call - ing to - day; Why from the sun-shine of love wilt thou roam
call - ing to - day; Bring Him thy bur - den and thou shalt be blest:
wait - ing to - day; Come with thy sins; at His feet low - ly bow;
hear Him to - day; They who be - lieve on His name shall re - joice;

REFRAIN

Far - ther and far - ther a - way? Call - ing to - day,
He will not turn thee a - way.
Come, and no long - er de - lay.
Quick - ly a - rise and a - way. Call-ing, call - ing to - day, to - day,

Call - ing to - day, Je - sus is
Call - ing, call - ing to - day, to - day, Je - sus is ten - der - ly

call - ing, Is ten - der - ly call - ing to - day. A-MEN.
call-ing to - day,

Music copyright. 1955. by John Ribble.
LIFE IN CHRIST: THE CALL OF CHRIST

"Come Unto Me, Ye Weary"

268

William C. Dix, 1867; alt.

BENTLEY: 7. 6. 7. 6. D.
John Hullah, 1867

1. "Come un - to Me, ye wea - ry, And I will give you rest."
2. "Come un - to Me, dear chil - dren, And I will give you light."
3. "Come un - to Me, ye faint - ing, And I will give you life."
4. "And who - so - ev - er com - eth I will not cast him out."

O bless - ed voice of Je - sus, Which comes to hearts op - pressed!
O lov - ing voice of Je - sus, Which comes to cheer the night!
O cheer - ing voice of Je - sus, Which comes to aid our strife!
O wel - come voice of Je - sus, Which drives a - way our doubt,

It tells of ben - e - dic - tion, Of par - don, grace, and peace,
Our hearts were filled with sad - ness, And we had lost our way;
The foe is stern and ea - ger, The fight is fierce and long;
Which calls us, ver - y sin - ners, Un - wor - thy though we be

Of joy that hath no end - ing, Of love which can - not cease.
But He hath brought us glad - ness And songs at break of day.
But Thou hast made us might - y And strong - er than the strong.
Of love so free and bound - less, To come, dear Lord, to Thee. A-MEN.

For lower key, see Hymn 418.
Alternative tune, "Llangloffan," Hymn 231.

LIFE IN CHRIST: THE CALL OF CHRIST

[233]

269 Jesus Calls Us

Cecil Frances Alexander, 1852

GALILEE: 8. 7. 8. 7.
William H. Jude, 1887

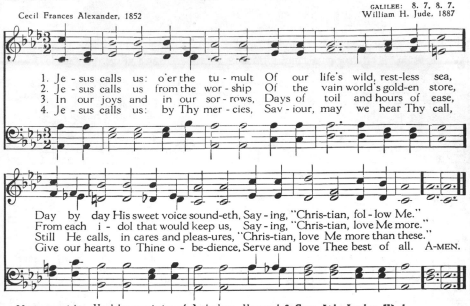

1. Je - sus calls us: o'er the tu - mult Of our life's wild, rest-less sea,
2. Je - sus calls us from the wor - ship Of the vain world's gold-en store,
3. In our joys and in our sor - rows, Days of toil and hours of ease,
4. Je - sus calls us: by Thy mer - cies, Sav - iour, may we hear Thy call,

Day by day His sweet voice sound-eth, Say-ing, "Chris-tian, fol-low Me."
From each i - dol that would keep us, Say-ing, "Chris-tian, love Me more."
Still He calls, in cares and pleas-ures, "Chris-tian, love Me more than these."
Give our hearts to Thine o - be-dience, Serve and love Thee best of all. A-MEN.

Music copyright. Used by permission of Ascherberg, Hopwood & Crew, Ltd., London, W. 1.
LIFE IN CHRIST: THE CALL OF CHRIST

270 Lord Jesus, Think on Me

Synesius of Cyrene (375-430)
Para. by Allen W. Chatfield, 1876

SOUTHWELL: S. M.
Damon's Psalter, 1579; alt.

1. Lord Je - sus, think on me, And purge a - way my sin;
2. Lord Je - sus, think on me, A - mid the bat - tle's strife;
3. Lord Je - sus, think on me, Nor let me go a - stray;
4. Lord Je - sus, think on me, That, when this life is past,

From earth-born pas-sions set me free, And make me pure with - in.
In all my pain and mis-er - y Be Thou my health and life.
Through dark-ness and per - plex - i - ty Point Thou the heaven-ly way.
I may th' e - ter - nal bright-ness see, And share Thy joy at last. A-MEN.

Alternative version on opposite page.
LIFE IN CHRIST: REPENTANCE AND FORGIVENESS

Lord Jesus, Think on Me

270

MELODY IN THE TENOR

SOUTHWELL: S. M.
Damon's Psalter, 1579; alt.
Arr. by Martin Shaw, 1915

Music copyright, 1915, by J. Curwen & Sons, Ltd. Used by permission.
This alternative version may be used for one or more stanzas, the congregation singing the melody.

Rock of Ages, Cleft for Me

271

Augustus M. Toplady, 1776

TOPLADY: 7. 7. 7. 7. 7. 7.
Thomas Hastings, 1830

1. Rock of A - ges, cleft for me, Let me hide my - self in Thee;
2. Not the la - bors of my hands Can ful - fill Thy law's de - mands;
3. Noth - ing in my hand I bring, Sim - ply to Thy cross I cling;
4. While I draw this fleet - ing breath, When my eye - lids close in death,

Let the wa - ter and the blood, From Thy wound - ed side which flowed,
Could my zeal no res - pite know, Could my tears for - ev - er flow,
Na - ked, come to Thee for dress, Help - less, look to Thee for grace;
When I soar to worlds un - known, See Thee on Thy judg - ment throne,

Be of sin the dou - ble cure, Cleanse me from its guilt and power.
All for sin could not a - tone, Thou must save, and Thou a - lone.
Foul, I to the foun - tain fly; Wash me, Sav - iour, or I die.
Rock of A - ges, cleft for me, Let me hide my - self in Thee. A - MEN.

Alternative tune, "Redhead, No. 76," Hymn 282.

LIFE IN CHRIST: REPENTANCE AND FORGIVENESS

272

Just as I Am, Without One Plea

Charlotte Elliott, 1836

WOODWORTH: L. M.
William B. Bradbury, 1849
Har. for this book, 1955

1. Just as I am, with-out one plea But that Thy blood was shed for me,
2. Just as I am, and wait-ing not To rid my soul of one dark blot,
3. Just as I am, though tossed a-bout With man-y a con-flict, man-y a doubt,
4. Just as I am, Thou wilt re-ceive, Wilt wel-come, par-don, cleanse, re-lieve;
5. Just as I am, Thy love un-known Has bro-ken ev-ery bar-rier down;

And that Thou biddest me come to Thee, O Lamb of God, I come, I come!
To Thee, whose blood can cleanse each spot, O Lamb of God, I come, I come!
Fight-ings and fears with-in, with-out, O Lamb of God, I come, I come!
Be-cause Thy prom-ise I be-lieve, O Lamb of God, I come, I come!
Now to be Thine, yea, Thine a-lone, O Lamb of God, I come, I come! A-MEN.

Music copyright, 1955, by John Ribble.

273

Depth of Mercy! Can There Be

SEYMOUR: 7. 7. 7. 7.
Arr. from Carl M. von Weber, 1826

Charles Wesley, 1740

1. Depth of mer-cy! can there be Mer-cy still re-served for me?
2. I have long with-stood His grace, Long pro-voked Him to His face;
3. Still for me the Sav-iour stands, Shows His wounds, and spreads His hands;

Can my God His wrath for-bear? Me, the chief of sin-ners, spare?
Would not heark-en to His calls, Grieved Him by a thou-sand falls.
God is love! I know, I feel; Je-sus weeps, and loves me still. A-MEN.

LIFE IN CHRIST: REPENTANCE AND FORGIVENESS

Because I Knew Not When My Life Was Good 274

Sarah Williams, 1868; alt.

PEACE: 10. 10. 10. 6.
George W. Chadwick, 1893

1. Be - cause I knew not when my life was good, And when there
2. Be - cause I held up - on my self - ish road, And left my
3. Be - cause I spent the strength Thou gav - est me In strug - gle
4. Be - cause I was im - pa - tient, would not wait, And thrust my

was a light up - on my path, But turned my soul per -
broth - er wound - ed by the way, And called am - bi - tion
which Thou nev - er didst or - dain, And have im - per - fect
will - ful hand a - cross Thy threads, And marred the pat - tern

verse - ly to the dark, O Lord, I do re - pent.
du - ty, and pressed on, O Lord, I do re - pent.
life to of - fer Thee, O Lord, I do re - pent.
drawn out for my life, O Lord, I do re - pent. A-MEN.

LIFE IN CHRIST: REPENTANCE AND FORGIVENESS

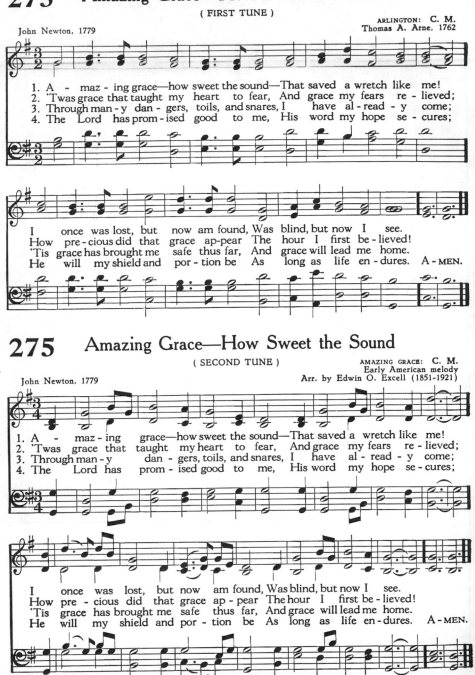

275 Amazing Grace—How Sweet the Sound
(FIRST TUNE)

John Newton, 1779

ARLINGTON: C. M.
Thomas A. Arne, 1762

1. A - maz - ing grace—how sweet the sound—That saved a wretch like me!
2. 'Twas grace that taught my heart to fear, And grace my fears re - lieved;
3. Through man - y dan - gers, toils, and snares, I have al - read - y come;
4. The Lord has prom - ised good to me, His word my hope se - cures;

I once was lost, but now am found, Was blind, but now I see.
How pre - cious did that grace ap-pear The hour I first be - lieved!
'Tis grace has brought me safe thus far, And grace will lead me home.
He will my shield and por - tion be As long as life en - dures. A - MEN.

275 Amazing Grace—How Sweet the Sound
(SECOND TUNE)

John Newton, 1779

AMAZING GRACE: C. M.
Early American melody
Arr. by Edwin O. Excell (1851-1921)

1. A - maz - ing grace—how sweet the sound—That saved a wretch like me!
2. 'Twas grace that taught my heart to fear, And grace my fears re - lieved;
3. Through man - y dan - gers, toils, and snares, I have al - read - y come;
4. The Lord has prom - ised good to me, His word my hope se - cures;

I once was lost, but now am found, Was blind, but now I see.
How pre - cious did that grace ap - pear The hour I first be - lieved!
'Tis grace has brought me safe thus far, And grace will lead me home.
He will my shield and por - tion be As long as life en - dures. A - MEN.

LIFE IN CHRIST: REPENTANCE AND FORGIVENESS

[238]

There Is a Fountain Filled with Blood 276

CLEANSING FOUNTAIN: C. M.
Early American melody
Arr. from Lowell Mason, 1830
Har. for this book, 1954

William Cowper, 1771

1. There is a foun-tain filled with blood Drawn from Em-man-uel's veins;
2. The dy-ing thief re-joiced to see That foun-tain in his day;
3. Dear dy-ing Lamb, Thy pre-cious blood Shall nev-er lose its power
4. E'er since by faith I saw the stream Thy flow-ing wounds sup-ply,
5. Then in a no-bler, sweet-er song, I'll sing Thy power to save,

And sin-ners, plunged be-neath that flood, Lose all their guilt-y stains,
And there may I, though vile as he, Wash all my sins a-way,
Till all the ran-somed Church of God Be saved, to sin no more,
Re-deem-ing love has been my theme, And shall be till I die,
When this poor lisp-ing, stam-mering tongue Lies si-lent in the grave,

Lose all their guilt-y stains, Lose all their guilt-y stains; And
Wash all my sins a-way, Wash all my sins a-way; And
Be saved, to sin no more, Be saved, to sin no more; Till
And shall be till I die, And shall be till I die; Re-
Lies si-lent in the grave, Lies si-lent in the grave; When

sin-ners, plunged be-neath that flood, Lose all their guilt-y stains.
there may I, though vile as he, Wash all my sins a-way.
all the ran-somed Church of God Be saved, to sin no more.
deem-ing love has been my theme, And shall be till I die.
this poor lisp-ing, stam-mering tongue Lies si-lent in the grave. A-MEN.

LIFE IN CHRIST: REPENTANCE AND FORGIVENESS

[239]

277 Lord, from the Depths to Thee I Cried

From Psalm 130
Scottish Psalter, 1650

SONG 67 (Gibbons): C. M.
Orlando Gibbons, 1623

1. Lord, from the depths to Thee I cried: My voice, Lord, do Thou hear:
2. Lord, who shall stand, if Thou, O Lord, Shouldst mark in - iq - ui - ty?
3. I wait for God, my soul doth wait; My hope is in His word.
4. I say, more than they that do watch The morn - ing light to see.
5. Re - demp-tion al - so plen - te - ous Is ev - er found with Him:

Un - to my sup - pli - ca-tion's voice Give an at - ten-tive ear.
But yet with Thee for - give-ness is, That feared Thou may-est be.
More than they that for morn-ing watch, My soul waits for the Lord;
Let Is - ra - el hope in the Lord, For with Him mer-cies be.
And from all his in - iq - ui - ties He Is - rael shall re - deem. A-MEN.

278 I Am Coming to the Cross

COMING TO THE CROSS: 7. 7. 7. 7.
William G. Fischer (1835-1912)
Har. for this book, 1953

William McDonald (1820-1901)

1. I am com - ing to the cross; I am poor and weak and blind;
2. Long my heart has sighed for Thee; Long has e - vil reigned with - in;
3. Here I give my all to Thee— Friends and time and earth - ly store;
4. Je - sus comes! He fills my soul! Per - fect - ed in Him I am;
5. I am trust - ing, Lord, in Thee, Bless - ed Lamb of Cal - va - ry;

I am count - ing all but dross; I shall full sal - va - tion find.
Je - sus sweet - ly speaks to me— "I will cleanse you from all sin."
Soul and bod - y Thine to be— Whol - ly Thine for - ev - er-more.
I am ev - ery whit made whole: Glo - ry, glo - ry to the Lamb!
Hum-bly at Thy cross I bow, Save me, Je - sus, save me now. A - MEN.

LIFE IN CHRIST: REPENTANCE AND FORGIVENESS

[240]

Jesus, I My Cross Have Taken

279

ELLESDIE: 8. 7. 8. 7. D.
Attributed to Wolfgang A. Mozart (1756-1791)
Arr. by Hubert P. Main, 1872

Henry Francis Lyte, 1824

1. Je - sus, I my cross have tak-en, All to leave, and fol-low Thee;
2. Man may trou-ble and dis-tress me, 'Twill but drive me to Thy breast;
3. Take, my soul, thy full sal-va-tion, Rise o'er sin and fear and care;
4. Haste, then, on from grace to glo-ry, Armed by faith and winged by prayer;

Des - ti-tute, de-spised, for-sak-en, Thou from hence my All shalt be:
Life with tri - als hard may press me, Heaven will bring me sweet-er rest;
Joy to find in ev - ery sta-tion Some-thing still to do or bear;
Heaven's e - ter - nal day's be - fore thee: God's own hand shall guide thee there.

Per - ish ev - ery fond am - bi - tion, All I've sought, or hoped, or known;
O 'tis not in grief to harm me While Thy love is left to me;
Think what Spir - it dwells with-in thee, What a Fa-ther's smile is thine,
Soon shall close thy earth - ly mis-sion; Swift shall pass thy pil - grim days;

Yet how rich is my con-di - tion: God and heaven are still my own.
O 'twere not in joy to charm me, Were that joy un-mixed with Thee.
What a Sav-iour died to win thee: Child of heaven, shouldst thou re-pine?
Hope soon change to glad fru-i - tion, Faith to sight, and prayer to praise. A-MEN.

For lower key, see Hymn 20.   LIFE IN CHRIST: REPENTANCE AND FORGIVENESS

[241]

280   I Heard the Voice of Jesus Say

Horatius Bonar, 1846

VOX DILECTI: C. M. D.
John B. Dykes, 1868

1. I heard the voice of Je - sus say, "Come un - to Me and rest;
2. I heard the voice of Je - sus say, "Be - hold, I free - ly give
3. I heard the voice of Je - sus say, "I am this dark world's Light;

Lay down, thou wea - ry one, lay down Thy head up - on My breast."
The liv - ing wa - ter; thirst - y one, Stoop down, and drink, and live."
Look un - to Me, thy morn shall rise, And all thy day be bright."

I came to Je - sus as I was, Wea - ry and worn and sad;
I came to Je - sus, and I drank Of that life - giv - ing stream;
I looked to Je - sus, and I found In Him my Star, my Sun;

I found in Him a rest - ing place, And He has made me glad.
My thirst was quenched, my soul re-vived, And now I live in Him.
And in that Light of life I'll walk, Till trav-eling days are done A - MEN.

LIFE IN CHRIST: REPENTANCE AND FORGIVENESS

How Blest Is He Whose Trespass

From Psalm 32
The Psalter, 1912; alt., 1950

RUTHERFORD: 7. 6. 7. 6. D.
Chrétien Urhan, 1734
Arr. by Edward F. Rimbault, 1867

281

1. How blest is he whose tres - pass Hath free - ly been for - given,
2. While I kept guilt - y si - lence My strength was spent with grief,
3. So let the god - ly seek Thee In times when Thou art near;

Whose sin is whol - ly cov - ered Be - fore the sight of heaven.
Thy hand was heav - y on me, My soul found no re - lief;
No whelm - ing floods shall reach them, Nor cause their hearts to fear.

To whom the Lord in mer - cy Im - put - eth not his sin,
But when I owned my tres - pass, My sin hid not from Thee,
In Thee, O Lord, I hide me, Thou sav - est me from ill,

Who hath a guile - less spir - it, Whose heart is true with - in.
When I con-fessed trans - gres - sion, Then Thou for - gav - est me.
And songs of Thy sal - va - tion My heart with rap - ture thrill. A-MEN.

LIFE IN CHRIST: REPENTANCE AND FORGIVENESS

282 God, Be Merciful to Me

From Psalm 51
The Psalter, 1912

REDHEAD, NO. 76: 7. 7. 7. 7. 7. 7.
Richard Redhead, 1853

1. God, be mer - ci - ful to me, On Thy grace I rest my plea;
2. My trans-gres-sions I con - fess, Grief and guilt my soul op - press;
3. I am e - vil, born in sin; Thou de - sir - est truth with - in.
4. Bro - ken, hum - bled to the dust By Thy wrath and judg - ment just,
5. Gra - cious God, my heart re - new, Make my spir - it right and true;

Plen-teous in com - pas - sion Thou, Blot out my trans - gres - sions now;
I have sinned a - gainst Thy grace And pro-voked Thee to Thy face;
Thou a - lone my Sav - iour art, Teach Thy wis - dom to my heart;
Let my con - trite heart re - joice And in glad - ness hear Thy voice;
Cast me not a - way from Thee, Let Thy Spir - it dwell in me;

Wash me, make me pure with - in, Cleanse, O cleanse me from my sin.
I con - fess Thy judg - ment just, Speech-less, I Thy mer - cy trust.
Make me pure, Thy grace be-stow, Wash me whit - er than the snow.
From my sins O hide Thy face, Blot them out in bound-less grace.
Thy sal - va-tion's joy im-part, Stead - fast make my will - ing heart. A-MEN.

LIFE IN CHRIST: REPENTANCE AND FORGIVENESS

283 Go, Labor On: Spend, and Be Spent

Horatius Bonar, 1843

PENTECOST: L. M.
William Boyd, c. 1864

1. Go, la - bor on: spend, and be spent, Thy joy to do the Fa-ther's will:
2. Go, la - bor on while it is day: The world's dark night is has-tening on;
3. Toil on, faint not, keep watch and pray, Be wise the err - ing soul to win;

LIFE IN CHRIST: DISCIPLESHIP AND SERVICE

[244]

Go, Labor On: Spend, and Be Spent

It is the way the Mas-ter went; Should not the serv-ant tread it still?
Speed, speed thy work, cast sloth a-way; It is not thus that souls are won.
Go forth in-to the world's high-way, Com-pel the wan-derer to come in. A-MEN.

Music used by permission of Novello & Co., Ltd.
Alternative tune, "Missionary Chant," Hymn 494.

Draw Thou My Soul, O Christ 284

ST. EDMUND: 6. 4. 6. 4. 6. 6. 6. 4.
Lucy Larcom, 1892
Arthur S. Sullivan, 1872; alt.

1. Draw Thou my soul, O Christ, Clos - er to Thine; Breathe in - to
2. Lead forth my soul, O Christ, One with Thine own, Joy - ful to
3. Not for my - self a - lone May my prayer be; Lift Thou Thy

ev - ery wish Thy will di - vine: Raised my low self a - bove, Won by Thy
fol - low Thee Through paths un-known: In Thee my strength re-new; Give me Thy
world, O Christ, Clos - er to Thee: Cleanse it from guilt and wrong; Teach it sal -

death-less love, Ev - er, O Christ, through mine Let Thy life shine.
work to do: Through me Thy truth be shown, Thy love made known.
va - tion's song, Till earth, as heaven, ful - fill God's ho - ly will. A-MEN.

LIFE IN CHRIST: DISCIPLESHIP AND SERVICE

285 Father, We Greet Thee

James G. Adderley, 1924

DONNE SECOURS: 11. 10. 11. 10.
Genevan Psalter, 1551

1. Fa - ther, we greet Thee, God of Love, whose glo - ry
2. Fa - ther, we dare, by our great Broth - er bid - den,
3. Here we pre - sent our - selves, our souls and bod - ies,
4. Friends at His ta - ble, priests a - round His al - tar,

Shines mir - rored in the face of Je - sus Christ,
Take up the cross and hum - bly fol - low Him:
Strength - ened with bread, the food of ev - ery man,
Sol - diers of Christ, dis - ci - ples of Thy Son,

Who by His per - fect life of love and la - bor
Send out Thy light and truth that they may lead us;
Read - y to love and work, but yet con - fess - ing
Fa - ther, we stand, pre - pared to do Thy bid - ding;

And in His per - fect death was sac - ri - ficed.
Show us the way a - mid the dark - ness dim.
Lone - ly we can - not, by His grace we can.
Come, God's own King - dom, and God's will be done. A - MEN.

Words used by permission of the author's heir.
LIFE IN CHRIST: DISCIPLESHIP AND SERVICE

I Bind My Heart This Tide 286

FEALTY: 6. 7. 7. 7. D.

Lauchlan MacLean Watt, 1907

Grace Wilbur Conant, 1927

1. I bind my heart this tide To the Gal - i - le - an's side,
2. I bind my heart in thrall To the God, the Lord of all,

To the wounds of Cal - va - ry, To the Christ who died for me.
To the God, the poor man's Friend, And the Christ whom He did send.

I bind my soul this day To the broth - er far a - way,
I bind my - self to peace, To make strife and en - vy cease,

And the broth - er near at hand, In this town, and in this land.
God, knit Thou sure the cord Of my thrall-dom to my Lord! A-MEN.

Words used by permission of the author. Music copyright, 1928. Used by permission of Fleming H. Revell Company.

LIFE IN CHRIST: DISCIPLESHIP AND SERVICE

287
Come, Labor On

Jane Laurie Borthwick, 1859, 1863
Stanza 4, line 5, alt.

ORA LABORA: 4. 10. 10. 10. 4.
T. Tertius Noble, 1918

In unison

1. Come, la - bor on. Who dares stand i - dle on the har-vest plain
2. Come, la - bor on. Claim the high call - ing an - gels can-not share—
3. Come, la - bor on. A - way with gloom-y doubts and faith-less fear!
4. Come, la - bor on. No time for rest, till glows the west-ern sky,

While all a - round him waves the gold - en grain? And to each serv - ant
To young and old the gos - pel glad-ness bear; Re - deem the time; its
No arm so weak but may do serv - ice here: By fee-blest a - gents
Till the long shad - ows o'er our path-way lie, And a glad sound comes

does the Mas - ter say, "Go work to - day."
hours too swift - ly fly. The night draws nigh.
may our God ful - fill His right - - - eous will.
with the set - ting sun, "Well done, well done!" A-MEN.

LIFE IN CHRIST: DISCIPLESHIP AND SERVICE

Lord God of Hosts, Whose Purpose, Never Swerving 288

Shepherd Knapp, 1907

WELWYN: 11. 10. 11. 10.
Alfred Scott-Gatty, 1902

1. Lord God of Hosts, whose pur - pose, nev - er swerv - ing,
2. Strong Son of God, whose work was His that sent Thee,
3. O Prince of Peace, Thou bring - er of good ti - dings,
4. Lord God, whose grace has called us to Thy serv - ice,

Leads toward the day of Je - sus Christ Thy Son,
One with the Fa - ther, thought and deed and word,
Teach us to speak Thy word of hope and cheer—
How good Thy thoughts toward us, how great their sum!

Grant us to march a - mong Thy faith - ful le - gions,
One make us all, true com-rades in Thy serv - ice,
Rest for the soul, and strength for all man's striv - ing,
We work with Thee, we go where Thou wilt lead us,

Armed with Thy cour - age, till the world is won.
And make us one in Thee with God the Lord.
Light for the path of life, and God brought near.
Un - til in all the earth Thy King - dom come. A - MEN.

Words used by permission of Mrs. Wilson M. Powell and Mrs. George A. Vondermuhll. Music used by permission of Mrs. Denis Hyde and the Abbot of Downside.

LIFE IN CHRIST: DISCIPLESHIP AND SERVICE

289 So Let Our Lips and Lives Express

Isaac Watts, 1707

HEBRON: L. M.
Lowell Mason, 1830

1. So let our lips and lives ex-press The ho - ly gos - pel we pro-fess;
2. Thus shall we best pro - claim a-broad The hon-ors of our Sav-iour God,
3. Our flesh and sense must be de-nied, Pas - sion and en - vy, lust and pride;
4. Re - li-gion bears our spir-its up, While we ex - pect that bless-ed hope,

So let our works and vir-tues shine, To prove the doc-trine all di - vine.
When His sal - va - tion reigns with-in, And grace sub-dues the power of sin.
While jus-tice, tem-perance, truth, and love, Our in-ward pi - e - ty ap-prove.
The bright ap-pear-ance of the Lord, And faith stands lean-ing on His word. A-MEN.

290 Must Jesus Bear the Cross Alone

Thomas Shepherd, 1693; alt.

MAITLAND: C. M.
George N. Allen (1812-1877)

1. Must Je - sus bear the cross a - lone, And all the world go free?
2. The con - se - crat - ed cross I'll bear, Till death shall set me free,
3. O pre-cious cross! O glo - rious crown! O res - ur - rec - tion day!

No, there's a cross for ev - ery one, And there's a cross for me.
And then go home my crown to wear, For there's a crown for me.
Ye an - gels, from the stars come down, And bear my soul a - way. A-MEN.

LIFE IN CHRIST: DISCIPLESHIP AND SERVICE

[250]

Hope of the World

291

Georgia Harkness, 1953

DONNE SECOURS: 11. 10. 11. 10.
Genevan Psalter, 1551

1. Hope of the world, Thou Christ of great com - pas - sion,
2. Hope of the world, God's Gift from high - est heav - en,
3. Hope of the world, a - foot on dust - y high - ways,
4. Hope of the world, who by Thy cross didst save us
5. Hope of the world, O Christ, o'er death vic - to - rious,

Speak to our fear - ful hearts by con - flict rent.
Bring - ing to hun - gry souls the bread of life,
Show - ing to wan - dering souls the path of light;
From death and dark de - spair, from sin and guilt;
Who by this sign didst con - quer grief and pain,

Save us, Thy peo - ple, from con - sum - ing pas - sion,
Still let Thy Spir - it un - to us be giv - en
Walk Thou be - side us lest the tempt - ing by - ways
We ren - der back the love Thy mer - cy gave us;
We would be faith - ful to Thy gos - pel glo - rious:

Who by our own false hopes and aims are spent.
To heal earth's wounds and end her bit - ter strife.
Lure us a - way from Thee to end - less night.
Take Thou our lives and use them as Thou wilt.
Thou art our Lord! Thou dost for - ev - er reign! A - MEN.

Words copyright, 1954, by The Hymn Society of America. Used by permission.

LIFE IN CHRIST: DISCIPLESHIP AND SERVICE

292 I'm Not Ashamed to Own My Lord

Isaac Watts, 1707
As in *Scottish Paraphrases*, 1781

BELMONT: C. M.
Arr. from William Gardiner's *Sacred Melodies*, 1812

1. I'm not a-shamed to own my Lord, Or to de-fend His cause,
2. Je - sus, my Lord! I know His name; His name is all my boast;
3. I know that safe with Him re-mains, Pro - tect - ed by His power,
4. Then will He own His serv-ant's name Be - fore His Fa-ther's face,

Main-tain the glo - ry of His cross, And hon - or all His laws.
Nor will He put my soul to shame, Nor let my hope be lost.
What I've com-mit-ted to His trust Till the de - ci - sive hour.
And in the new Je - ru - sa - lem Ap - point my soul a place. A-MEN.

293 "Take Up Thy Cross," the Saviour Said

BRESLAU: L. M.
As *hymnodus sacer*, Leipzig, 1625
Modern form

Charles W. Everest, 1833; alt.

1. "Take up thy cross," the Sav-iour said, "If thou wouldst My dis - ci-ple be;
2. Take up thy cross; let not its weight Fill thy weak spir - it with a-larm;
3. Take up thy cross, nor heed the shame; Nor let thy fool - ish pride re - bel;
4. Take up thy cross and fol-low Christ, Nor think till death to lay it down;

Take up thy cross with will - ing heart And hum-bly fol - low aft - er Me."
His strength shall bear thy spir - it up, And brace thy heart, and nerve thine arm.
Thy Lord for thee the cross en-dured, To save thy soul from death and hell.
For on - ly he who bears the cross May hope to wear the glo-rious crown. A-MEN.

LIFE IN CHRIST: DISCIPLESHIP AND SERVICE

[252]

We Thank Thee, Lord

294

Calvin W. Laufer, 1919

FIELD: 10. 10. 10. 10.
Calvin W. Laufer, 1919

1. We thank Thee, Lord, Thy paths of serv-ice lead
2. We've sought and found Thee in the se-cret place
3. We've felt Thy touch in sor-row's dark-ened way
4. We've seen Thy glo-ry like a man-tle spread

To bla-zoned heights and down the slopes of need;
And mar-veled at the ra-diance of Thy face;
A-bound with love and sol-ace for the day;
O'er hill and dale in saf-fron flame and red;

They reach Thy throne, en-com-pass land and sea,
But of-ten in some far-off Gal-i-lee
And, 'neath the bur-dens there, Thy sov-ereign-ty
But in the eyes of men, re-deemed and free,

And he who jour-neys in them walks with Thee.
Be-held Thee fair-er yet while serv-ing Thee.
Has held our hearts en-thralled while serv-ing Thee.
A splen-dor great-er yet while serv-ing Thee. A-MEN.

LIFE IN CHRIST: DISCIPLESHIP AND SERVICE

[253]

295 Christ of the Upward Way

Walter J. Mathams, c. 1915

SURSUM CORDA: 6. 4. 6. 4. 10. 10.
George Lomas (1834-1884)

1. Christ of the Up-ward Way, My Guide di-vine,
2. Give me the heart to hear Thy voice and will,
3. Give me the good stout arm To shield the right,
4. Christ of the Up-ward Way, My Guide di-vine,

Where Thou hast set Thy feet May I place mine;
That with-out fault or fear I may ful-fill
And wield Thy sword of truth With all my might,
Where Thou hast set Thy feet May I place mine;

And move and march wher-ev-er Thou hast trod,
Thy pur-pose with a glad and ho-ly zest,
That, in the war-fare I must wage for Thee,
And when Thy last call comes se-rene and clear,

Keep-ing face for-ward up the hill of God.
Like one who would not bring less than his best.
More than a vic-tor I may ev-er be.
Calm may my an-swer be, "Lord, I am here." A-MEN.

LIFE IN CHRIST: DISCIPLESHIP AND SERVICE

Come, Ye That Fear the Lord

From Psalm 66
The Psalter, 1912

ANCYRA: C. M. D.
Benjamin C. Unseld, 1901
Har. for this book, 1953

296

1. Come, ye that fear the Lord, and hear What He has done for me;
2. If in my heart I sin re-gard, My prayer He will not hear;
3. Here in Thy house I give to Thee The life that Thou dost bless,

My cry for help is turned to praise, For He has set me free.
But, tru-ly, God has heard my voice, My prayer has reached His ear.
And pay the sol-emn vows I made When I was in dis-tress.

Through pain and trou-ble Thou hast led, And hum-bled all our pride,
O let the Lord, our gra-cious God, For-ev-er bless-ed be,
O all ye peo-ples, bless our God, A-loud pro-claim His praise,

But, in the end, to lib-er-ty And wealth Thy hand did guide.
Who has not turned my prayer from Him, Nor yet His grace from me.
Who safe-ly holds our soul in life, And stead-fast makes our ways. A-MEN.

Music copyright, 1901, 1928. Used by permission of the United Presbyterian Board of Christian Education.

LIFE IN CHRIST: DISCIPLESHIP AND SERVICE

297 Work, for the Night Is Coming

WORK SONG: 7. 6. 7. 5. D.

Anna L. Coghill, 1854
Alt. by Lowell Mason, 1864

Lowell Mason, 1864
Har. for this book, 1954

1. Work, for the night is com - ing, Work through the morn-ing hours; Work while the
2. Work, for the night is com - ing, Work through the sun-ny noon; Fill bright-est
3. Work, for the night is com - ing, Un - der the sun-set skies; While their bright

dew is spark - ling, Work 'mid spring-ing flowers; Work when the day grows bright-er,
hours with la - bor, Rest comes sure and soon. Give ev - er-y fly - ing min-ute,
tints are glow - ing, Work, for day-light flies. Work till the last beam fad - eth,

Work in the glow-ing sun; Work, for the night is com - ing, When man's work is done.
Some-thing to keep in store; Work, for the night is com - ing, When man works no more.
Fad-eth to shine no more; Work while the night is dark-'ning, When man's work is o'er. A-MEN.

Words used by permission of A. C. Dalzell.

298 Lord, Speak to Me, that I May Speak

CANONBURY: L. M.

Frances Ridley Havergal, 1872

Robert Schumann, 1839

1. Lord, speak to me, that I may speak In liv - ing ech - oes of Thy tone;
2. O lead me, Lord, that I may lead The wan-dering and the wa-vering feet;
3. O teach me, Lord, that I may teach The pre-cious things Thou dost im - part;
4. O fill me with Thy full - ness, Lord, Un - til my ver - y heart o'er-flow
5. O use me, Lord, use e - ven me, Just as Thou wilt, and when, and where;

LIFE IN CHRIST: DEDICATION AND CONSECRATION

Lord, Speak to Me, that I May Speak

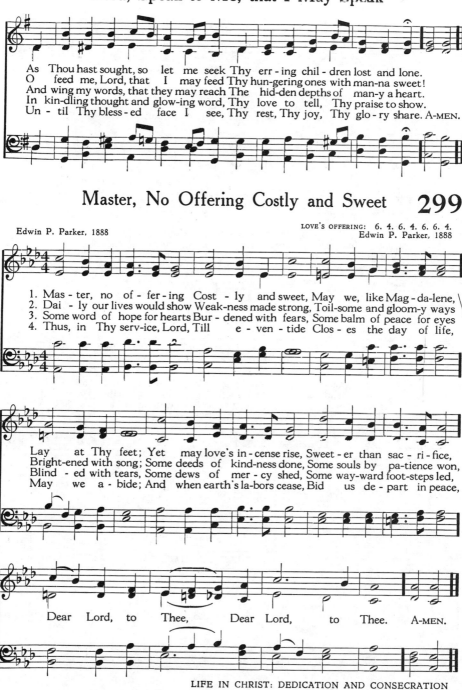

As Thou hast sought, so let me seek Thy err-ing chil-dren lost and lone.
O feed me, Lord, that I may feed Thy hun-gering ones with man-na sweet!
And wing my words, that they may reach The hid-den depths of man-y a heart.
In kin-dling thought and glow-ing word, Thy love to tell, Thy praise to show.
Un-til Thy bless-ed face I see, Thy rest, Thy joy, Thy glo-ry share. A-MEN.

Master, No Offering Costly and Sweet   299

Edwin P. Parker, 1888

LOVE'S OFFERING: 6. 4. 6. 4. 6. 6. 4.
Edwin P. Parker, 1888

1. Mas-ter, no of-fer-ing Cost-ly and sweet, May we, like Mag-da-lene,
2. Dai-ly our lives would show Weak-ness made strong, Toil-some and gloom-y ways
3. Some word of hope for hearts Bur-dened with fears, Some balm of peace for eyes
4. Thus, in Thy serv-ice, Lord, Till e-ven-tide Clos-es the day of life,

Lay at Thy feet; Yet may love's in-cense rise, Sweet-er than sac-ri-fice,
Bright-ened with song; Some deeds of kind-ness done, Some souls by pa-tience won,
Blind-ed with tears, Some dews of mer-cy shed, Some way-ward foot-steps led,
May we a-bide; And when earth's la-bors cease, Bid us de-part in peace,

Dear Lord, to Thee, Dear Lord, to Thee. A-MEN.

LIFE IN CHRIST: DEDICATION AND CONSECRATION

300 Take Time to Be Holy

William D. Longstaff (1822-1894)

LONGSTAFF: 6. 5. 6. 5. D.
George C. Stebbins, 1890

1. Take time to be ho-ly, Speak oft with thy Lord; A-bide in Him
2. Take time to be ho-ly, The world rush-es on; Much time spend in
3. Take time to be ho-ly, Let Him be thy Guide, And run not be-
4. Take time to be ho-ly, Be calm in thy soul; Each thought and each

al-ways, And feed on His Word. Make friends of God's chil-dren; Help those who are
se-cret With Je-sus a-lone; By look-ing to Je-sus, Like Him thou shalt
fore Him, What-ev-er be-tide; In joy or in sor-row, Still fol-low thy
mo-tive Be-neath His con-trol; Thus led by His Spir-it To foun-tains of

weak; For-get-ting in noth-ing His bless-ing to seek.
be; Thy friends in thy con-duct His like-ness shall see.
Lord, And, look-ing to Je-sus, Still trust in His Word.
love, Thou soon shalt be fit-ted For serv-ice a-bove. A-MEN.

301 A Charge to Keep I Have

Charles Wesley, 1762; alt.

BOYLSTON: S. M.
Lowell Mason, 1832

1. A charge to keep I have, A God to glo-ri-fy,
2. To serve the pres-ent age, My call-ing to ful-fill;
3. Arm me with jeal-ous care, As in Thy sight to live;
4. Help me to watch and pray, And on Thy-self re-ly,

LIFE IN CHRIST: DEDICATION AND CONSECRATION

A Charge to Keep I Have

A nev-er-dy-ing soul to save, And fit it for the sky.
O may it all my powers en-gage To do my Mas-ter's will!
And oh, Thy serv-ant, Lord, pre-pare A strict ac-count to give!
And let me ne'er my trust be-tray, But press to realms on high. A-MEN.

Have Thine Own Way, Lord! 302

Adelaide A. Pollard, 1902

ADELAIDE: 5. 4. 5. 4. D.
George C. Stebbins, 1907

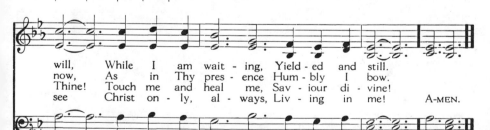

1. Have Thine own way, Lord! Have Thine own way! Thou art the
2. Have Thine own way, Lord! Have Thine own way! Search me and
3. Have Thine own way, Lord! Have Thine own way! Wound-ed and
4. Have Thine own way, Lord! Have Thine own way! Hold o'er my

Pot-ter; I am the clay. Mold me and make me Aft-er Thy
try me, Mas-ter, to-day! Whit-er than snow, Lord, Wash me just
wea-ry, Help me, I pray! Pow-er—all pow-er—Sure-ly is
be-ing Ab-so-lute sway! Fill with Thy Spir-it Till all shall

will, While I am wait-ing, Yield-ed and still.
now, As in Thy pres-ence Hum-bly I bow.
Thine! Touch me and heal me, Sav-iour di-vine!
see Christ on-ly, al-ways, Liv-ing in me! A-MEN.

Words and music copyright, 1907; renewal, 1935, by George C. Stebbins. Assigned to Hope Publishing Company. Used by permission.

LIFE IN CHRIST: DEDICATION AND CONSECRATION

303

Be Thou My Vision

Ancient Irish
Trans. by Mary Byrne. 1927
Versified by Eleanor Hull, 1927

SLANE: 10. 10. 9. 10.
Traditional Irish melody
Har. by David Evans, 1927

In unison

1. Be Thou my Vi - sion, O Lord of my heart;
2. Be Thou my Wis - dom, and Thou my true Word;
3. Rich - es I heed not, nor man's emp - ty praise,
4. High King of heav - en, my vic - to - ry won,

Nought be all else to me, save that Thou art—
I ev - er with Thee and Thou with me, Lord;
Thou mine in - her - it - ance, now and al - ways:
May I reach heav - en's joys, O bright heaven's Sun!

Thou my best thought, by day or by night,
Thou my great Fa - ther, I Thy true son;
Thou and Thou on - ly, first in my heart,
Heart of my own heart, what - ev - er be - fall,

Wak - ing or sleep - ing, Thy pres - ence my light.
Thou in me dwell - ing, and I with Thee one.
High King of heav - en, my Treas - ure Thou art.
Still be my Vi - sion, O Rul - er of all. A - MEN.

Words used by permission of Miss Hull's executors and Chatto & Windus, Ltd. Melody used by permission of The Educational Company of Ireland, Ltd. Harmony copyright; from *The Church Hymnary*, Revised Edition; used by permission of Oxford University Press.

LIFE IN CHRIST: DEDICATION AND CONSECRATION

O Master, Let Me Walk with Thee 304

Washington Gladden, 1879

MARYTON: L. M.
Henry Percy Smith, 1874

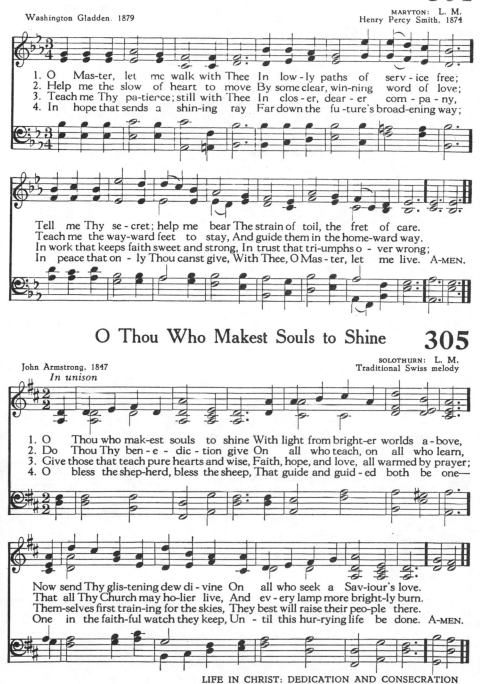

1. O Mas-ter, let me walk with Thee In low-ly paths of serv-ice free;
2. Help me the slow of heart to move By some clear, win-ning word of love;
3. Teach me Thy pa-tience; still with Thee In clos-er, dear-er com-pa-ny,
4. In hope that sends a shin-ing ray Far down the fu-ture's broad-ening way;

Tell me Thy se-cret; help me bear The strain of toil, the fret of care.
Teach me the way-ward feet to stay, And guide them in the home-ward way.
In work that keeps faith sweet and strong, In trust that tri-umphs o - ver wrong;
In peace that on - ly Thou canst give, With Thee, O Mas-ter, let me live. A-MEN.

O Thou Who Makest Souls to Shine 305

John Armstrong, 1847
In unison

SOLOTHURN: L. M.
Traditional Swiss melody

1. O Thou who mak-est souls to shine With light from bright-er worlds a-bove,
2. Do Thou Thy ben - e - dic-tion give On all who teach, on all who learn,
3. Give those that teach pure hearts and wise, Faith, hope, and love, all warmed by prayer;
4. O bless the shep-herd, bless the sheep, That guide and guid - ed both be one—

Now send Thy glis-tening dew di - vine On all who seek a Sav-iour's love.
That all Thy Church may ho-lier live, And ev - ery lamp more bright-ly burn.
Them-selves first train-ing for the skies, They best will raise their peo-ple there.
One in the faith-ful watch they keep, Un - til this hur-rying life be done. A-MEN.

LIFE IN CHRIST: DEDICATION AND CONSECRATION

[261]

306 Take Thou Our Minds, Dear Lord

William Hiram Foulkes, 1918

HALL: 10. 10. 10. 10.
Calvin W. Laufer, 1918

1. Take Thou our minds, dear Lord, we hum-bly pray;
2. Take Thou our hearts, O Christ, they are Thine own;
3. Take Thou our wills, Most High! Hold Thou full sway;
4. Take Thou our-selves, O Lord, heart, mind, and will;

Give us the mind of Christ each pass-ing day;
Come Thou with-in our souls and claim Thy throne;
Have in our in-most souls Thy per-fect way;
Through our sur-ren-dered souls Thy plans ful-fill.

Teach us to know the truth that sets us free;
Help us to shed a-broad Thy death-less love;
Guard Thou each sa-cred hour from self-ish ease;
We yield our-selves to Thee— time, tal-ents, all;

Grant us in all our thoughts to hon-or Thee.
Use us to make the earth like heaven a-bove.
Guide Thou our or-dered lives as Thou dost please.
We hear, and hence-forth heed, Thy sov-ereign call. A-MEN.

LIFE IN CHRIST: DEDICATION AND CONSECRATION

O Jesus, I Have Promised

307

John E. Bode, 1868

ANGEL'S STORY: 7. 6. 7. 6. D.
Arthur H. Mann, 1881

1. O Je - sus, I have prom - ised To serve Thee to the end;
2. O let me feel Thee near me! The world is ev - er near;
3. O let me hear Thee speak - ing In ac - cents clear and still,
4. O Je - sus, Thou hast prom - ised To all who fol - low Thee

Be Thou for - ev - er near me, My Mas - ter and my Friend:
I see the sights that daz - zle, The tempt - ing sounds I hear;
A - bove the storms of pas - sion, The mur - murs of self - will!
That where Thou art in glo - ry There shall Thy serv - ant be;

I shall not fear the bat - tle If Thou art by my side,
My foes are ev - er near me, A - round me and with - in;
O speak to re - as - sure me, To has - ten or con - trol!
And, Je - sus, I have prom - ised To serve Thee to the end;

Nor wan - der from the path - way If Thou wilt be my Guide.
But, Je - sus, draw Thou near - er, And shield my soul from sin.
O speak, and make me lis - ten, Thou Guard-ian of my soul!
O give me grace to fol - low, My Mas - ter and my Friend! A-MEN.

Music used by permission of E. R. Goodliffe.

LIFE IN CHRIST: DEDICATION AND CONSECRATION

[263]

308 Make Me a Captive, Lord

ST. BRIDE: S. M.
Samuel Howard, 1762
Har. by David Evans, 1927

George Matheson, 1890

1. Make me a cap-tive, Lord, And then I shall be free;
2. I sink in life's a-larms When by my-self I stand;
3. My heart is weak and poor Un-til it mas-ter find;
4. It can-not free-ly move Till Thou hast wrought its chain;
5. My will is not my own Till Thou hast made it Thine;
6. It on-ly stands un-bent A-mid the clash-ing strife,

Force me to ren-der up my sword, And I shall con-queror be.
Im-pris-on me with-in Thine arms, And strong shall be my hand.
It has no spring of ac-tion sure—It var-ies with the wind.
En-slave it with Thy match-less love, And death-less it shall reign.
If it would reach a mon-arch's throne, It must its crown re-sign;
When on Thy bos-om it has leant, And found in Thee its life. A-MEN.

Music from *The Church Hymnary*, Revised Edition. Used by permission of Oxford University Press.

308 Make Me a Captive, Lord

MELODY IN THE TENOR

ST. BRIDE: S. M.
Samuel Howard, 1762
Arr. by Geoffrey Shaw (1879-1943)

Music from the *Tenor Tune Book*. Used by permission of The Faith Press, Ltd.
This alternative arrangement may be used for one or more stanzas, the congregation singing the melody only.

LIFE IN CHRIST: DEDICATION AND CONSECRATION

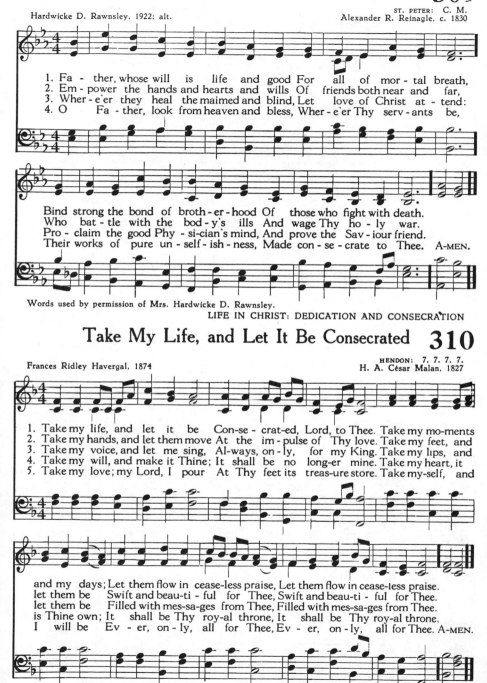

Father, Whose Will Is Life and Good 309

Hardwicke D. Rawnsley, 1922; alt.

ST. PETER: C. M.
Alexander R. Reinagle, c. 1830

1. Fa - ther, whose will is life and good For all of mor - tal breath,
2. Em - power the hands and hearts and wills Of friends both near and far,
3. Wher - e'er they heal the maimed and blind, Let love of Christ at - tend:
4. O Fa - ther, look from heaven and bless, Wher - e'er Thy serv - ants be,

Bind strong the bond of broth - er - hood Of those who fight with death.
Who bat - tle with the bod - y's ills And wage Thy ho - ly war.
Pro - claim the good Phy - si - cian's mind, And prove the Sav - iour friend.
Their works of pure un - self - ish - ness, Made con - se - crate to Thee. A-MEN.

Words used by permission of Mrs. Hardwicke D. Rawnsley.

LIFE IN CHRIST: DEDICATION AND CONSECRATION

Take My Life, and Let It Be Consecrated 310

Frances Ridley Havergal, 1874

HENDON: 7. 7. 7. 7.
H. A. César Malan, 1827

1. Take my life, and let it be Con-se - crat-ed, Lord, to Thee. Take my mo-ments
2. Take my hands, and let them move At the im - pulse of Thy love. Take my feet, and
3. Take my voice, and let me sing, Al-ways, on - ly, for my King. Take my lips, and
4. Take my will, and make it Thine; It shall be no long-er mine. Take my heart, it
5. Take my love; my Lord, I pour At Thy feet its treas-ure store. Take my-self, and

and my days; Let them flow in cease-less praise, Let them flow in cease-less praise.
let them be Swift and beau-ti - ful for Thee, Swift and beau-ti - ful for Thee.
let them be Filled with mes-sa-ges from Thee, Filled with mes-sa-ges from Thee.
is Thine own; It shall be Thy roy-al throne, It shall be Thy roy-al throne.
I will be Ev - er, on - ly, all for Thee, Ev - er, on - ly, all for Thee. A-MEN.

[265]

LIFE IN CHRIST: STEWARDSHIP

311
Saviour! Thy Dying Love

SOMETHING FOR JESUS: 6. 4. 6. 4. 6. 6. 6. 4.

Sylvanus D. Phelps, 1862

Robert Lowry, 1871

1. Sav - iour! Thy dy - ing love Thou gav - est me,
2. At the blest mer - cy seat, Plead - ing for me,
3. Give me a faith - ful heart, Guid - ed by Thee,
4. All that I am and have— Thy gifts so free—

Nor should I aught with - hold, Dear Lord, from Thee:
My fee - ble faith looks up, Je - sus, to Thee;
That each de - part - ing day Hence - forth may see
In joy, in grief, through life, Dear Lord, for Thee;

In love my soul would bow, My heart ful - fill its vow,
Help me the cross to bear, Thy won-drous love de - clare,
Some work of love be - gun, Some deed of kind - ness done,
And when Thy face I see, My ran - somed soul shall be,

Some of - fering bring Thee now, Some - thing for Thee.
Some song to raise, or prayer, Some - thing for Thee.
Some wan - derer sought and won, Some - thing for Thee.
Through all e - ter - ni - ty, Of - fered for Thee. A - MEN.

LIFE IN CHRIST: STEWARDSHIP

[266]

We Give Thee but Thine Own 312

William Walsham How. 1858

SCHUMANN: S. M.
Mason and Webb's *Cantica Laudis*, 1850

1. We give Thee but Thine own, What-e er the gift may be:
2. May we Thy boun - ties thus As stew - ards true re - ceive,
3. To com - fort and to bless, To find a balm for woe,
4. The cap - tive to re - lease, To God the lost to bring,
5. And we be - lieve Thy Word, Though dim our faith may be:

All that we have is Thine a - lone, A trust, O Lord, from Thee.
And glad - ly, as Thou bless-est us, To Thee our first fruits give.
To tend the lone and fa - ther - less, Is an - gels' work be - low.
To teach the way of life and peace—It is a Christ-like thing.
What-e'er for Thine we do, O Lord, We do it un - to Thee. A-MEN.

All Things Are Thine; No Gift Have We 313

John Greenleaf Whittier, 1873

GERMANY: L. M.
William Gardiner's *Sacred Melodies*, 1815

1. All things are Thine; no gift have we, Lord of all gifts, to of - fer Thee;
2. Thy will was in the build-ers' thought; Thy hand un-seen a - midst us wrought;
3. In weak-ness and in want we call On Thee for whom the heavens are small;
4. O Fa-ther, deign these walls to bless; Fill with Thy love their emp - ti - ness;

And hence with grate-ful hearts to - day Thine own be - fore Thy feet we lay.
Through mor-tal mo-tive, scheme, and plan, Thy wise e - ter - nal pur - pose ran.
Thy glo - ry is Thy chil-dren's good, Thy joy Thy ten - der Fa - ther-hood.
And let their door a gate-way be To lead us from our-selves to Thee. A-MEN.

Words used by permission of Houghton Mifflin Company, authorized publishers.

LIFE IN CHRIST: STEWARDSHIP

314 Christ, of All My Hopes the Ground

Ralph Wardlaw, 1817

HENDON: 7. 7. 7. 7.
H. A. César Malan, 1827

1. Christ, of all my hopes the Ground, Christ, the Spring of all my joy, Still in Thee may
2. Let Thy love my heart in-flame; Keep Thy fear be-fore my sight; Be Thy praise my
3. Foun-tain of o'er-flow-ing grace, Free-ly from Thy full-ness give; Till I close my
4. Firm-ly trust-ing in Thy blood, Noth-ing shall my heart con-found; Safe-ly I shall
5. Thus, O thus, an en-trance give To the land of cloud-less sky; Hav-ing known it

I be found, Still for Thee my powers em-ploy, Still for Thee my powers em-ploy.
high-est aim; Be Thy smile my chief de-light, Be Thy smile my chief de-light.
earth-ly race, May I prove it Christ to live, May I prove it Christ to live.
pass the flood, Safe-ly reach Em-man-uel's ground, Safe-ly reach Em-man-uel's ground.
Christ to live, Let me know it gain to die, Let me know it gain to die. A-MEN.

315 From Thee All Skill and Science Flow

Charles Kingsley, 1871

ST. PETER: C. M.
Alexander R. Reinagle, c. 1830

1. From Thee all skill and sci-ence flow, All pit-y, care, and love,
2. And part them, Lord, to each and all, As each and all shall need,
3. And has-ten, Lord, that per-fect day When pain and death shall cease,
4. When ev-er blue the sky shall gleam, And ev-er green the sod;

All calm and cour-age, faith and hope; O pour them from a-bove.
To rise like in-cense, each to Thee, In no-ble thought and deed.
And Thy just rule shall fill the earth With health, and light, and peace;
And man's rude work de-face no more The Par-a-dise of God. A-MEN.

Alternative tune, "Gräfenberg," Hymn 243.
LIFE IN CHRIST: HOPE AND ASPIRATION

More About Jesus Would I Know

Eliza E. Hewitt (1851-1920)

MORE ABOUT JESUS: 8. 8. 8. 8. with Refrain
John R. Sweney, 1887

1. More a-bout Je - sus would I know, More of His grace to oth - ers show;
2. More a-bout Je - sus let me learn, More of His ho - ly will dis - cern.
3. More a-bout Je - sus; in His Word Hold-ing com-mun - ion with my Lord;
4. More a-bout Je - sus; on His throne, Rich - es in glo - ry all His own;

More of His sav - ing full - ness see, More of His love who died for me.
Spir - it of God, my teach - er be, Show - ing the things of Christ to me.
Hear - ing His voice in ev - ery line, Mak - ing each faith-ful say - ing mine.
More of His King-dom's sure in-crease; More of His com - ing, Prince of Peace.

REFRAIN

More, more a - bout Je - sus, More, more a - bout Je - sus,

More of His sav - ing full-ness see, More of His love who died for me. A-MEN.

LIFE IN CHRIST: HOPE AND ASPIRATION

317 Lord, I Want to Be a Christian

Negro spiritual

I WANT TO BE A CHRISTIAN: Irregular
Negro melody

1. Lord, I want to be a Chris-tian In my heart, in my heart,
2. Lord, I want to be more lov-ing In my heart, in my heart,
3. Lord, I want to be more ho-ly In my heart, in my heart,
4. Lord, I want to be like Je-sus In my heart, in my heart,

Lord, I want to be a Chris-tian In my heart.
Lord, I want to be more lov-ing In my heart.
Lord, I want to be more ho-ly In my heart.
Lord, I want to be like Je-sus In my heart.

In my heart,............ In my heart,............
In my heart, In my heart,

Lord, I want to be a Chris-tian In my heart.
Lord, I want to be more lov-ing In my heart.
Lord, I want to be more ho-ly In my heart.
Lord, I want to be like Je-sus In my heart. A-MEN.

LIFE IN CHRIST: HOPE AND ASPIRATION

There Is a Place of Quiet Rest

318

Cleland B. McAfee (1866-1944)

MCAFEE: 8. 6. 8. 6. with Refrain
Cleland B. McAfee (1866-1944)

1. There is a place of qui - et rest, Near to the heart of God,
2. There is a place of com - fort sweet, Near to the heart of God,
3. There is a place of full re - lease, Near to the heart of God,

A place where sin can - not mo-lest, Near to the heart of God.
A place where we our Sav - iour meet, Near to the heart of God.
A place where all is joy and peace, Near to the heart of God.

REFRAIN

O Je - sus, blest Re - deem - er, Sent from the heart of God,

Hold us, who wait be - fore Thee, Near to the heart of God. A-MEN.

Words and music copyright, 1903, 1931, by Lorenz Publishing Company as "Near to the Heart of God." Used by permission.

LIFE IN CHRIST: HOPE AND ASPIRATION

319

O for a Closer Walk with God
(FIRST TUNE)

William Cowper, 1772

DALEHURST: C. M.
Arthur Cottman, 1874

1. O for a clos-er walk with God, A calm and heaven-ly frame,
2. Re-turn, O ho-ly Dove, re-turn, Sweet mes-sen-ger of rest!
3. The dear-est i-dol I have known, What-e'er that i-dol be,
4. So shall my walk be close with God, Calm and se-rene my frame;

A light to shine up-on the road That leads me to the Lamb!
I hate the sins that made Thee mourn And drove Thee from my breast.
Help me to tear it from Thy throne, And wor-ship on-ly Thee.
So pur-er light shall mark the road That leads me to the Lamb. A-men.

319

O for a Closer Walk with God
(SECOND TUNE)

William Cowper, 1772

BEATITUDO: C. M.
John B. Dykes, 1875

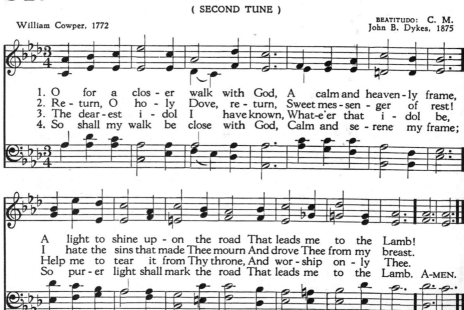

1. O for a clos-er walk with God, A calm and heaven-ly frame,
2. Re-turn, O ho-ly Dove, re-turn, Sweet mes-sen-ger of rest!
3. The dear-est i-dol I have known, What-e'er that i-dol be,
4. So shall my walk be close with God, Calm and se-rene my frame;

A light to shine up-on the road That leads me to the Lamb!
I hate the sins that made Thee mourn And drove Thee from my breast.
Help me to tear it from Thy throne, And wor-ship on-ly Thee.
So pur-er light shall mark the road That leads me to the Lamb. A-men.

LIFE IN CHRIST: HOPE AND ASPIRATION

I Am Thine, O Lord

320

Fanny Crosby, 1875

I AM THINE: 10. 7. 10. 7. with Refrain
William H. Doane, 1875

1. I am Thine, O Lord, I have heard Thy voice, And it
told Thy love to me; But I long to rise in the arms of faith,
And be clos - er drawn to Thee.

2. O the pure de - light of a sin - gle hour That be -
fore Thy throne I spend, When I kneel in prayer, and with Thee, my God,
I com-mune as friend with friend!

3. Con - se - crate me now to Thy serv - ice, Lord, By the
power of grace di - vine; Let my soul look up with a stead-fast hope,
And my will be lost in Thine.

REFRAIN

Draw me near - er, near - er, bless - ed Lord, To the cross where Thou hast died; Draw me near - er, near - er, near - er, bless - ed Lord, To Thy pre - cious, bleed - ing side. A-MEN.

LIFE IN CHRIST: HOPE AND ASPIRATION

[273]

321 My Spirit Longs for Thee

FINGAL: 6. 6. 6. 6. D.
Traditional Irish melody
Arr. by Leopold L. Dix (1861-1935)

John Byrom, 1773; alt.

1. My spir-it longs for Thee With-in my trou-bled breast,
2. Un-less it come from Thee, In vain I look a-round;

Though I un-wor-thy be Of so di-vine a Guest.
In all that I can see No rest is to be found.

Of so di-vine a Guest Un-wor-thy though I be,
No rest is to be found But in Thy bless-ed love:

Yet has my heart no rest, Un-less it come from Thee,
O let my wish be crowned, And send it from a-bove! A - - MEN.

Music used by permission of R. G. Leigh.

LIFE IN CHRIST: HOPE AND ASPIRATION

As Pants the Hart for Cooling Streams

322

From Psalm 42
Nahum Tate and Nicholas Brady, 1696

SPOHR: C. M.
Arr. from Louis Spohr, 1835

1. As pants the hart for cool-ing streams When heat-ed in the chase,
2. For Thee, my God, the liv-ing God, My thirst-y soul doth pine;
3. Why rest-less, why cast down, my soul? Trust God; and He'll em-ploy
4. Why rest-less, why cast down, my soul? Hope still; and thou shalt sing

So longs my soul, O God, for Thee, And Thy re-fresh-ing grace.
O when shall I be-hold Thy face, Thou Maj-es-ty di-vine!
His aid for thee, and change these sighs To thank-ful hymns of joy.
The praise of Him who is thy God, Thy health's e-ter-nal Spring. A-MEN.

Alternative tune, "Martyrdom," Hymn 199.

O Let My Supplicating Cry

323

From Psalm 119
The Psalter, 1912

MELCOMBE: L. M.
Samuel Webbe, 1782

1. O let my sup-pli-cat-ing cry By Thee, my gra-cious Lord, be heard;
2. In-struct-ed in Thy ho-ly law, To praise Thy word I lift my voice;
3. For Thy sal-va-tion I have longed, And in Thy law is my de-light;
4. Thy serv-ant like a wan-dering sheep Has lost the path and gone a-stray;

Give wis-dom and de-liv-er me Ac-cord-ing to Thy faith-ful word.
O Lord, be Thou my pres-ent help, For Thy com-mand-ments are my choice.
En-rich my soul with life di-vine, And help me by Thy judg-ments right.
Re-store my soul and lead me home, For Thy com-mands I would o-bey. A-MEN.

LIFE IN CHRIST: HOPE AND ASPIRATION

324 I Need Thee Every Hour

Annie S. Hawks, 1872
Refrain by Robert Lowry, 1872

NEED: 6. 4. 6. 4. with Refrain
Robert Lowry, 1872

1. I need Thee ev-ery hour, Most gra-cious Lord; No oth-er voice but Thine
2. I need Thee ev-ery hour; Stay Thou near by; Temp-ta-tions lose their power
3. I need Thee ev-ery hour; Teach me Thy will, And Thy rich prom-is-es
4. I need Thee ev-ery hour, Most Ho-ly One; O make me Thine in-deed,

REFRAIN

Can peace af-ford.
When Thou art nigh. I need Thee, O I need Thee, Ev-ery hour I
In me ful-fill.
Thou bless-ed Son.

need Thee! O bless me now, my Sav-iour— I come to Thee! A-MEN.

325 O for a Heart to Praise My God!

Charles Wesley, 1742

BEATITUDO: C. M.
John B. Dykes, 1875

1. O for a heart to praise my God! A heart from sin set free;
2. A heart re-signed, sub-mis-sive, meek, My great Re-deem-er's throne,
3. A hum-ble, low-ly, con-trite heart, Be-liev-ing, true, and clean,
4. A heart in ev-ery thought re-newed, And full of love di-vine,
5. Thy na-ture, gra-cious Lord, im-part; Come quick-ly from a-bove;

LIFE IN CHRIST: HOPE AND ASPIRATION

[276]

O for a Heart to Praise My God!

A heart that al - ways feels Thy blood, So free - ly shed for me;
Where on - ly Christ is heard to speak, Where Je - sus reigns a - lone;
Which nei - ther life nor death can part From Him that dwells with - in;
Per - fect and right and pure and good, A cop - y, Lord, of Thine!
Write Thy new name up - on my heart, Thy new, best name of Love. A - MEN.

Nearer, My God, to Thee 326

BETHANY: 6. 4. 6. 4. 6. 6. 6. 4.

Sarah F. Adams, 1841

Lowell Mason, 1856

1. Near - er, my God, to Thee, Near - er to Thee! E'en though it
2. Though like the wan - der - er, The sun gone down, Dark-ness be
3. There let the way ap - pear Steps un - to heaven: All that Thou
4. Then, with my wak - ing thoughts Bright with Thy praise, Out of my
5. Or if on joy - ful wing Cleav - ing the sky, Sun, moon, and

be a cross That rais - eth me; Still all my song shall be, Near - er, my
o - ver me, My rest a stone; Yet in my dreams I'd be Near - er, my
send - est me In mer - cy given: An - gels to beck - on me Near - er, my
ston - y griefs Beth - el I'll raise; So by my woes to be Near - er, my
stars for - got, Up - ward I fly, Still all my song shall be, Near - er, my

God, to Thee, Near - er, my God, to Thee, Near - er to Thee! A - MEN.

LIFE IN CHRIST: HOPE AND ASPIRATION

[277]

327

O Lord, My God, Most Earnestly

STRACATHRO: C. M.
Charles Hutcheson, 1832
Har. by Geoffrey Shaw, 1925

From Psalm 63
The Psalter, 1912

1. O Lord, my God, most ear - nest - ly My heart would seek Thy face,
2. A - part from Thee I long and thirst, And nought can sat - is - fy;
3. The lov - ing - kind - ness of my God Is more than life to me;
4. In Thee my soul is sat - is - fied, My dark - ness turns to light,
5. My Sav - iour, 'neath Thy shel - tering wings My soul de - lights to dwell;

With - in Thy ho - ly house once more To see Thy glo - rious grace.
I wan - der in a des - ert land Where all the streams are dry.
So I will bless Thee while I live And lift my prayer to Thee.
And joy - ful med - i - ta - tions fill The watch - es of the night.
Still clos - er to Thy side I press, For near Thee all is well. A-MEN.

Music from *Songs of Praise*, Enlarged Edition. Used by permission of Oxford University Press.

328

Father of Peace, and God of Love

Stanzas 1 to 3, Philip Doddridge (1702-1751)
As in *Scottish Paraphrases*, 1751
Stanza 4, William Cameron, 1781

ST. PAUL: C. M.
James Chalmers' Collection, 1749

1. Fa - ther of peace, and God of love, We own Thy power to save,
2. Him from the dead Thou broughtest a-gain, When by His sa - cred blood
3. O may Thy Spir - it seal our souls, And mold them to Thy will,
4. That to per - fec - tion's sa - cred height We near - er still may rise,

That power by which our Shep-herd rose Vic - to - rious o'er the grave.
Con - firmed and sealed for - ev - er-more Th' e - ter - nal cov-enant stood.
That our weak hearts no more may stray, But keep Thy pre - cepts still;
And all we think, and all we do, Be pleas - ing in Thine eyes. A-MEN.

LIFE IN CHRIST: HOPE AND ASPIRATION

O God, Regard My Humble Plea — 329

From Psalm 61
The Psalter, 1912

MERIBAH: 8. 8. 6. D.
Lowell Mason, 1839

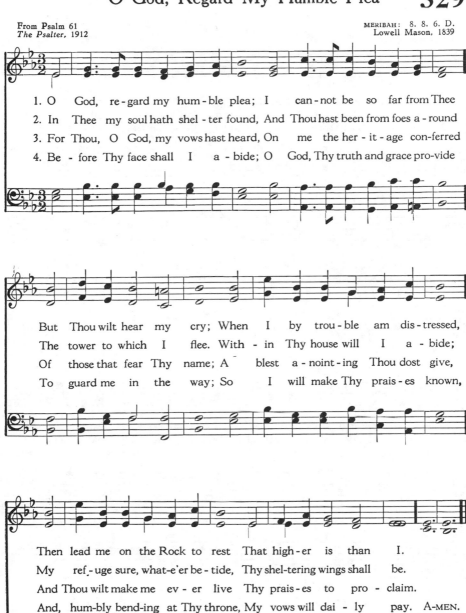

1. O God, re-gard my hum-ble plea; I can-not be so far from Thee
2. In Thee my soul hath shel-ter found, And Thou hast been from foes a-round
3. For Thou, O God, my vows hast heard, On me the her-it-age con-ferred
4. Be-fore Thy face shall I a-bide; O God, Thy truth and grace pro-vide

But Thou wilt hear my cry; When I by trou-ble am dis-tressed,
The tower to which I flee. With-in Thy house will I a-bide;
Of those that fear Thy name; A blest a-noint-ing Thou dost give,
To guard me in the way; So I will make Thy prais-es known,

Then lead me on the Rock to rest That high-er is than I.
My ref-uge sure, what-e'er be-tide, Thy shel-ter-ing wings shall be.
And Thou wilt make me ev-er live Thy prais-es to pro-claim.
And, hum-bly bend-ing at Thy throne, My vows will dai-ly pay. A-MEN.

LIFE IN CHRIST: HOPE AND ASPIRATION

330 Rise, My Soul, and Stretch Thy Wings

AMSTERDAM: 7. 6. 7. 6. 7. 7. 7. 6.
German choral
In *The Foundery Collection*, 1742

Robert Seagrave, 1742; alt.

1. Rise, my soul, and stretch thy wings, Thy bet-ter por-tion trace;
2. Riv-ers to the o-cean run, Nor stay in all their course;
3. Cease, my soul, then, cease to mourn, Press on-ward to the prize;

Rise from tran-si-to-ry things Toward heaven, thy des-tined place.
Fire as-cend-ing seeks the sun; Both speed them to their source:
Soon the Sav-iour will re-turn Tri-um-phant in the skies:

Sun and moon and stars de-cay, Time shall soon this earth re-move;
So my soul, de-rived from God, Longs to view His glo-rious face,
Yet a sea-son, and we know Hap-py en-trance will be given,

Rise, my soul, and haste a-way To seats pre-pared a-bove.
For-ward tends to His a-bode, To rest in His em-brace.
All our sor-rows left be-low, And earth ex-changed for heaven. A-MEN.

LIFE IN CHRIST: HOPE AND ASPIRATION

Lead, Kindly Light

331

John Henry Newman, 1833

LUX BENIGNA: 10. 4. 10. 4. 10. 10.
John B. Dykes, 1865

1. Lead, kind - ly Light, a - mid th' en - cir - cling gloom,
2. I was not ev - er thus, nor prayed that Thou
3. So long Thy power hath blest me, sure it still

Lead Thou me on; The night is dark, and I am far from home;
Shouldst lead me on; I loved to choose and see my path; but now
Will lead me on, O'er moor and fen, o'er crag and tor - rent, till

Lead Thou me on: Keep Thou my feet; I do not ask to see
Lead Thou me on. I loved the gar - ish day, and, spite of fears,
The night is gone; And with the morn those an - gel fa - ces smile,

The dis - tant scene— one step e - nough for me.
Pride ruled my will: re - mem - ber not past years.
Which I have loved long since, and lost a - while. A - MEN.

Alternative tune, "Sandon," Hymn 108.

LIFE IN CHRIST: PILGRIMAGE AND GUIDANCE

Lead On, O King Eternal

LANCASHIRE: 7. 6. 7. 6. D.
Henry Smart, c. 1835

Ernest W. Shurtleff, 1888

1. Lead on, O King E-ter-nal, The day of march has come;
2. Lead on, O King E-ter-nal, Till sin's fierce war shall cease,
3. Lead on, O King E-ter-nal: We fol-low, not with fears;

Hence-forth in fields of con-quest Thy tents shall be our home:
And Ho-li-ness shall whis-per The sweet A-men of peace;
For glad-ness breaks like morn-ing Wher-e'er Thy face ap-pears;

Through days of prep-a-ra-tion Thy grace has made us strong,
For not with swords' loud clash-ing, Nor roll of stir-ring drums,
Thy cross is lift-ed o'er us; We jour-ney in its light:

And now, O King E-ter-nal, We lift our bat-tle song.
With deeds of love and mer-cy, The heaven-ly King-dom comes.
The crown a-waits the con-quest; Lead on, O God of might. A-MEN.

Alternative tune, "Llangloffan," opposite page.
LIFE IN CHRIST: PILGRIMAGE AND GUIDANCE

O Brothers, Lift Your Voices

333

LLANGLOFFAN: 7. 6. 7. 6. D.
Welsh hymn melody
D. Evans' *Hymnau a Thonau*, 1865

Edward H. Bickersteth, 1848

1. O broth-ers, lift your voi - ces, Tri - um-phant songs to raise;
2. O Chris-tian broth-ers, glo - rious Shall be the con-flict's close;
3. Not un - to us, Lord Je - sus: To Thee all praise be due,
4. Great God of our sal - va - tion, Thy pres-ence we a - dore;

Till heaven on high re-joi - ces, And earth is filled with praise:
The cross hath been vic-to - rious, And shall be o'er its foes:
Whose blood-bought mer - cy frees us, Has freed our breth-ren too.
Praise, glo - ry, ad - o - ra - tion Be Thine for - ev - er - more;

Ten thou-sand hearts are bound-ing With ho - ly hopes and free;
Faith is our bat - tle to - ken; Our Lead - er all con - trols;
Not un - to us: in glo - ry The an - gels catch the strain,
Still on in con - flict press-ing On Thee Thy peo - ple call,

The gos-pel trump is sound - ing, The trump of ju - bi - lee.
Our tro-phies, fet-ters bro - ken; Our cap-tives, ran-somed souls.
And cast their crowns be - fore Thee Ex - ult - ing - ly a - gain.
Thee King of Kings con - fess - ing, Thee crown-ing Lord of all. A-MEN.

Words copyright by the Church Society. Used by permission.
Alternative tune, "Lancashire," opposite page.

LIFE IN CHRIST: PILGRIMAGE AND GUIDANCE

[283]

334

Jesus, Lead the Way

Nicolaus L. von Zinzendorf, 1721
Trans. by Arthur W. Farlander, 1939

SEELENBRÄUTIGAM: 5. 5. 8. 8. 5. 5.
Adam Drese, 1698

1. Je - sus, lead the way Through our life's long day, And with
2. Should our lot be hard, Keep us on our guard; E - ven
3. When we need re - lief From an in - ner grief, Or when
4. Or - der Thou our ways, Sav - iour, all our days. If Thou

faith - ful foot-step stead - y, We will fol - low, ev - er read - y.
through se - ver - est tri - al Make us brave in self - de - ni - al:
e - vils come al - lur - ing, Make us pa - tient and en - dur - ing:
lead us through rough pla - ces, Grant us Thy sus - tain-ing gra - ces.

Guide us by Thy hand To the Fa - ther - land.
Tran - sient pain may be But a way to Thee.
Let us fol - low still Thy most ho - ly will.
When our course is o'er, O - pen heav - en's door. A - MEN.

Words used by permission of The Church Pension Fund.

335

O Grant Us Light

ILLSLEY: L. M.
John Bishop (1665-1737)

Lawrence Tuttiett, 1864

1. O grant us light, that we may know The wis - dom Thou a - lone canst give;
2. O grant us light, that we may learn How dead is life from Thee a - part,
3. O grant us light, in grief and pain, To lift our bur-dened hearts a - bove,
4. O grant us light, when, soon or late, All earth - ly scenes shall pass a - way,

LIFE IN CHRIST: PILGRIMAGE AND GUIDANCE

[284]

O Grant Us Light

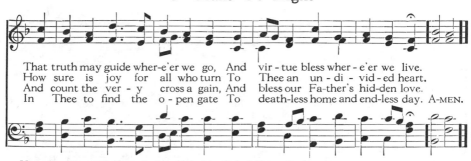

That truth may guide wher-e'er we go, And vir-tue bless wher-e'er we live.
How sure is joy for all who turn To Thee an un-di-vid-ed heart.
And count the ver - y cross a gain, And bless our Fa-ther's hid-den love.
In Thee to find the o - pen gate To death-less home and end-less day. A-MEN.

Music from *The BBC Hymn Book*, published by Oxford University Press.
Alternative tune, "Quebec," Hymn 215.

Jesus, Saviour, Pilot Me

336

PILOT: 7. 7. 7. 7. 7. 7.

Edward Hopper, 1871

John E. Gould, 1871

1. Je - sus, Sav - iour, pi - lot me O - ver life's tem-pes-tuous sea;
2. As a moth - er stills her child, Thou canst hush the o - cean wild;
3. When at last I near the shore, And the fear - ful break-ers roar

Un - known waves be - fore me roll, Hid - ing rock and treach-erous shoal;
Bois - terous waves o - bey Thy will When Thou sayest to them, "Be still!"
'Twixt me and the peace-ful rest, Then, while lean - ing on Thy breast,

Chart and com - pass come from Thee: Je - sus, Sav - iour, pi - lot me.
Won-drous Sov - ereign of the sea, Je - sus, Sav - iour, pi - lot me.
May I hear Thee say to me, "Fear not, I will pi - lot thee." A-MEN.

337 Far Off I See the Goal

MOAB: 6. 5. 6. 5. 6. 6. 6. 5.

Robert Rowland Roberts, 1925

John Roberts (Ieuan Gwyllt), 1870

1. Far off I see the goal— O Sav - iour, guide me;
2. When - e'er Thy way seems strange, Go Thou be - fore me;
3. Should earth - ly pleas - ures wane, And joy for - sake me,
4. There, with the ran - somed throng Who praise for - ev - er

I feel my strength is small— Be Thou be - side me;
And, lest my heart should change, O Lord, watch o'er me;
And lone - ly hours of pain At length o'er - take me,
The love that made them strong To serve for - ev - er,

With vi - sion ev - er clear, With love that con - quers fear,
But, should my faith prove frail, And I through blind - ness fail,
My hand in Thine hold fast Till sor - row be o'er - past,
I too would seek Thy face, Thy fin - ished work re - trace,

And grace to per - se - vere, O Lord, pro - vide me.
O let Thy grace pre - vail, And still re - store me.
And gen - tle death at last For heaven a - wake me.
And mag - ni - fy Thy grace, Re - deemed for - ev - er. A - MEN.

Words used by permission of Mrs. Robert R. Roberts. Music used by permission of the Calvinistic Methodist Connexion.

LIFE IN CHRIST: PILGRIMAGE AND GUIDANCE

[286]

He Leadeth Me: O Blessed Thought! 338

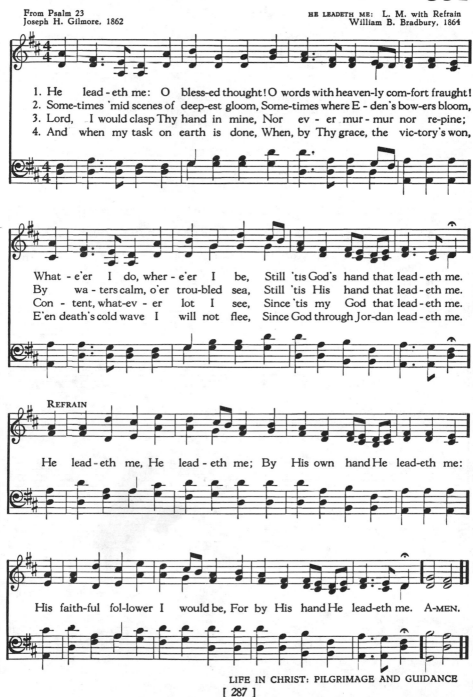

From Psalm 23
Joseph H. Gilmore, 1862

HE LEADETH ME: L. M. with Refrain
William B. Bradbury, 1864

1. He lead-eth me: O bless-ed thought! O words with heaven-ly com-fort fraught!
2. Some-times 'mid scenes of deep-est gloom, Some-times where E - den's bow-ers bloom,
3. Lord, I would clasp Thy hand in mine, Nor ev - er mur - mur nor re-pine;
4. And when my task on earth is done, When, by Thy grace, the vic-tory's won,

What - e'er I do, wher - e'er I be, Still 'tis God's hand that lead-eth me.
By wa - ters calm, o'er trou-bled sea, Still 'tis His hand that lead-eth me.
Con - tent, what-ev - er lot I see, Since 'tis my God that lead-eth me.
E'en death's cold wave I will not flee, Since God through Jor-dan lead-eth me.

REFRAIN

He lead-eth me, He lead-eth me; By His own hand He lead-eth me:

His faith-ful fol-lower I would be, For by His hand He lead-eth me. A-MEN.

LIFE IN CHRIST: PILGRIMAGE AND GUIDANCE

[287]

339 Guide Me, O Thou Great Jehovah

(FIRST TUNE)

Welsh, William Williams, 1745
Stanza 1 trans. by Peter Williams, 1771
Stanzas 2, 3, trans. by William Williams, c. 1772

CWM RHONDDA: 8. 7. 8. 7. 8. 7.
John Hughes, 1907

1. Guide me, O Thou great Je - ho - vah, Pil - grim through this bar - ren land; I am weak, but Thou art might - y; Hold me with Thy power - ful hand; Bread of heav - en, Bread of heav - en, Feed me till I want no more, Feed me till I want no more.

2. O - pen now the crys - tal foun - tain, Whence the heal - ing stream doth flow; Let the fire and cloud - y pil - lar Lead me all my jour - ney through; Strong De - liv - erer, strong De - liv - erer, Be Thou still my Strength and Shield, Be Thou still my Strength and Shield.

3. When I tread the verge of Jor - dan, Bid my anx - ious fears sub - side; Death of death, and hell's de - struc - tion, Land me safe on Ca - naan's side; Songs of prais - es, songs of prais - es I will ev - er give to Thee, I will ev - er give to Thee. A-MEN.

Music used by permission of Mrs. John Hughes.
LIFE IN CHRIST: PILGRIMAGE AND GUIDANCE

Guide Me, O Thou Great Jehovah   **339**

(SECOND TUNE)

SEGUR: 8. 7. 8. 7. 8. 7.
Joseph P. Holbrook, 1862
Har. for this book, 1953

For words, see opposite page.

Children of the Heavenly King   **340**

John Cennick, 1742

PLEYEL'S HYMN: 7. 7. 7. 7.
Arr. from Ignaz J. Pleyel, 1790

1. Chil-dren of the Heaven-ly King, As we jour-ney, sweet-ly sing;
2. We are trav-eling home to God In the way the fa-thers trod;
3. Fear not, breth-ren; joy-ful stand On the bor-ders of your land;
4. Lord, o-be-dient-ly we go, Glad-ly leav-ing all be-low;

Sing our Sav-iour's wor-thy praise, Glo-rious in His works and ways.
They are hap-py now, and we Soon their hap-pi-ness shall see.
Je-sus Christ, your Fa-ther's Son, Bids you un-dis-mayed go on.
On-ly Thou our Lead-er be, And we still will fol-low Thee. A-MEN.

LIFE IN CHRIST: PILGRIMAGE AND GUIDANCE

[289]

341 Lead Us, O Father, in the Paths of Peace

William Henry Burleigh, 1859

LANGRAN: 10. 10. 10. 10.
James Langran, 1862

1. Lead us, O Fa-ther, in the paths of peace: With-out Thy guid-ing
2. Lead us, O Fa-ther, in the paths of truth: Un-helped by Thee, in
3. Lead us, O Fa-ther, in the paths of right: Blind-ly we stum-ble
4. Lead us, O Fa-ther, to Thy heaven-ly rest, How-ev-er rough and

hand we go a-stray, And doubts ap-pall, and sor-rows still in-crease;
er-ror's maze we grope, While pas-sion stains and fol-ly dims our youth,
when we walk a-lone, In-volved in shad-ows of a dark-ening night;
steep the path-way be, Through joy or sor-row, as Thou deem-est best,

Lead us through Christ, the true and liv-ing Way.
And age comes on un-cheered by faith or hope.
On-ly with Thee we jour-ney safe-ly on.
Un-til our lives are per-fect-ed in Thee. A-MEN.

Music used by permission of Novello & Co., Ltd.

342 O God of Beth-el

Philip Doddridge, 1736, and
John Logan, 1781

DUNDEE (FRENCH): C. M.
Scottish Psalter, 1615

1. O God of Beth-el, by whose hand Thy peo-ple still are fed;
2. Our vows, our prayers, we now pre-sent Be-fore Thy throne of grace;
3. Through each per-plex-ing path of life Our wan-dering foot-steps guide;
4. O spread Thy cov-ering wings a-round Till all our wan-derings cease,

LIFE IN CHRIST: PILGRIMAGE AND GUIDANCE

O God of Beth-el

Who through this wea - ry pil - grim-age Hast all our fa - thers led,
God of our fa - thers, be the God Of their suc-ceed - ing race.
Give us each day our dai - ly bread, And rai - ment fit pro - vide.
And at our Fa-ther's loved a - bode Our souls ar - rive in peace. A-MEN.

For alternative arrangement, see Hymn 112.

Lead Us, Heavenly Father, Lead Us 343

James Edmeston, 1821

DULCE CARMEN (CORINTH): 8. 7. 8. 7. 8. 7.
An Essay on the Church Plain Chant, 1782

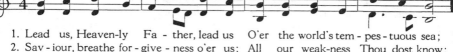

1. Lead us, Heaven-ly Fa - ther, lead us O'er the world's tem - pes - tuous sea;
2. Sav - iour, breathe for - give - ness o'er us; All our weak-ness Thou dost know;
3. Spir - it of our God, de - scend-ing, Fill our hearts with heaven - ly joy;

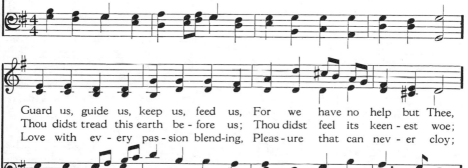

Guard us, guide us, keep us, feed us, For we have no help but Thee,
Thou didst tread this earth be - fore us; Thou didst feel its keen - est woe;
Love with ev - ery pas - sion blend-ing, Pleas-ure that can nev - er cloy;

Yet pos - sess - ing ev - ery bless-ing, If our God our Fa-ther be.
Lone and drear - y, faint and wea - ry, Thru the des - ert Thou didst go.
Thus pro - vid - ed, par-doned, guid-ed, Noth-ing can our peace de - stroy. A-MEN.

LIFE IN CHRIST: PILGRIMAGE AND GUIDANCE

344   If Thou but Suffer God to Guide Thee

From Psalm 55
Georg Neumark, 1657
Trans. by Catherine Winkworth, 1855, 1863

NEUMARK: 9. 8. 9. 8. 8. 8.
Georg Neumark, 1657

1. If thou but suf - fer God to guide thee, And hope in
2. On - ly be still, and wait His lei - sure In cheer - ful
3. Sing, pray, and swerve not from His ways, But do thine

Him through all thy ways, He'll give thee strength, what-e'er be - tide thee,
hope, with heart con - tent To take what - e'er thy Fa - ther's pleas-ure
own part faith - ful - ly; Trust His rich prom - is - es of grace,

And bear thee through the e - vil days; Who trusts in God's un -
And all - dis - cern - ing love hath sent; Nor doubt our in - most
So shall they be ful - filled in thee; God nev - er yet for -

chang - ing love Builds on the rock that nought can move.
wants are known To Him who chose us for His own.
sook at need The soul that trust - ed Him in - deed. A - MEN.

Music from the *Common Service Book of the Lutheran Church.* Used by permisssion.

LIFE IN CHRIST: PILGRIMAGE AND GUIDANCE

He Who Would Valiant Be

John Bunyan, 1684; alt., 1906

ST. DUNSTAN'S: 6. 5. 6. 5. 6. 6. 6. 5.
Charles Winfred Douglas, 1917

345

1. He who would val - iant be 'Gainst all dis - as - ter,
2. Who - so be - set him round With dis - mal sto - ries
3. Since, Lord, Thou dost de - fend Us with Thy Spir - it,

Let him in con - stan - cy Fol - low the Mas - ter.
Do but them - selves con - found— His strength the more is.
We know we at the end Shall life in - her - it.

There's no dis - cour - age - ment Shall make him once re - lent
No foes shall stay his might; Though he with gi - ants fight,
Then fan - cies flee a - way! I'll fear not what men say,

His first a - vowed in - tent To be a pil - grim.
He will make good his right To be a pil - grim.
I'll la - bor night and day To be a pil - grim. A - MEN.

Words used by permission of Oxford University Press. Music used by permission of The Church Pension Fund.

LIFE IN CHRIST: PILGRIMAGE AND GUIDANCE

346 Awake, My Soul, Stretch Every Nerve

CHRISTMAS: C. M.

Philip Doddridge, 1755

Arr. from Georg Friedrich Handel, 1728

1. A-wake, my soul, stretch ev-ery nerve, And press with vig-or on; A heaven-ly race de-
2. A cloud of wit-ness-es a - round Hold thee in full sur - vey: For-get the steps al-
3. 'Tis God's all an - i - mat-ing voice That calls thee from on high; 'Tis His own hand pre-
4. Blest Sav-iour, in-tro-duced by Thee, Have I my race be-gun; And, crowned with vic-tory,

mands thy zeal, And an im-mor-tal crown, And an im-mor-tal crown.
read - y trod, And on-ward urge thy way, And on - ward urge thy way.
sents the prize To thine as-pir-ing eye, To thine as-pir-ing eye.
at Thy feet I'll lay my hon-ors down, I'll lay my hon-ors down. A-MEN.

347 God Is My Strong Salvation

MEIN LEBEN: 7. 6. 7. 6.

From Psalm 27
James Montgomery, 1822

Melchior Vulpius, 1609

1. God is my strong Sal - va - tion; What foe have I to fear?
2. Though hosts en - camp a - round me, Firm to the fight I stand;
3. Place on the Lord re - li - ance, My soul, with cour-age wait;
4. His might thy heart shall strength - en, His love thy joy in - crease;

In dark-ness and temp-ta - tion My Light, my Help, is near.
What ter - ror can con - found me, With God at my right hand?
His truth be thine af - fi - ance, When faint and des - o - late.
Mer - cy thy days shall length - en; The Lord will give thee peace. A-MEN.

LIFE IN CHRIST: LOYALTY AND COURAGE

Faith of Our Fathers!

ST. CATHERINE: 8. 8. 8. 8. 8. 8.
Henri F. Hemy, 1865
Alt. by James G. Walton, 1871

Frederick W. Faber, 1849; alt.

348

1. Faith of our fa - thers! liv - ing still In spite of dun - geon, fire, and sword, O how our hearts beat high with joy When - e'er we hear that glo - rious word: Faith of our fa - thers, ho - ly faith! We will be true to thee till death.

2. Faith of our fa - thers! God's great power Shall win all na - tions un - to thee; And through the truth that comes from God Man - kind shall then be tru - ly free: Faith of our fa - thers, ho - ly faith! We will be true to thee till death.

3. Faith of our fa - thers! we will love Both friend and foe in all our strife, And preach thee, too, as love knows how By kind - ly words and vir - tuous life: Faith of our fa - thers, ho - ly faith! We will be true to thee till death. A - MEN.

LIFE IN CHRIST: LOYALTY AND COURAGE

349 Stand Up, Stand Up for Jesus

George Duffield, 1858

WEBB: 7. 6. 7. 6. D.
George J. Webb, 1837

1. Stand up, stand up for Je - sus, Ye sol - diers of the cross;
2. Stand up, stand up for Je - sus, The trum - pet call o - bey;
3. Stand up, stand up for Je - sus, Stand in His strength a - lone;
4. Stand up, stand up for Je - sus, The strife will not be long;

Lift high His roy - al ban - ner, It must not suf - fer loss:
Forth to the might - y con - flict, In this His glo - rious day:
The arm of flesh will fail you, Ye dare not trust your own:
This day the noise of bat - tle, The next the vic - tor's song:

From vic - tory un - to vic - tory His ar - my shall He lead,
Ye that are men now serve Him A - gainst un - num - bered foes;
Put on the gos - pel ar - mor, Each piece put on with prayer;
To him that o - ver - com - eth A crown of life shall be;

Till ev - ery foe is van-quished, And Christ is Lord in - deed.
Let cour - age rise with dan - ger, And strength to strength op-pose.
Where du - ty calls, or dan - ger, Be nev - er want - ing there.
He with the King of Glo - ry Shall reign e - ter - nal - ly. A-MEN.

LIFE IN CHRIST: LOYALTY AND COURAGE

Onward, Christian Soldiers

ST. GERTRUDE: 6. 5. 6. 5. D. with Refrain

Sabine Baring-Gould, 1864

Arthur S. Sullivan, 1871

1. On - ward, Chris-tian sol - diers, March-ing as to war, With the cross of
2. Like a might-y ar - my Moves the Church of God; Broth-ers, we are
3. Crowns and thrones may per - ish, King-doms rise and wane, But the Church of
4. On - ward, then, ye peo - ple, Join our hap-py throng, Blend with ours your

Je - sus Go - ing on be - fore: Christ the roy - al Mas-ter Leads a -
tread-ing Where the saints have trod; We are not di - vid - ed, All one
Je - sus Con-stant will re - main; Gates of hell can nev - er 'Gainst that
voi - ces In the tri-umph song; Glo - ry, laud, and hon - or Un - to

gainst the foe; For - ward in - to bat - tle, See, His ban-ners go.
bod - y we, One in hope and doc - trine, One in char - i - ty.
Church pre - vail; We have Christ's own prom - ise, And that can - not fail.
Christ the King; This through count-less a - ges Men and an - gels sing.

REFRAIN

On - ward, Chris - tian sol - diers, March - ing as to war,

With the cross of Je - sus Go - ing on be - fore. A - MEN.

Words copyright by J. Curwen & Sons, Ltd. Used by permission.

LIFE IN CHRIST: LOYALTY AND COURAGE

351   March On, O Soul, with Strength!

George T. Coster, 1900

ARTHUR'S SEAT: 6. 6. 6. 6. 8. 8.
John Goss, 1874

1. March on, O soul, with strength! Like those strong men of old
2. The sons of fa - thers we By whom our faith is taught
3. March on, O soul, with strength, As strong the bat - tle rolls!
4. Not long the con - flict: soon The ho - ly war shall cease,

Who 'gainst en - thron - ed wrong Stood con - fi - dent and bold;
To fear no ill, to fight The ho - ly fight they fought:
'Gainst lies and lusts and wrongs, Let cour - age rule our souls:
Faith's war - fare end - ed, won The home of end - less peace!

Who, thrust in prison or cast to flame,
He - ro - ic war - riors, ne'er from Christ
In keen - est strife, Lord, may we stand,
Look up! the vic - tor's crown at length!

Still made their glo - ry in Thy name.
By an - y lure or guile en - ticed.
Up - held and strength - ened by Thy hand.
March on, O soul, march on, with strength! A-MEN.

LIFE IN CHRIST: LOYALTY AND COURAGE

Rise Up, O Men of God!

William Pierson Merrill, 1911

FESTAL SONG: S. M.
William H. Walter, 1894

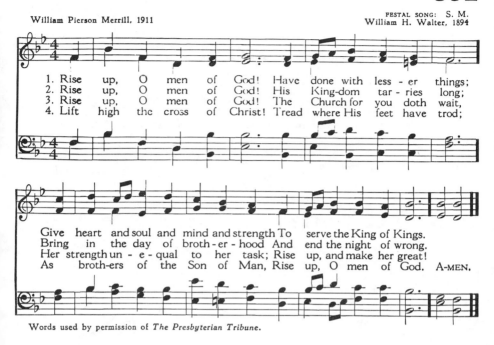

1. Rise up, O men of God! Have done with less - er things;
2. Rise up, O men of God! His King-dom tar - ries long;
3. Rise up, O men of God! The Church for you doth wait,
4. Lift high the cross of Christ! Tread where His feet have trod;

Give heart and soul and mind and strength To serve the King of Kings.
Bring in the day of broth - er - hood And end the night of wrong.
Her strength un - e - qual to her task; Rise up, and make her great!
As broth-ers of the Son of Man, Rise up, O men of God. A-MEN.

Words used by permission of *The Presbyterian Tribune.*

Am I a Soldier of the Cross

ARLINGTON: C. M.
Thomas A. Arne, 1762

Isaac Watts, 1724

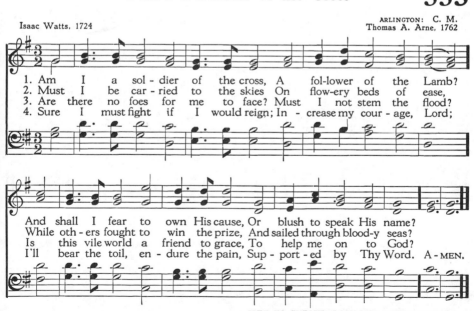

1. Am I a sol - dier of the cross, A fol-low-er of the Lamb?
2. Must I be car - ried to the skies On flow-ery beds of ease,
3. Are there no foes for me to face? Must I not stem the flood?
4. Sure I must fight if I would reign; In - crease my cour - age, Lord;

And shall I fear to own His cause, Or blush to speak His name?
While oth - ers fought to win the prize, And sailed through blood-y seas?
Is this vile world a friend to grace, To help me on to God?
I'll bear the toil, en - dure the pain, Sup - port - ed by Thy Word. A - MEN.

LIFE IN CHRIST: LOYALTY AND COURAGE

354 The Son of God Goes Forth to War

ALL SAINTS NEW: C. M. D.
Reginald Heber, 1827
Henry S. Cutler, 1872

1. The Son of God goes forth to war, A king-ly crown to gain;
2. The mar-tyr first, whose ea-gle eye Could pierce be-yond the grave,
3. A glo-rious band, the cho-sen few On whom the Spir-it came,
4. A no-ble ar-my, men and boys, The ma-tron and the maid,

His blood-red ban-ner streams a-far: Who fol-lows in His train?
Who saw his Mas-ter in the sky, And called on Him to save:
Twelve val-iant saints, their hope they knew, And mocked the cross and flame:
A-round the Sav-iour's throne re-joice, In robes of light ar-rayed:

Who best can drink his cup of woe, Tri-um-phant o-ver pain,
Like Him, with par-don on his tongue In midst of mor-tal pain,
They met the ty-rant's bran-dished steel, The li-on's gor-y mane;
They climbed the steep as-cent of heaven Through per-il, toil, and pain:

Who pa-tient bears his cross be-low, He fol-lows in His train.
He prayed for them that did the wrong: Who fol-lows in his train?
They bowed their necks the death to feel: Who fol-lows in their train?
O God, to us may grace be given To fol-low in their train! A-MEN.

LIFE IN CHRIST: LOYALTY AND COURAGE

Who Is on the Lord's Side?

ARMAGEDDON: 6. 5. 6. 5. 6. 5. D.
German melody
Adapted by John Goss, 1871

Frances Ridley Havergal, 1877

1. Who is on the Lord's side? Who will serve the King?
2. Not for weight of glo - ry, Not for crown and palm,
3. Fierce may be the con - flict, Strong may be the foe,

Who will be His help - ers, Oth - er lives to bring? Who will leave the
En - ter we the ar - my, Raise the war - rior psalm; But for Love that
But the King's own ar - my None can o - ver - throw: Round His stand-ard

world's side? Who will face the foe? Who is on the Lord's side?
claim - eth Lives for whom He died: He whom Je - sus nam - eth
rang - ing, Vic - tory is se - cure; For His truth un - chang - ing

Who for Him will go? By Thy call of mer - cy, By Thy grace di - vine,
Must be on His side. By Thy love con-strain-ing, By Thy grace di - vine,
Makes the tri-umph sure. Joy - ful - ly en - list - ing By Thy grace di - vine,

We are on the Lord's side, Sav - iour, we are Thine.
We are on the Lord's side, Sav - iour, we are Thine.
We are on the Lord's side, Sav - iour, we are Thine. A-MEN.

LIFE IN CHRIST: LOYALTY AND COURAGE

356 We Are Living, We Are Dwelling

Arthur Cleveland Coxe, 1840; alt.

BLAENHAFREN: 8. 7. 8. 7. D.
Traditional Welsh melody

1. We are liv - ing, we are dwell - ing In a grand and aw - ful time,
2. Will ye play, then? will ye dal - ly Far be - hind the bat - tle line?
3. Sworn to yield, to wa - ver, nev - er; Con - se - crat - ed, born a - gain;

In an age on a - ges tell - ing; To be liv - ing is sub - lime.
Up! it is Je - ho - vah's ral - ly; God's own arm hath need of thine.
Sworn to be Christ's sol - diers ev - er, O for Christ at least be men!

Hark! the wak - ing up of na - tions, Hosts ad - vanc - ing to the fray;
Worlds are charg - ing, heaven be - hold - ing; Thou hast but an hour to fight;
O let all the soul with - in you For the truth's sake go a - broad!

Hark! what sound - eth is cre - a - tion's Groan - ing for the lat - ter day.
Now, the bla - zoned cross un - fold - ing, On, right on - ward for the right!
Strike! let ev - ery nerve and sin - ew Tell on a - ges, tell for God. A-MEN.

Alternative tune. "Austrian Hymn." Hymn 434.
LIFE IN CHRIST: TRIAL AND CONFLICT

[302]

Now Israel May Say

357

From Psalm 124
The Psalter, 1912; alt., 1953

OLD 124TH: 10. 10. 10. 10. 10.
Genevan Psalter, 1551

1. Now Is - ra - el may say, and that in truth, If that the
Lord had not our right main - tained, If that the Lord had
not with us re - mained, When cru - el men a - gainst us rose to
strive, We sure - ly had been swal-lowed up a - live.

2. Yea, when their wrath a - gainst us fierce - ly rose, The swell - ing
tide had o'er us spread its wave, The rag - ing stream had
then be-come our grave, The surg - ing flood, in proud-ly swell - ing
roll, Most sure - ly then had o - ver-whelmed our soul.

3. Blest be the Lord, who made us not their prey; As from the
snare a bird es - cap - eth free, Their net is rent and
so es-caped are we; Our on - ly help is in God's ho - ly
name, Who made the earth and all the heaven - ly frame. A-MEN.

LIFE IN CHRIST: TRIAL AND CONFLICT

[303]

358 God of Grace and God of Glory

Harry Emerson Fosdick, 1930

CWM RHONDDA: 8. 7. 8. 7. 8. 7.
John Hughes, 1907

1. God of grace and God of glo - ry, On Thy peo - ple
2. Lo! the hosts of e - vil round us Scorn Thy Christ, as -
3. Cure Thy chil - dren's war - ring mad - ness, Bend our pride to
4. Set our feet on loft - y pla - ces; Gird our lives that
5. Save us from weak res - ig - na - tion To the e - vils

pour Thy power; Crown Thine an-cient Church's sto - ry; Bring her bud to
sail His ways! From the fears that long have bound us Free our hearts to
Thy con - trol; Shame our wan - ton, self - ish glad-ness, Rich in things and
they may be Ar - mored with all Christ-like gra - ces In the fight to
we de - plore; Let the search for Thy sal - va - tion Be our glo - ry

glo - rious flower. Grant us wis - dom, grant us cour - age,
faith and praise. Grant us wis - dom, grant us cour - age,
poor in soul. Grant us wis - dom, grant us cour - age,
set men free. Grant us wis - dom, grant us cour - age,
ev - er - more. Grant us wis - dom, grant us cour - age,

For the fac - ing of this hour, For the fac - ing of this hour.
For the liv - ing of these days, For the liv - ing of these days.
Lest we miss Thy King-dom's goal, Lest we miss Thy King-dom's goal.
That we fail not man nor Thee! That we fail not man nor Thee!
Serv - ing Thee whom we a - dore, Serv - ing Thee whom we a - dore. A-MEN.

Words used by permission of the author. Music used by permission of Mrs. John Hughes.
Alternative tune, "Regent Square," Hymn 168.
LIFE IN CHRIST: TRIAL AND CONFLICT

Fight the Good Fight

359

(FIRST TUNE)

PENTECOST: L. M.
William Boyd, c. 1864

John S. B. Monsell, 1863

1. Fight the good fight with all thy might; Christ is thy Strength, and Christ thy Right:
2. Run the straight race through God's good grace, Lift up thine eyes, and seek His face;
3. Cast care a - side, lean on thy Guide; His bound-less mer - cy will pro - vide;
4. Faint not nor fear, His arms are near; He chang-eth not, and thou art dear;

Lay hold on life, and it shall be Thy joy and crown e - ter - nal - ly.
Life with its way be-fore us lies, Christ is the Path, and Christ the Prize.
Trust, and thy trust-ing soul shall prove Christ is its Life, and Christ its Love.
On - ly be-lieve, and thou shalt see That Christ is All in all to thee. A-MEN.

Music used by permission of Novello & Co., Ltd.

Fight the Good Fight

359

(SECOND TUNE)

CANNOCK: L. M.
Walter K. Stanton, 1951

John S. B. Monsell, 1863

1. Fight the good fight with all thy might; Christ is thy Strength, and Christ thy Right:
2. Run the straight race through God's good grace, Lift up thine eyes, and seek His face;
3. Cast care a - side, lean on thy Guide; His bound-less mer - cy will pro - vide;
4. Faint not nor fear, His arms are near; He chang-eth not, and thou art dear;

Lay hold on life, and it shall be Thy joy and crown e - ter - nal - ly.
Life with its way be - fore us lies, Christ is the Path, and Christ the Prize.
Trust, and thy trust-ing soul shall prove Christ is its Life, and Christ its Love.
On - ly be-lieve, and thou shalt see That Christ is All in all to thee. A-MEN.

Music from *The BBC Hymn Book.* Used by permission of Oxford University Press.

LIFE IN CHRIST: TRIAL AND CONFLICT

360 Christian, Dost Thou See Them

Ascribed to Andrew of Crete (660-732)
Trans. by John Mason Neale, 1862; alt.

ST. ANDREW OF CRETE: 6. 5. 6. 5. D.
John B. Dykes, 1868

1. Chris - tian, dost thou see them On the ho - ly ground,
2. Chris - tian, dost thou feel them, How they work with - in,
3. Chris - tian, dost thou hear them, How they speak thee fair?
4. "Well I know thy trou - ble, O My serv - ant true,

How the powers of dark - ness Rage thy steps a - round?
Striv - ing, tempt - ing, lur - ing, Goad - ing in - to sin?
"Al - ways fast and vig - il? Al - ways watch and prayer?"
Thou art ver - y wea - ry— I was wea - ry too;

Chris - tian, up and smite them, Count - ing gain but loss,
Chris - tian, nev - er trem - ble; Nev - er be down - cast;
Chris - tian, an - swer bold - ly, "While I breathe I pray!"
But that toil shall make thee Some - day all Mine own,

In the strength that com - eth By the ho - ly cross.
Gird thee for the bat - tle; Thou shalt win at last.
Peace shall fol - low bat - tle, Night shall end in day.
And the end of sor - row Shall be near My throne." A - MEN.

LIFE IN CHRIST: TRIAL AND CONFLICT

[306]

Once to Every Man and Nation

361

EBENEZER (TON-Y-BOTEL): 8. 7. 8. 7. D.
Thomas John Williams, 1890

James Russell Lowell, 1845; alt.

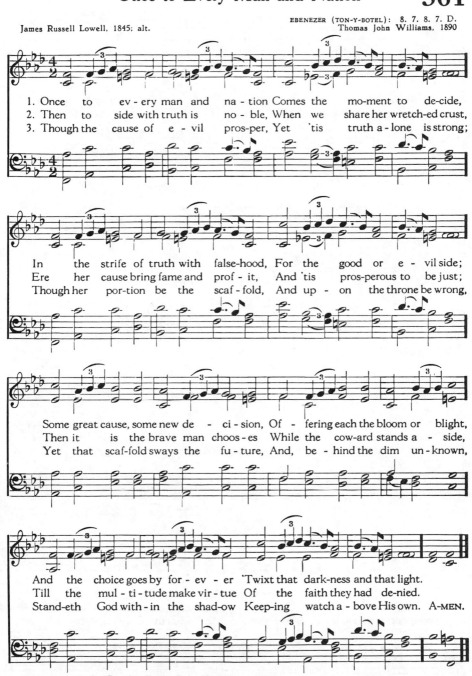

1. Once to ev-ery man and na-tion Comes the mo-ment to de-cide,
2. Then to side with truth is no-ble, When we share her wretch-ed crust,
3. Though the cause of e-vil pros-per, Yet 'tis truth a-lone is strong;

In the strife of truth with false-hood, For the good or e-vil side;
Ere her cause bring fame and prof-it, And 'tis pros-perous to be just;
Though her por-tion be the scaf-fold, And up-on the throne be wrong,

Some great cause, some new de-ci-sion, Of-fering each the bloom or blight,
Then it is the brave man choos-es While the cow-ard stands a-side,
Yet that scaf-fold sways the fu-ture, And, be-hind the dim un-known,

And the choice goes by for-ev-er 'Twixt that dark-ness and that light.
Till the mul-ti-tude make vir-tue Of the faith they had de-nied.
Stand-eth God with-in the shad-ow Keep-ing watch a-bove His own. A-MEN.

Music copyright by Gwenlyn Evans, Ltd. Used by permission.

LIFE IN CHRIST: TRIAL AND CONFLICT

[307]

Charles Wesley, 1749

DIADEMATA: S. M. D.
George J. Elvey, 1868

1. Sol - diers of Christ, a - rise, And put your ar - mor on,
2. Stand, then, in His great might, With all His strength en - dued;
3. Leave no un - guard - ed place, No weak - ness of the soul;

Strong in the strength which God sup - plies Through His e - ter - nal Son.
And take, to arm you for the fight, The pan - o - ply of God:
Take ev - ery vir - tue, ev - ery grace, And for - ti - fy the whole.

Strong in the Lord of Hosts, And in His might - y power,
That, hav - ing all things done, And all your con - flicts passed,
From strength to strength go on; Wres - tle, and fight, and pray;

Who in the strength of Je - sus trusts Is more than con - quer - or.
Ye may o'er-come, through Christ a-lone, And stand com-plete at last.
Tread all the powers of dark-ness down, And win the well-fought day. A-MEN.

LIFE IN CHRIST: TRIAL AND CONFLICT

My Soul, Be on Thy Guard

363

George Heath, 1781; alt.

LABAN: S. M.
Lowell Mason, 1830

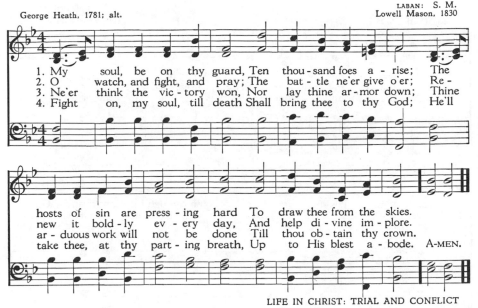

1. My soul, be on thy guard, Ten thou-sand foes a - rise; The
2. O watch, and fight, and pray; The bat - tle ne'er give o'er; Re -
3. Ne'er think the vic - tory won, Nor lay thine ar-mor down; Thine
4. Fight on, my soul, till death Shall bring thee to thy God; He'll

hosts of sin are press - ing hard To draw thee from the skies.
new it bold - ly ev - ery day, And help di - vine im - plore.
ar - duous work will not be done Till thou ob - tain thy crown.
take thee, at thy part - ing breath, Up to His blest a - bode. A-MEN.

LIFE IN CHRIST: TRIAL AND CONFLICT

Give to the Winds Thy Fears

364

Paul Gerhardt, 1656
Trans. by John Wesley, 1739

ST. BRIDE: S. M.
Samuel Howard, 1762
Har. by David Evans, 1927

1. Give to the winds thy fears; Hope and be un - dis - mayed;
2. Through waves, and clouds, and storms, He gent - ly clears thy way;
3. Leave to His sov - ereign sway To choose and to com - mand;
4. Far, far a - bove thy thought His coun - sel shall ap - pear,

God hears thy sighs and counts thy tears, God shall lift up thy head.
Wait thou His time; so shall this night Soon end in joy-ous day.
So shalt thou, won-dering, own His way, How wise, how strong His hand!
When ful - ly He the work hath wrought That caused thy need-less fear. A-MEN.

Music from *The Church Hymnary*, Revised Edition. Used by permission of Oxford University Press.
For alternative arrangement, see Hymn 308.   LIFE IN CHRIST: FAITH AND ASSURANCE

365 All the Way My Saviour Leads Me

ALL THE WAY: 8. 7. 8. 7. D.
Robert Lowry, 1875
Har. for this book, 1953

Fanny Crosby, 1875

1. All the way my Sav-iour leads me; What have I to ask be-side?
2. All the way my Sav-iour leads me, Cheers each wind-ing path I tread,
3. All the way my Sav-iour leads me; Oh, the full-ness of His love!

Can I doubt His ten-der mer-cy, Who through life has been my Guide?
Gives me grace for ev-ery tri - al, Feeds me with the liv-ing bread.
Per - fect rest to me is prom-ised In my Fa-ther's house a-bove.

Heaven-ly peace, di - vin-est com-fort, Here by faith in Him to dwell!
Though my wea - ry steps may fal - ter, And my soul a-thirst may be,
When my spir - it, clothed im - mor - tal, Wings its flight to realms of day,

For I know, what-e'er be-fall me, Je - sus do-eth all things well;
Gush-ing from the Rock be-fore me, Lo! a spring of joy I see;
This my song through end-less a - ges: Je - sus led me all the way;

For I know, what-e'er be-fall me, Je-sus do-eth all things well.
Gush-ing from the Rock be-fore me, Lo! a spring of joy I see.
This my song through end-less a - ges: Je - sus led me all the way. A - MEN.

LIFE IN CHRIST: FAITH AND ASSURANCE

Whate'er My God Ordains Is Right

366

WAS GOTT THUT DAS IST WOHLGETHAN: 8. 7. 8. 7. 4. 4. 8. 8.

Samuel Rodigast. c. 1675
Trans. by Catherine Winkworth, 1863

Severus Gastorius
Weimar Gesangbuch, 1681

1. What-e'er my God or-dains is right; His ho-ly will a-bid-eth;
2. What-e'er my God or-dains is right; He nev-er will de-ceive me;
3. What-e'er my God or-dains is right; Here shall my stand be tak-en;

I will be still, what-e'er He doth, And fol-low where He guid-eth.
He leads me by the prop-er path; I know He will not leave me,
Though sor-row, need, or death be mine, Yet am I not for-sak-en;

He is my God; Though dark my road, He holds me that I
And take, con-tent, What He hath sent; His hand can turn my
My Fa-ther's care Is round me there; He holds me that I

shall not fall; Where-fore to Him I leave it all.
griefs a-way, And pa-tient-ly I wait His day.
shall not fall, And so to Him I leave it all. A-MEN.

Music from the *Common Service Book of the Lutheran Church.* Used by permission.

LIFE IN CHRIST: FAITH AND ASSURANCE

[311]

367 My Jesus, as Thou Wilt!

JEWETT: 6. 6. 6. 6. D.
Carl M. von Weber, 1820
Arr. by Joseph P. Holbrook, 1862
Har. for this book, 1953

Benjamin Schmolck, c. 1704
Trans. by Jane Laurie Borthwick, 1854

1. My Je - sus, as Thou wilt! O may Thy will be mine! In - to Thy hand of love I would my all re - sign. Through sor - row or through joy, Con - duct me as Thine own; And help me still to say, "My Lord, Thy will be done."

2. My Je - sus, as Thou wilt! Though seen through man - y a tear, Let not my star of hope Grow dim or dis - ap - pear. Since Thou on earth hast wept, And sor - rowed oft a - lone, If I must weep with Thee, My Lord, Thy will be done.

3. My Je - sus, as Thou wilt! All shall be well for me; Each chang - ing fu - ture scene I glad - ly trust with Thee. Straight to my home a - bove I trav - el calm - ly on, And sing, in life or death, "My Lord, Thy will be done." A - MEN.

LIFE IN CHRIST: FAITH AND ASSURANCE

[312]

My Hope Is Built on Nothing Less 368

Edward Mote, c. 1834

SOLID ROCK: L. M. with Refrain
William B. Bradbury, 1863

1. My hope is built on noth - ing less Than Je - sus' blood and
2. When dark-ness veils His love - ly face, I rest on His un -
3. His oath, His cov - e - nant, His blood, Sup - port me in the
4. When He shall come with trum - pet sound, Oh, may I then in

right - eous - ness; I dare not trust the sweet - est frame, But
chang - ing grace; In ev - ery high and storm - y gale, My
whelm - ing flood; When all a - round my soul gives way, He
Him be found; Dressed in His right - eous - ness a - lone, Fault -

REFRAIN

whol - ly lean on Je - sus' name.
an - chor holds with - in the veil.   On Christ, the sol - id Rock, I stand; All
then is all my hope and stay.
less to stand be - fore the throne.

oth - er ground is sink-ing sand, All oth - er ground is sink-ing sand. A - MEN.

LIFE IN CHRIST: FAITH AND ASSURANCE

How Firm a Foundation

(FIRST TUNE)

K.
Rippon's *A Selection of Hymns*, 1787; alt.

ADESTE FIDELES: 11. 11. 11. 11.
J. F. Wade's *Cantus Diversi*, 1751

1. How firm a foun-da-tion, ye saints of the Lord, Is laid for your
2. "Fear not, I am with thee, O be not dis-mayed, For I am thy
3. "When through the deep wa-ters I call thee to go, The riv-ers of
4. "The soul that on Je-sus hath leaned for re-pose, I will not, I

faith in His ex-cel-lent word! What more can He say than to
God, I will still give thee aid; I'll strength-en thee, help thee, and
sor-row shall not o-ver-flow; For I will be near thee, thy
will not de-sert to his foes; That soul, though all hell should en-

you He hath said, To you who for ref-uge to Je-sus have fled?
cause thee to stand, Up-held by My right-eous, om-nip-o-tent hand,
trou-bles to bless, And sanc-ti-fy to thee thy deep-est dis-tress,
deav-or to shake, I'll nev-er, no, nev-er, no, nev-er for-sake,

To you who for ref-uge to Je-sus have fled?
Up-held by My right-eous, om-nip-o-tent hand.
And sanc-ti-fy to thee thy deep-est dis-tress.
I'll nev-er, no, nev-er, no, nev-er for-sake." A-MEN.

LIFE IN CHRIST: FAITH AND ASSURANCE

How Firm a Foundation

369

(SECOND TUNE)

FOUNDATION: 11. 11. 11. 11.
Early American melody
Har. for this book, 1953

I Love the Lord, His Strength Is Mine

370

From Psalm 18
The Psalter, 1912

MENDON: L. M.
German melody
Arr. attributed to Samuel Dyer, 1824

1. I love the Lord, His strength is mine; He is my God, I trust His grace;
2. From God the vic - tory I re - ceive; Most per-fect is His ho - ly way;
3. For who is God, and strong to save, Be - side the Lord, our God of might?
4. Thy free sal - va - tion is my shield, My sure de-fense in ev - ery strait;

My for-tress high, my shield di - vine, My Sav-iour and my hid - ing place.
His word is tried, they who be-lieve Will find the Lord their shield and stay.
'Tis He that makes me strong and brave, The Lord who guides my steps a-right.
Thy hand up-holds me, lest I yield; Thy gen-tle-ness has made me great. A-MEN.

LIFE IN CHRIST: FAITH AND ASSURANCE

371 Ask Ye What Great Thing I Know

Johann C. Schwedler (1672-1730)
Trans. by Benjamin H. Kennedy, 1863

HENDON: 7. 7. 7. 7. 7.
H. A. César Malan, 1827

1. Ask ye what great thing I know That de - lights and
2. Who de - feats my fierc - est foes? Who con - soles my
3. Who is life in life to me? Who the death of
4. This is that great thing I know; This de - lights and

stirs me so? What the high re - ward I win? Whose the name I
sad - dest woes? Who re - vives my faint-ing heart, Heal - ing all its
death will be? Who will place me on His right, With the count-less
stirs me so: Faith in Him who died to save, Him who tri-umphed

glo - ry in? Je - sus Christ, the Cru - ci - fied.
hid - den smart? Je - sus Christ, the Cru - ci - fied.
hosts of light? Je - sus Christ, the Cru - ci - fied.
o'er the grave, Je - sus Christ, the Cru - ci - fied. A-MEN.

372 Grace and Truth Shall Mark the Way

From Psalm 25
The Psalter, 1912; alt., 1953

HOLLEY: 7. 7. 7. 7.
George Hews, 1835

1. Grace and truth shall mark the way Where the Lord His own will lead;
2. For Thy name's sake hear Thou me, For Thy mer - cy, Lord, I wait;
3. He who walks in god - ly fear In the path of truth shall go;
4. They that fear and love the Lord Shall His ho - ly friend-ship know;

LIFE IN CHRIST: FAITH AND ASSURANCE

[316]

Grace and Truth Shall Mark the Way

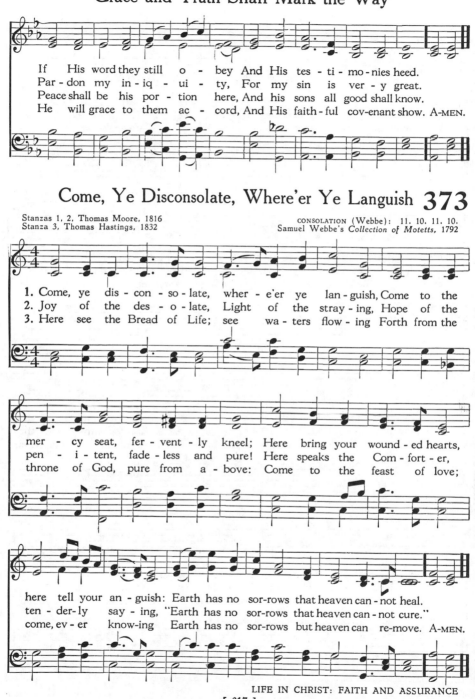

If His word they still o - bey And His tes - ti - mo - nies heed.
Par - don my in - iq - ui - ty, For my sin is ver - y great.
Peace shall be his por - tion here, And his sons all good shall know.
He will grace to them ac - cord, And His faith - ful cov - enant show. A-MEN.

Come, Ye Disconsolate, Where'er Ye Languish 373

Stanzas 1, 2, Thomas Moore, 1816
Stanza 3, Thomas Hastings, 1832

CONSOLATION (Webbe): 11. 10. 11. 10.
Samuel Webbe's *Collection of Motetts*, 1792

1. Come, ye dis - con - so - late, wher - e'er ye lan - guish, Come to the
2. Joy of the des - o - late, Light of the stray - ing, Hope of the
3. Here see the Bread of Life; see wa - ters flow - ing Forth from the

mer - cy seat, fer - vent - ly kneel; Here bring your wound - ed hearts,
pen - i - tent, fade - less and pure! Here speaks the Com - fort - er,
throne of God, pure from a - bove: Come to the feast of love;

here tell your an - guish: Earth has no sor-rows that heaven can - not heal.
ten - der - ly say - ing, "Earth has no sor-rows that heaven can - not cure."
come, ev - er know-ing Earth has no sor-rows but heaven can re-move. A-MEN.

LIFE IN CHRIST: FAITH AND ASSURANCE

374 Be Still, My Soul

From Psalm 46
Katharina von Schlegel, 1752
Trans. by Jane Laurie Borthwick, 1855

FINLANDIA: 10. 10. 10. 10. 10. 10.
Jean Sibelius, 1899
Arr. for *The Hymnal*, 1933

1. Be still, my soul: the Lord is on thy side; Bear pa-tient-ly the
2. Be still, my soul: thy God doth un-der-take To guide the fu-ture
3. Be still, my soul: the hour is has-tening on When we shall be for-

cross of grief or pain; Leave to thy God to or-der and pro-vide;
as He has the past. Thy hope, thy con-fi-dence, let noth-ing shake;
ev-er with the Lord, When dis-ap-point-ment, grief, and fear are gone,

In ev-ery change He faith-ful will re-main. Be still, my soul: thy
All now mys-te-rious shall be bright at last. Be still, my soul: the
Sor-row for-got, love's pur-est joys re-stored. Be still, my soul: when

best, thy heaven-ly Friend Through thorn-y ways leads to a joy-ful end.
waves and winds still know His voice who ruled them while He dwelt be-low.
change and tears are past, All safe and bless-ed we shall meet at last. A-MEN.

Melody used by permission of Breitkopf & Härtel, Wiesbaden; all rights reserved. Arrangement copyright 1933, by the Presbyterian Board of Christian Education. Used by permission.

LIFE IN CHRIST: FAITH AND ASSURANCE

Who Trusts in God, a Strong Abode 375

Stanza 1, Joachim Magdeburg, 1572
Stanzas 2, 3, Anon.
Trans. by Benjamin H. Kennedy, 1863
Alt. by William Walsham How, 1864

BISHOPGARTH: 8. 7. 8. 7. D.
Arthur S. Sullivan, 1897

1. Who trusts in God, a strong a-bode In heaven and earth pos-sess-es;
2. Though Sa-tan's wrath be-set our path, And world-ly scorn as-sail us,
3. In all the strife of mor-tal life, Our feet shall stand se-cure-ly:

Who looks in love to Christ a-bove, No fear his heart op-press-es.
While Thou art near we will not fear, Thy strength shall nev-er fail us.
Temp-ta-tion's hour shall lose its power, For Thou shalt guard us sure-ly.

In Thee a-lone, dear Lord, we own Sweet hope and con-so-la-tion;
Thy rod and staff shall keep us safe, And guide our steps for-ev-er;
O God, re-new, with heaven-ly dew, Our bod-y, soul and spir-it,

Our shield from foes, our balm for woes, Our great and sure sal-va-tion.
Nor shades of death, nor hell be-neath, Our souls from Thee shall sev-er.
Un-til we stand at Thy right hand, Through Je-sus' sav-ing mer-it. A-MEN.

LIFE IN CHRIST: FAITH AND ASSURANCE

376
Jesus, Keep Me Near the Cross

NEAR THE CROSS: 7. 6. 7. 6. with Refrain

Fanny Crosby, 1869

William H. Doane, 1869

1. Je - sus, keep me near the cross; There a pre - cious foun-tain, Free to all— a
2. Near the cross, a trem-bling soul, Love and mer - cy found me; There the bright and
3. Near the cross! O Lamb of God, Bring its scenes be - fore me; Help me walk from
4. Near the cross I'll watch and wait, Hop - ing, trust - ing ev - er, Till I reach the

REFRAIN

heal-ing stream—Flows from Cal-vary's moun-tain. In the cross, in the cross, Be my glo-ry
morn - ing Star Shed its beams a - round me.
day to day With its shad - ow o'er me.
gold - en strand Just be-yond the riv - er.

ev - er, Till my rap - tured soul shall find Rest be-yond the riv - er. A - MEN.

377
I to the Hills Will Lift My Eyes

From Psalm 121
The Psalter, 1912

DUNDEE (FRENCH): C. M.
Scottish Psalter, 1615

1. I to the hills will lift my eyes; O whence shall come my aid?
2. He will not let thy foot be moved, Thy Guard-ian nev - er sleeps;
3. Thy faith - ful Keep - er is the Lord, Thy Shel - ter and thy Shade;
4. From e - vil He will keep thee safe, For thee He will pro - vide;

LIFE IN CHRIST: FAITH AND ASSURANCE

[320]

I to the Hills Will Lift My Eyes

My help is from the Lord a - lone, Who heaven and earth has made.
With watch-ful and un - slum-bering care His own He safe - ly keeps.
'Neath sun or moon, by day or night, Thou shalt not be a - fraid.
Thy go - ing out, thy com - ing in, For - ev - er He will guide. A - MEN.

For alternative arrangement, see Hymn 112.

My Faith Looks Up to Thee 378

Ray Palmer, 1830

OLIVET: 6. 6. 4. 6. 6. 6. 4.
Lowell Mason, 1832

1. My faith looks up to Thee, Thou Lamb of Cal - va - ry,
2. May Thy rich grace im - part Strength to my faint - ing heart,
3. While life's dark maze I tread, And griefs a - round me spread,
4. When ends life's tran - sient dream, When death's cold, sul - len stream

Sav - iour di - vine: Now hear me while I pray, Take all my
My zeal in - spire; As Thou hast died for me, O may my
Be Thou my Guide; Bid dark - ness turn to day, Wipe sor - row's
Shall o'er me roll, Blest Sav - iour, then, in love, Fear and dis-

guilt a - way, O let me from this day Be whol - ly Thine!
love to Thee Pure, warm, and change-less be, A liv - ing fire!
tears a - way, Nor let me ev - er stray From Thee a - side.
trust re-move; O bear me safe a - bove, A ran-somed soul! A - MEN.

LIFE IN CHRIST: FAITH AND ASSURANCE

[321]

379 Come, Thou Fount of Every Blessing

Robert Robinson, 1758

NETTLETON: 8. 7. 8. 7. D.
John Wyeth, 1813

1. Come, Thou Fount of ev-ery bless-ing, Tune my heart to sing Thy grace;
2. Here I raise my Eb-en-e-zer, Hith-er by Thy help I'm come;
3. O to grace how great a debt-or Dai-ly I'm con-strained to be!

Streams of mer-cy, nev-er ceas-ing, Call for songs of loud-est praise.
And I hope, by Thy good pleas-ure, Safe-ly to ar-rive at home.
Let that grace now, like a fet-ter, Bind my wan-dering heart to Thee:

Teach me some me-lo-dious son-net, Sung by flam-ing tongues a-bove;
Je-sus sought me when a stran-ger, Wan-dering from the fold of God;
Prone to wan-der, Lord, I feel it, Prone to leave the God I love;

Praise the mount! I'm fixed up-on it, Mount of God's un-chang-ing love!
He, to res-cue me from dan-ger, In-ter-posed His pre-cious blood.
Here's my heart, O take and seal it, Seal it for Thy courts a-bove. A-MEN.

LIFE IN CHRIST: FAITH AND ASSURANCE

Saviour, Like a Shepherd Lead Us

380

Ascribed to Dorothy A. Thrupp
Hymns for the Young, 1836

BRADBURY: 8. 7. 8. 7. 8. 7.
William B. Bradbury, 1859

1. Sav - iour, like a Shep-herd lead us, Much we need Thy ten - der care;
2. Thou hast prom-ised to re - ceive us, Poor and sin - ful though we be;
3. Ear - ly let us seek Thy fa - vor; Ear - ly let us do Thy will;

In Thy pleas-ant pas-tures feed us, For our use Thy folds pre - pare:
Thou hast mer - cy to re - lieve us, Grace to cleanse, and power to free:
Bless - ed Lord and on - ly Sav - iour, With Thy love our bos-oms fill:

Bless - ed Je - sus, Bless - ed Je - sus, Thou hast bought us, Thine we are;
Bless - ed Je - sus, Bless - ed Je - sus, Ear - ly let us turn to Thee;
Bless - ed Je - sus, Bless - ed Je - sus, Thou hast loved us, love us still;

Bless - ed Je - sus, Bless-ed Je - sus, Thou hast bought us, Thine we are.
Bless - ed Je - sus, Bless-ed Je - sus, Ear - ly let us turn to Thee.
Bless - ed Je - sus, Bless-ed Je - sus, Thou hast loved us, love us still. A-MEN.

Alternative tune, "Sicilian Mariners," Hymn 79.

LIFE IN CHRIST: FAITH AND ASSURANCE

[323]

381 God Is Our Refuge and Our Strength

From Psalm 46
The Psalter, 1912

WINCHESTER OLD: C. M.
Based on Christopher Tye, 1553
In Este's Psalter, 1592

1. God is our Ref - uge and our Strength, Our ev - er - pres - ent aid,
2. Though hills a - midst the seas be cast, Though foam - ing wa - ters roar,
3. A riv - er flows whose streams make glad The cit - y of our God,
4. Since God is in the midst of her, Un - moved her walls shall stand,

And, there - fore, though the earth re - move, We will not be a - fraid;
Yea, though the might - y bil - lows shake The moun - tains on the shore.
The ho - ly place where - in the Lord Most High has His a - bode;
For God will be her ear - ly help, When trou - ble is at hand. A - MEN.

382 Not So in Haste, My Heart!

DOLOMITE CHANT: 6. 6. 6. 6.
Austrian melody
Har. by Joseph T. Cooper, 1877

Bradford Torrey, 1875

1. Not so in haste, my heart! Have faith in God and wait;
2. He nev - er com - eth late; He know - eth what is best;
3. Un - til He com - eth, rest, Nor grudge the hours that roll;
4. Are soon - est at the goal That is not gained by speed;

Al - though He lin - ger long, He nev - er comes too late.
Vex not thy - self in vain; Un - til He com - eth, rest.
The feet that wait for God Are soon - est at the goal;
Then 'hold thee still, my heart, For I shall wait His lead. A - MEN.

LIFE IN CHRIST: FAITH AND ASSURANCE

I Love to Tell the Story

Katherine Hankey, 1866
Refrain, William G. Fischer, 1869

HANKEY: 7. 6. 7. 6. D. with Refrain
William G. Fischer, 1869

1. I love to tell the sto - ry Of un - seen things a - bove, Of
2. I love to tell the sto - ry; 'Tis pleas - ant to re - peat What
3. I love to tell the sto - ry; For those who know it best Seem

Je - sus and His glo - ry, Of Je - sus and His love. I love to tell the
seems, each time I tell it, More won - der-ful - ly sweet. I love to tell the
hun - ger - ing and thirst-ing To hear it, like the rest. And when, in scenes of

sto - ry, Be - cause I know 'tis true; It sat - is - fies my long-ings
sto - ry, For some have nev - er heard The mes - sage of sal - va - tion
glo - ry, I sing the new, new song, 'Twill be the old, old sto - ry

REFRAIN

As noth-ing else could do. I love to tell the sto-ry, 'Twill be my theme in glo - ry
From God's own ho-ly Word.
That I have loved so long.

To tell the old, old sto - ry Of Je - sus and His love. A - MEN.

Words used by permission of Sybil Tremellen.

LIFE IN CHRIST: FAITH AND ASSURANCE

384 Father, in Thy Mysterious Presence Kneeling

HENLEY: 11. 10. 11. 10.
Lowell Mason, 1854
Har. for this book, 1953

Samuel Johnson, 1846

1. Fa - ther, in Thy mys - te - rious pres - ence kneel - ing,
2. Lord, we have wan - dered forth through doubt and sor - row,
3. Now, Fa - ther, now in Thy dear pres - ence kneel - ing,

Fain would our souls feel all Thy kin - dling love;
And Thou hast made each step an on - ward one;
Our spir - its yearn to feel Thy kin - dling love;

For we are weak, and need some deep re - veal - ing
And we will ev - er trust each un - known mor - row;
Now make us strong; we need Thy deep re - veal - ing

Of trust and strength and calm - ness from a - bove.
Thou wilt sus - tain us till its work is done.
Of trust and strength and calm - ness from a - bove. A-MEN.

Alternative tune. "Welwyn," Hymn 288.
LIFE IN CHRIST: PRAYER AND INTERCESSION

What a Friend We Have in Jesus

385

Joseph Scriven, c. 1855

WHAT A FRIEND: 8. 7. 8. 7. D.
C. C. Converse, 1868

1. What a Friend we have in Je - sus, All our sins and griefs to bear!
2. Have we tri - als and temp - ta - tions? Is there trou - ble an - y - where?
3. Are we weak and heav - y - lad - en, Cum-bered with a load of care?

What a priv - i - lege to car - ry Ev - ery-thing to God in prayer!
We should nev - er be dis - cour - aged: Take it to the Lord in prayer!
Pre - cious Sav - iour, still our Ref - uge— Take it to the Lord in prayer!

O what peace we of - ten for - feit, O what need-less pain we bear,
Can we find a friend so faith - ful, Who will all our sor-rows share?
Do thy friends de - spise, for - sake thee? Take it to the Lord in prayer!

All be-cause we do not car - ry Ev - ery-thing to God in prayer!
Je - sus knows our ev - ery weak - ness— Take it to the Lord in prayer!
In His arms He'll take and shield thee, Thou wilt find a sol-ace there. A-MEN.

LIFE IN CHRIST: PRAYER AND INTERCESSION

386 Approach, My Soul, the Mercy Seat

BALLERMA: C. M.
Melody by François H. Barthélémon (1741-1808)
Adapted by Robert Simpson; pub. 1833

John Newton, 1779

1. Ap - proach, my soul, the mer - cy seat, Where Je - sus an - swers prayer;
2. Thy prom - ise is my on - ly plea, With this I ven - ture nigh;
3. Bowed down be - neath a load of sin, By Sa - tan sore - ly pressed,
4. Be Thou my shield and hid - ing place, That, shel - tered near Thy side,
5. O won-drous love! to bleed and die, To bear the cross and shame,

There hum-bly fall be - fore His feet, For none can per - ish there.
Thou call - est bur-dened souls to Thee, And such, O Lord, am I.
By war with-out and fears with-in, I come to Thee for rest.
I may my fierce ac - cus - er face, And tell him Thou hast died!
That guilt - y sin - ners, such as I, Might plead Thy gra - cious name. A-MEN.

387 To God My Earnest Voice I Raise

ROCKINGHAM OLD: L. M.
Source unknown
Adapted by Edward Miller, 1790

From Psalm 142
The Psalter, 1912

1. To God my ear - nest voice I raise, To God my voice im - plor - ing prays;
2. When gloom and sor - row com-pass me, The path I take is known to Thee,
3. O Lord, my Sav - iour, now to Thee, With - out a hope be - sides, I flee,
4. Be Thou my help when trou-bles throng, For I am weak and foes are strong;

Be - fore His face my grief I show And tell my trou - ble and my woe.
And all the toils that foes do lay To snare Thy serv-ant in his way.
To Thee, my shel-ter from the strife, My por - tion in the land of life.
My cap-tive soul from pris-on bring, And thank-ful prais-es I will sing. A - MEN.

LIFE IN CHRIST: PRAYER AND INTERCESSION
[328]

O Lord Most High, with All My Heart 388

From Psalm 9
The Psalter, 1912; alt., 1953

MOZART: L. M.
Attributed to Wolfgang A. Mozart (1756-1791)

1. O Lord Most High, with all my heart Thy won-drous works I will pro-claim;
2. A might-y for-tress is our God, A ref-uge strong for all op-pressed,
3. All they, O Lord, that know Thy name Their con-fi-dence in Thee will place,
4. Sing prais-es to the Lord Most High, To Him who doth in Zi-on dwell;

I will be glad and give Thee thanks And sing the prais-es of Thy name.
A safe re-treat, where wea-ry souls In trou-blous times may sure-ly rest.
For Thou hast ne'er for-sak-en them Who ear-nest-ly have sought Thy face.
De-clare His might-y deeds a-broad, His deeds a-mong the na-tions tell. A-MEN.

Where High the Heavenly Temple Stands 389

Ascribed to Michael Bruce, c. 1764
As in *Scottish Paraphrases*, 1781

SOLDAU: L. M.
Geystliche Gesangk Buchleyn, 1524
Har. by David Evans, 1927

1. Where high the heaven-ly tem-ple stands, The house of God not made with hands,
2. He who for men their sure-ty stood, And poured on earth His pre-cious blood,
3. Though now as-cend-ed up on high, He bends on earth a broth-er's eye;
4. Our fel-low suf-fer-er yet re-tains A fel-low feel-ing of our pains;
5. In ev-ery pang that rends the heart The Man of Sor-rows had a part;
6. With bold-ness, there-fore, at the throne, Let us make all our sor-rows known;

A great High Priest our na-ture wears, The Guard-ian of man-kind ap-pears.
Pur-sues in heaven His might-y plan, The Sav-iour and the Friend of man.
Par-tak-er of the hu-man name, He knows the frail-ty of our frame.
And still re-mem-bers in the skies His tears, His ag-o-nies, and cries.
He sym-pa-thiz-es with our grief, And to the suf-fer-er sends re-lief.
And ask the aids of heaven-ly power To help us in the e-vil hour. A-MEN.

Music from *The Church Hymnary*, Revised Edition. Used by permission of Oxford University Press.

LIFE IN CHRIST: PRAYER AND INTERCESSION

390 Open My Eyes, that I May See

OPEN MY EYES: 8. 8. 9. 8. 8. 8. 8. 4.

Clara H. Scott, 1895

Clara H. Scott, 1895

1. O-pen my eyes, that I may see Glimps-es of truth Thou hast for me;
2. O-pen my ears, that I may hear Voi-ces of truth Thou send-est clear;
3. O-pen my mouth, and let me bear Glad-ly the warm truth ev-ery-where;

Place in my hands the won-der-ful key That shall un-clasp, and set me free.
And while the wave notes fall on my ear, Ev-ery-thing false will dis-ap-pear.
O-pen my heart, and let me pre-pare Love with Thy chil-dren thus to share.

Si-lent-ly now I wait for Thee, Read-y, my God, Thy will to see;
Si-lent-ly now I wait for Thee, Read-y, my God, Thy will to see;
Si-lent-ly now I wait for Thee, Read-y, my God, Thy will to see;

O-pen my eyes, il-lu-mine me, Spir-it di-vine!
O-pen my ears, il-lu-mine me, Spir-it di-vine!
O-pen my heart, il-lu-mine me, Spir-it di-vine! A-MEN.

LIFE IN CHRIST: PRAYER AND INTERCESSION

[330]

Prayer Is the Soul's Sincere Desire 391

James Montgomery, 1818

ST. AGNES: C. M.
John B. Dykes, 1866

1. Prayer is the soul's sin - cere de - sire, Un - ut - tered or ex - pressed;
2. Prayer is the bur - den of a sigh, The fall - ing of a tear,
3. Prayer is the con - trite sin - ner's voice, Re - turn - ing from his ways,
4. Prayer is the Chris-tian's vi - tal breath, The Chris-tian's na - tive air,
5. O Thou, by whom we come to God, The Life, the Truth, the Way;

The mo - tion of a hid - den fire That trem-bles in the breast.
The up - ward glanc-ing of an eye, When none but God is near.
While an - gels in their songs re - joice And cry, "Be - hold, he prays!"
His watch-word at the gates of death; He en - ters heaven with prayer.
The path of prayer Thy - self hast trod: Lord, teach us how to pray! A-MEN.

O Lord, Make Haste to Hear My Cry 392

From Psalm 141
The Psalter, 1912

CANNONS: L. M.
Georg Friedrich Handel (1685-1759)

1. O Lord, make haste to hear my cry. To Thee I call, on Thee re - ly.
2. When in the morn-ing un - to Thee I lift my voice and bring my plea,
3. When un - to Thee I look and pray With lift - ed hands at close of day,
4. Guard Thou my thoughts, I Thee im-plore, And of my lips keep Thou the door;

In - cline to me a gra-cious ear, And, when I call, in mer - cy hear.
Then let my prayer as in-cense rise To God en-throned a - bove the skies.
Then as the eve-ning sac - ri - fice Let my re - quest ac - cept-ed rise.
Nor leave my sin - ful heart to stray Where e - vil foot-steps lead the way. A-MEN.

LIFE IN CHRIST: PRAYER AND INTERCESSION

393 Thy Loving-kindness, Lord, Is Good and Free

From Psalm 69
The Psalter. 1912

ELLERS: 10. 10. 10. 10.
Edward J. Hopkins, 1869

1. Thy lov - ing - kind - ness, Lord, is good and free,
2. Need - y and sor - row - ful, to Thee I cry;
3. With joy the meek shall see my soul re - stored;
4. Let heaven a - bove His grace and glo - ry tell,

In ten - der mer - cy turn Thou un - to me;
Let Thy sal - va - tion set my soul on high;
Your heart shall live, ye saints that seek the Lord;
Let earth and sea and all that in them dwell;

Hide not Thy face from me in my dis - tress,
Then I will sing and praise Thy ho - ly name,
He helps the need - y and re - gards their cries,
Sal - va - tion to His peo - ple God will give,

In mer - cy hear my prayer, Thy serv - ant bless.
My thank - ful song Thy mer - cy shall pro - claim.
Those in dis - tress the Lord will not de - spise.
And they that love His name with Him shall live. A - MEN.

LIFE IN CHRIST: PRAYER AND INTERCESSION

In the Hour of Trial

James Montgomery, 1834; alt.

PENITENCE: 6. 5. 6. 5. D.
Spencer Lane, 1879

1. In the hour of tri - al, Je - sus, plead for me;
2. With its witch - ing pleas - ures Would this vain world charm,
3. When in dust and ash - es To the grave I sink,

Lest by base de - ni - al I de - part from Thee;
Or its sor - did treas - ures Spread to work me harm,
While heaven's glo - ry flash - es O'er the shelv - ing brink,

When Thou seest me wa - ver, With a look re - call,
Bring to my re - mem - brance Sad Geth - sem - a - ne,
On Thy truth re - ly - ing Through that mor - tal strife,

Nor for fear or fa - vor Suf - fer me to fall.
Or, in dark - er sem - blance, Cross-crowned Cal - va - ry.
Lord, re - ceive me, dy - ing, To e - ter - nal life. A - MEN.

For higher key, see Hymn 52.

LIFE IN CHRIST: PRAYER AND INTERCESSION

[333]

God Be in My Head

Sarum Primer, 1558

GOD BE IN MY HEAD: Irregular
Henry Walford Davies, 1910

God be in my head, And in my un-der-stand-ing;

God be in mine eyes, And in my look-ing; God be in my mouth,

And in my speak-ing; God be in my heart, And in my think-ing;

God be at mine end, And at my de-part-ing.

Music copyright in the U.S.A., 1910, 1938, by H. Walford Davies. Used by permission of his trustees.

396 O Gracious God, Forsake Me Not

From Psalm 71
The Psalter, 1912

MARTYRDOM (AVON): C. M.
Hugh Wilson, 1825

1. O gra-cious God, for-sake me not When I am old and gray,
2. Thy per-fect right-eous-ness, O God, The height of heaven ex-ceeds;
3. Thou who hast sent me man-y griefs Wilt yet my soul re-store;
4. O turn a-gain and com-fort me, My wan-ing strength in-crease,
5. Thou Ho-ly One of Is-ra-el, To Thee sweet songs I raise;

LIFE IN CHRIST: PRAYER AND INTERCESSION

O Gracious God, Forsake Me Not

That un-to those that fol-low me I may Thy might dis-play.
O who is like to Thee, who hast Per-formed such might-y deeds?
And out of sor-row's low-est depths Wilt bring me forth once more.
And for Thy faith-ful-ness, O God, My praise shall nev-er cease.
The soul Thou hast re-deemed from death Shall give Thee joy-ful praise. A-MEN.

More Love to Thee, O Christ
397

MORE LOVE TO THEE: 6. 4. 6. 4. 6. 6. 4. 4.

Elizabeth P. Prentiss, 1856

William H. Doane, 1868

1. More love to Thee, O Christ, More love to Thee! Hear Thou the
2. Once earth-ly joy I craved, Sought peace and rest; Now Thee a-
3. Then shall my lat-est breath Whis-per Thy praise; This be the

prayer I make On bend-ed knee; This is my ear-nest plea,
lone I seek; Give what is best: This all my prayer shall be,
part-ing cry My heart shall raise; This still its prayer shall be,

More love, O Christ, to Thee, More love to Thee, More love to Thee! A-MEN.

LIFE IN CHRIST: PRAYER AND INTERCESSION

[335]

398 Sweet Hour of Prayer

William W. Walford, c. 1842

SWEET HOUR: L. M. D.
William B. Bradbury, 1859

1. Sweet hour of prayer, sweet hour of prayer, That calls me from a world of care,
2. Sweet hour of prayer, sweet hour of prayer, Thy wings shall my pe - ti - tion bear

And bids me at my Fa-ther's throne Make all my wants and wish-es known!
To Him, whose truth and faith-ful-ness En - gage the wait-ing soul to bless.

In sea-sons of dis-tress and grief, My soul has of - ten found re - lief,
And since He bids me seek His face, Be - lieve His word and trust His grace,

And oft es-caped the tempt-er's snare, By thy re-turn, sweet hour of prayer.
I'll cast on Him my ev - ery care, And wait for thee, sweet hour of prayer. A-MEN.

LIFE IN CHRIST: PRAYER AND INTERCESSION

Love Divine, All Loves Excelling

399

BEECHER: 8. 7. 8. 7. D.

Charles Wesley, 1747

John Zundel, 1870

1. Love di - vine, all loves ex - cell - ing, Joy of heaven, to earth come down,
2. Breathe, O breathe Thy lov - ing Spir - it In - to ev - ery trou - bled breast!
3. Come, Al - might - y to de - liv - er, Let us all Thy life re - ceive;
4. Fin - ish, then, Thy new cre - a - tion; Pure and spot - less let us be;

Fix in us Thy hum - ble dwell - ing, All Thy faith - ful mer - cies crown!
Let us all in Thee in - her - it, Let us find the prom - ised rest;
Sud - den - ly re - turn, and nev - er, Nev - er - more Thy tem - ples leave.
Let us see Thy great sal - va - tion Per - fect - ly re - stored in Thee;

Je - sus, Thou art all com - pas - sion, Pure, un - bound - ed love Thou art;
Take a - way the love of sin - ning; Al - pha and O - me - ga be;
Thee we would be al - ways bless - ing, Serve Thee as Thy hosts a - bove;
Changed from glo - ry in - to glo - ry, Till in heaven we take our place,

Vis - it us with Thy sal - va - tion, En - ter ev - ery trem - bling heart.
End of faith, as its Be - gin - ning, Set our hearts at lib - er - ty.
Pray, and praise Thee with - out ceas - ing, Glo - ry in Thy per - fect love.
Till we cast our crowns be - fore Thee, Lost in won - der, love, and praise. A-MEN.

Alternative tune, "Hyfrydol," Hymn 123.

LIFE IN CHRIST: LOVE

[337]

400 O Love That Wilt Not Let Me Go

George Matheson, 1882

ST. MARGARET: 8. 8. 8. 8. 6.
Albert L. Peace, 1884

1. O Love that wilt not let me go, I rest my
2. O Light that fol-lowest all my way, I yield my
3. O Joy that seek-est me through pain, I can-not
4. O Cross that lift-est up my head, I dare not

wea-ry soul in Thee; I give Thee back the life I owe,
flick-ering torch to Thee; My heart re-stores its bor-rowed ray,
close my heart to Thee; I trace the rain-bow through the rain,
ask to fly from Thee; I lay in dust life's glo-ry dead,

That in Thine o-cean depths its flow May rich-er, full-er be.
That in Thy sun-shine's blaze its day May bright-er, fair-er be.
And feel the prom-ise is not vain That morn shall tear-less be.
And from the ground there blos-soms red Life that shall end-less be. A-MEN.

Words and music used by permission of Novello & Co., Ltd.

401 Jesus, the Very Thought of Thee

Latin, 11th century
Trans. by Edward Caswall, 1849

ST. AGNES: C. M.
John B. Dykes, 1866

1. Je - sus, the ver - y thought of Thee With sweet-ness fills my breast;
2. Nor voice can sing, nor heart can frame, Nor can the mem - ory find
3. O Hope of ev - ery con - trite heart, O joy of all the meek,
4. But what to those who find? Ah, this Nor tongue nor pen can show:
5. Je - sus, our on - ly Joy be Thou, As Thou our Prize wilt be;

LIFE IN CHRIST: LOVE

[338]

Jesus, the Very Thought of Thee

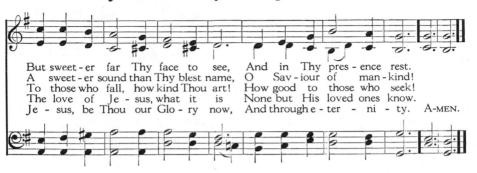

But sweet-er far Thy face to see, And in Thy pres-ence rest.
A sweet-er sound than Thy blest name, O Sav-iour of man-kind!
To those who fall, how kind Thou art! How good to those who seek!
The love of Je-sus, what it is None but His loved ones know.
Je-sus, be Thou our Glo-ry now, And through e-ter-ni-ty. A-MEN.

I Sought the Lord, and Afterward I Knew 402

Anon., 1880
Rev. in *The Pilgrim Hymnal*, 1904

PEACE: 10. 10. 10. 6.
George W. Chadwick, 1893

1. I sought the Lord, and aft-er-ward I knew He moved my
2. Thou didst reach forth Thy hand and mine en-fold; I walked and
3. I find, I walk, I love, but O the whole Of love is

soul to seek Him, seek-ing me; It was not I that
sank not on the storm-vexed sea; 'Twas not so much that
but my an-swer, Lord, to Thee! For Thou wert long be-

found, O Sav-iour true; No, I was found of Thee.
I on Thee took hold As Thou, dear Lord, on me.
fore-hand with my soul; Al-ways Thou lov-edst me. A-MEN.

LIFE IN CHRIST: LOVE

403 Tell Me the Old, Old Story

Katherine Hankey, 1866

EVANGEL: 7. 6. 7. 6. D. with Refrai
William H. Doane, 1870

1. Tell me the old, old sto - ry Of un - seen things a - bove, Of Je - sus
2. Tell me the sto - ry slow - ly, That I may take it in— That won-der-
3. Tell me the sto - ry soft - ly, With ear - nest tones and grave; Re - mem-ber,

and His glo - ry, Of Je - sus and His love. Tell me the sto - ry
ful re - demp-tion, God's rem-e - dy for sin. Tell me the sto - ry
I'm the sin - ner Whom Je - sus came to save. Tell me the sto - ry

sim - ply, As to a lit - tle child, For I am weak and wea - ry,
of - ten, For I for - get so soon; The ear - ly dew of morn-ing
al - ways, If you would real-ly be, In an - y time of trou - ble,

REFRAIN

And help - less and de - filed.
Has passed a - way at noon. Tell me the old, old sto - ry, Tell me the
A com - fort - er to me.

old, old sto - ry, Tell me the old, old sto - ry Of Je - sus and His love. A-MEN.

Words used by permission of Sybil Tremellen.
LIFE IN CHRIST: LOVE   [340]

Jesus, Thy Boundless Love to Me

404

Paul Gerhardt, 1653
Trans. by John Wesley, 1739; alt.

ST. CATHERINE: 8. 8. 8. 8. 8. 8.
Henri F. Hemy, 1865
Alt. by James G. Walton, 1871

1. Je - sus, Thy bound - less love to me No thought can
2. O grant that noth - ing in my soul May dwell, but
3. O Love, how gra - cious is Thy way! All fear be -

reach, no tongue de - clare; O knit my thank - ful heart to Thee,
Thy pure love a - lone; O may Thy love pos - sess me whole,
fore Thy pres - ence flies; Care, an - guish, sor - row, melt a - way,

And reign with - out a ri - val there! Thine whol - ly, Thine a -
My joy, my treas - ure, and my crown! All cold - ness from my
Wher - e'er Thy heal - ing beams a - rise. O Je - sus, noth - ing

lone, I'd live, My - self to Thee en - tire - ly give.
heart re - move; May ev - ery act, word, thought, be love.
may I see, Noth - ing de - sire, or seek, but Thee. A - MEN.

LIFE IN CHRIST: LOVE

405 My Jesus, I Love Thee

GORDON: 11. 11. 11. 11.
Adoniram J. Gordon, 1894
Har. alt., 1953

William R. Featherstone, 1864

1. My Je - sus, I love Thee, I know Thou art mine;
2. I love Thee, be - cause Thou hast first lov - ed me,
3. In man - sions of glo - ry and end - less de - light,

For Thee all the fol - lies of sin I re - sign;
And pur - chased my par - don on Cal - va - ry's tree,
I'll ev - er a - dore Thee in heav - en so bright;

My gra - cious Re - deem - er, my Sav - iour art Thou;
I love Thee for wear - ing the thorns on Thy brow;
I'll sing with the glit - ter - ing crown on my brow,

If ev - er I loved Thee, my Je - sus, 'tis now. A-MEN.

LIFE IN CHRIST: LOVE

[342]

My Heart Is Resting, O My God

406

Anna Laetitia Waring, 1850

PENTATONE: C. M. D.
Henry Walford Davies, 1923

1. My heart is rest-ing, O my God, I will give thanks and sing;
2. I have a her-it-age of joy, That yet I must not see;
3. My heart is rest-ing, O my God, My heart is in Thy care;

My heart is at the se-cret source Of ev-ery pre-cious thing.
But the hand that bled to make it mine Is keep-ing it for me.
I hear the voice of joy and health Re-sound-ing ev-ery-where.

I thirst for springs of heaven-ly life, And here all day they rise;
And a new song is in my mouth, To long-loved mu-sic set:
"Thou art my por-tion, saith my soul," Ten thou-sand voi-ces say,

I seek the treas-ure of Thy love, And close at hand it lies.
"Glo-ry to Thee for all the grace I have not tast-ed yet."
And the mu-sic of their glad A-men Will nev-er die a-way. A-MEN.

Words copyright by the author's heirs. Music from *A Students' Hymnal*; used by permission of Oxford University Press.

LIFE IN CHRIST: JOY

407 Rejoice, Ye Pure in Heart

Edward H. Plumptre, 1865

MARION: S. M. with Refrain
Arthur H. Messiter, 1883

1. Re - joice, ye pure in heart, Re - joice, give thanks, and sing:
2. Still lift your stand - ard high, Still march in firm ar - ray;
3. Yes, on through life's long path, Still chant - ing as ye go;
4. Then on, ye pure in heart, Re - joice, give thanks, and sing;

Your fes - tal ban - ner wave on high, The cross of Christ your King.
As war - riors through the dark - ness toil Till dawns the gold - en day.
From youth to age, by night and day, In glad - ness and in woe.
Your fes - tal ban - ner wave on high, The cross of Christ your King.

REFRAIN

Re - joice, re - joice, Re - joice, give thanks, and sing! A-MEN.

Re - joice, re - joice,

408 Come, We That Love the Lord

Isaac Watts, 1709; alt.

ST. THOMAS: S. M.
Williams' Psalmody, 1770

1. Come, we that love the Lord, And let our joys be known;
2. Let those re - fuse to sing Who nev - er knew our God;
3. The men of grace have found Glo - ry be - gun be - low;
4. The hill of Zi - on yields A thou - sand sa - cred sweets
5. Then let our songs a - bound, And ev - ery tear be dry;

LIFE IN CHRIST: JOY

[344]

Come, We That Love the Lord

Join in a song with sweet ac-cord, And thus sur-round the throne.
But chil-dren of the heaven-ly King Should speak their joys a - broad.
Ce - les-tial fruits on earth-ly ground From faith and hope may grow.
Be - fore we reach the heaven-ly fields, Or walk the gold-en streets.
We're march-ing through Em-man-uel's ground To fair - er worlds on high. A-MEN.

My God, I Thank Thee

409

Adelaide Anne Procter, 1858

WENTWORTH: 8. 4. 8. 4. 8. 4.
Frederick C. Maker, 1876

1. My God, I thank Thee, who hast made The earth so bright,
2. I thank Thee, too, that Thou hast made Joy to a - bound;
3. I thank Thee, Lord, that Thou hast kept The best in store;

So full of splen - dor and of joy, Beau - ty and light;
So man - y gen - tle thoughts and deeds Cir - cling us round,
We have e - nough, yet not too much To long for more:

So man - y glo - rious things are here, No - ble and right.
That in the dark - est spot of earth Some love is found.
A yearn - ing for a deep - er peace Not known be - fore. A-MEN.

Music copyright by The Psalms and Hymns Trust. Used by permission.

LIFE IN CHRIST: JOY

410 The King of Glory Standeth

GOSTERWOOD: 7. 6. 7. 6. D.
Traditional English melody
Arr. by R. Vaughan Williams, 1906

Charitie Lees de Chenez, 1867

1. The King of Glo-ry stand-eth Be-side the heart of sin;
2. At times, with sud-den glo-ry, He speaks, and all is done;
3. O Christ, Thy love is might-y; Long-suf-fering is Thy grace;

His might-y voice com-mand-eth The rag-ing waves with-in;
With-out one stroke of bat-tle The vic-to-ry is won,
And glo-rious is the splen-dor That beam-eth from Thy face.

The floods of deep-est an-guish Roll back-ward at His will,
While we, with joy be-hold-ing, Can scarce be-lieve it true
Our hearts up-leap in glad-ness When we be-hold that love,

As o'er the storm a-ris-eth His man-date, "Peace, be still."
That e'en our king-ly Je-sus Can form such hearts a-new.
As we go sing-ing on-ward, To dwell with Thee a-bove. A-MEN.

Music from *Songs of Praise*, Enlarged Edition. Used by permission of Oxford University Press.
LIFE IN CHRIST: JOY

Take the Name of Jesus with You

411

PRECIOUS NAME: 8. 7. 8. 7. with Refrain
William H. Doane, 1871
Har. for this book, 1954

Lydia Baxter, 1870

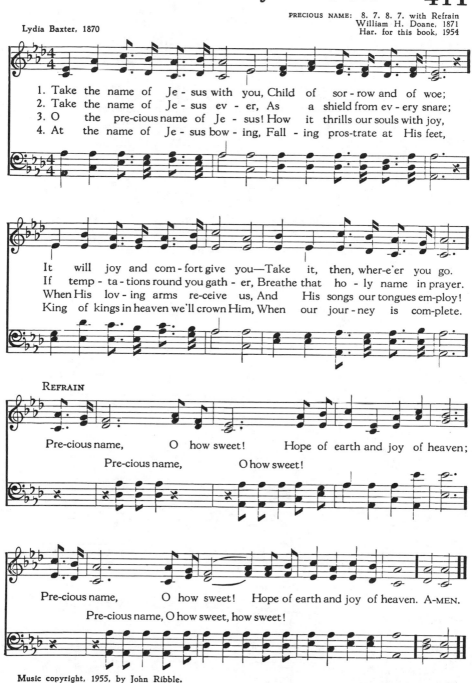

1. Take the name of Je-sus with you, Child of sor-row and of woe;
2. Take the name of Je-sus ev-er, As a shield from ev-ery snare;
3. O the pre-cious name of Je-sus! How it thrills our souls with joy,
4. At the name of Je-sus bow-ing, Fall-ing pros-trate at His feet,

It will joy and com-fort give you—Take it, then, wher-e'er you go.
If temp-ta-tions round you gath-er, Breathe that ho-ly name in prayer.
When His lov-ing arms re-ceive us, And His songs our tongues em-ploy!
King of kings in heaven we'll crown Him, When our jour-ney is com-plete.

REFRAIN

Pre-cious name, O how sweet! Hope of earth and joy of heaven;
Pre-cious name, O how sweet!

Pre-cious name, O how sweet! Hope of earth and joy of heaven. A-MEN.
Pre-cious name, O how sweet, how sweet!

Music copyright, 1955, by John Ribble.

LIFE IN CHRIST: JOY

412 The Lord I Will at All Times Bless

From Psalm 34
The Psalter, 1912

AMES: L. M.
Sigismund Neukomm (1778-1858)

1. The Lord I will at all times bless, My mouth His prais-es shall ex-press;
2. O mag-ni-fy the Lord with me, Let us to praise His name a-gree;
3. Who look to Him shall walk in light, With joy their fa-ces shall be bright.
4. A-round His saints as watch and ward En-camps the an-gel of the Lord;

In Him shall all my boast-ing be, While all the meek re-joice with me.
I sought the Lord, He an-swered me, And from my fears He set me free.
Dis-tressed, they cried; the Lord a-rose And saved them out of all their woes.
That God is good, O taste and see, Who trusts in Him shall bless-ed be. A-MEN.

413 I Waited for the Lord My God

From Psalm 40
The Psalter, 1912

ABRIDGE: C. M.
Isaac Smith, c. 1770

1. I wait-ed for the Lord my God, Yea, pa-tient-ly drew near,
2. He took me from de-struc-tion's pit, From out the mir-y clay;
3. A new and joy-ful song of praise My thank-ful heart He taught,
4. And man-y who be-hold how good The Lord has been to me

And He at length in-clined to me, My plead-ing cry to hear.
He set my feet up-on a rock, And stead-fast made my way.
A song of glo-ry to our God For all that He has wrought.
Shall learn to fear, and in His name Their trust hence-forth shall be. A-MEN.

LIFE IN CHRIST: JOY

Jesus, Priceless Treasure

Johann Franck, 1650
Trans. by Catherine Winkworth, 1863

JESU, MEINE FREUDE: 6. 6. 5. 6. 6. 5. 7. 8. 6.
Crüger's *Praxis Pietatis Melica*, 1653
Har. by Johann Sebastian Bach, 1723

1. Je - sus, price - less treas - ure, Source of pur - est pleas - ure,
2. In Thine arm I rest me; Foes who would mo - lest me
3. Hence, all thoughts of sad - ness! For the Lord of glad - ness,

Tru-est friend to me; Long my heart hath pant - ed, Till it well-nigh
Can-not reach me here. Though the earth be shak - ing, Ev - ery heart be
Je - sus, en - ters in: Those who love the Fa - ther, Though the storms may

faint - ed, Thirst-ing af - ter Thee. Thine I am, O spot - less Lamb,
quak - ing, God dis - pels our fear; Sin and hell in con - flict fell
gath - er, Still have peace with - in; Yea, what-e'er we here must bear,

I will suf - fer nought to hide Thee, Ask for nought be - side Thee.
With their heav-iest storms as- sail us: Je - sus will not fail us.
Still in Thee lies pur - est pleas - ure, Je - sus, price-less treas - ure! A-MEN.

LIFE IN CHRIST: JOY

[349]

415 O Morning Star, How Fair and Bright

Philipp Nicolai, 1599
Trans. by Catherine Winkworth, 1863

FRANKFORT: 8. 8. 7. 8. 8. 7. 4. 8. 4. 8.
Philipp Nicolai, 1599
Har. by Johann Sebastian Bach (1685-1750)

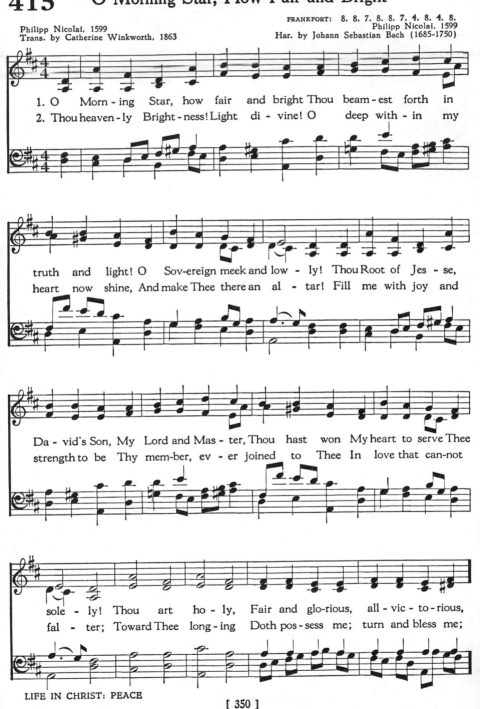

1. O Morn-ing Star, how fair and bright Thou beam-est forth in truth and light! O Sov-ereign meek and low-ly! Thou Root of Jes-se, Da-vid's Son, My Lord and Mas-ter, Thou hast won My heart to serve Thee sole-ly! Thou art ho-ly, Fair and glo-rious, all-vic-to-rious,

2. Thou heaven-ly Bright-ness! Light di-vine! O deep with-in my heart now shine, And make Thee there an al-tar! Fill me with joy and strength to be Thy mem-ber, ev-er joined to Thee In love that can-not fal-ter; Toward Thee long-ing Doth pos-sess me; turn and bless me;

LIFE IN CHRIST: PEACE

[350]

O Morning Star, How Fair and Bright

Rich in bless - ing, Rule and might o'er all pos - sess - ing.
Here in sad - ness Eye and heart long for Thy glad - ness! A-MEN.

Dear Lord and Father of Mankind

416

John Greenleaf Whittier, 1872

REST: 8. 6. 8. 8. 6.
Frederick C. Maker, 1887

1. Dear Lord and Fa - ther of man-kind, For - give our fool - ish ways;
2. In sim - ple trust like theirs who heard, Be - side the Syr - ian sea,
3. O Sab - bath rest by Gal - i - lee, O calm of hills a - bove,
4. Drop Thy still dews of qui - et - ness, Till all our striv-ings cease;
5. Breathe through the heats of our de - sire Thy cool-ness and Thy balm;

Re - clothe us in our right - ful mind, In pur - er lives Thy
The gra - cious call - ing of the Lord, Let us, like them, with -
Where Je - sus knelt to share with Thee The si - lence of e -
Take from our souls the strain and stress, And let our or - dered
Let sense be dumb, let flesh re - tire; Speak through the earth-quake,

serv - ice find, In deep - er rev - erence, praise.
out a word Rise up and fol - low Thee.
ter - ni - ty, In - ter - pret - ed by love!
lives con - fess The beau - ty of Thy peace.
wind, and fire, O still, small voice of calm! A - MEN.

Words used by permission of Houghton Mifflin Company, authorized publishers. Music copyright by The Psalms & Hymns Trust. Used by permission.

LIFE IN CHRIST: PEACE

417   In Heavenly Love Abiding

NYLAND: 7. 6. 7. 6. D.
Traditional Finnish melody
Har. by David Evans, 1927

Anna Laetitia Waring, 1850

1. In heaven-ly love a - bid - ing, No change my heart shall fear,
2. Wher - ev - er He may guide me, No want shall turn me back;
3. Green pas - tures are be - fore me, Which yet I have not seen;

And safe is such con - fid - ing, For noth - ing chan-ges here.
My shep - herd is be - side me, And noth - ing can I lack.
Bright skies will soon be o'er me, Where dark - est clouds have been.

The storm may roar with - out me, My heart may low be laid;
His wis - dom ev - er wak - eth, His sight is nev - er dim;
My hope I can - not meas - ure, The path to life is free;

But God is round a - bout me, And can I be dis-mayed?
He knows the way He tak - eth, And I will walk with Him.
My Sav - iour has my treas - ure, And He will walk with me. A-MEN.

Words copyright by the author's heirs. Music from *The Church Hymnary*, Revised Edition; used by permission of Oxford University Press.
Alternative tunes. "Meirionydd," Hymn 200, and "Bentley," opposite page.
LIFE IN CHRIST: PEACE

Sometimes a Light Surprises

418

William Cowper, 1779

BENTLEY: 7. 6. 7. 6. D.
John Hullah, 1867

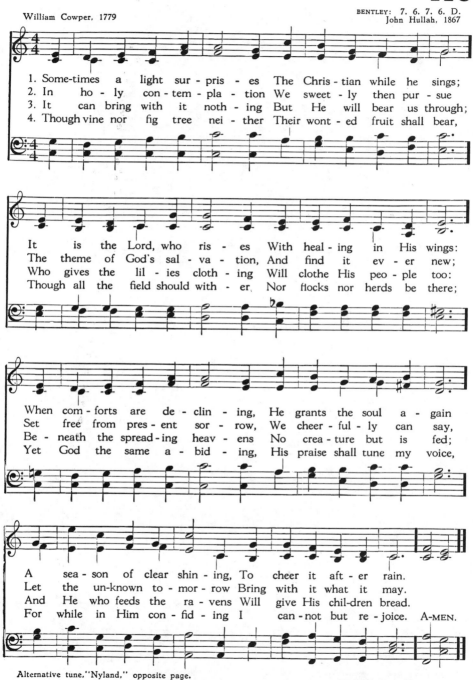

1. Some-times a light sur-pris - es The Chris - tian while he sings;
2. In ho - ly con - tem - pla - tion We sweet - ly then pur - sue
3. It can bring with it noth - ing But He will bear us through;
4. Though vine nor fig tree nei - ther Their wont - ed fruit shall bear,

It is the Lord, who ris - es With heal - ing in His wings:
The theme of God's sal - va - tion, And find it ev - er new;
Who gives the lil - ies cloth - ing Will clothe His peo - ple too:
Though all the field should with - er, Nor flocks nor herds be there;

When com - forts are de - clin - ing, He grants the soul a - gain
Set free from pres - ent sor - row, We cheer - ful - ly can say,
Be - neath the spread-ing heav - ens No crea - ture but is fed;
Yet God the same a - bid - ing, His praise shall tune my voice,

A sea - son of clear shin - ing, To cheer it aft - er rain.
Let the un-known to - mor - row Bring with it what it may.
And He who feeds the ra - vens Will give His chil-dren bread.
For while in Him con - fid - ing I can - not but re - joice. A-MEN.

Alternative tune, "Nyland," opposite page.

LIFE IN CHRIST: PEACE

419 From Every Stormy Wind That Blows

Hugh Stowell, 1828, 1831; alt.

RETREAT: L. M.
Thomas Hastings, 1842

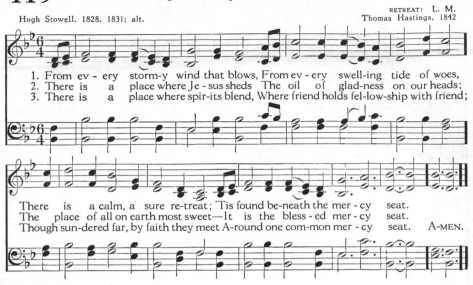

1. From ev - ery storm-y wind that blows, From ev - ery swell-ing tide of woes,
2. There is a place where Je - sus sheds The oil of glad-ness on our heads;
3. There is a place where spir-its blend, Where friend holds fel-low-ship with friend;

There is a calm, a sure re-treat; 'Tis found be-neath the mer - cy seat.
The place of all on earth most sweet—It is the bless - ed mer - cy seat.
Though sun-dered far, by faith they meet A-round one com-mon mer - cy seat. A-MEN.

420 Peace, Perfect Peace, in This Dark World of Sin?

PAX TECUM: 10. 10.
George T. Caldbeck, 1877
Arr. by Charles J. Vincent, 1877

Edward H. Bickersteth, 1875

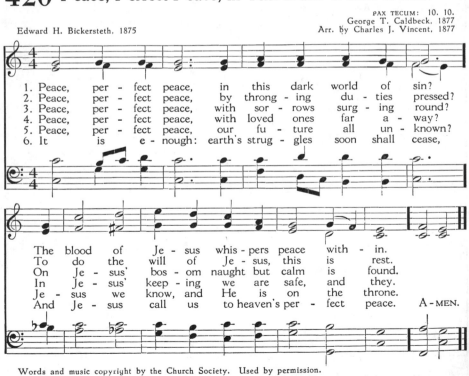

1. Peace, per - fect peace, in this dark world of sin?
2. Peace, per - fect peace, by throng - ing du - ties pressed?
3. Peace, per - fect peace, with sor - rows surg - ing round?
4. Peace, per - fect peace, with loved ones far a - way?
5. Peace, per - fect peace, our fu - ture all un - known?
6. It is e - nough: earth's strug - gles soon shall cease,

The blood of Je - sus whis - pers peace with - in.
To do the will of Je - sus, this is rest.
On Je - sus' bos - om naught but calm is found.
In Je - sus' keep - ing we are safe, and they.
Je - sus we know, and He is on the throne.
And Je - sus call us to heaven's per - fect peace. A-MEN.

Words and music copyright by the Church Society. Used by permission.
LIFE IN CHRIST: PEACE

They Cast Their Nets in Galilee 421

William Alexander Percy, 1924; alt.

GEORGETOWN: C. M.
David McK. Williams, 1941

In unison

1. They cast their nets in Gal-i-lee Just off the hills of brown;
2. Con-tent-ed, peace - ful fish-er-men, Be - fore they ev - er knew
3. Young John who trimmed the flap-ping sail, Home-less, in Pat-mos died.
4. The peace of God, it is no peace, But strife closed in the sod.

Such hap-py, sim - ple fish-er-folk, Be - fore the Lord came down.
The peace of God that filled their hearts Brim - ful, and broke them too.
Pe - ter, who hauled the teem-ing net, Head down was cru - ci - fied.
Yet, broth-ers, pray for but one thing—The mar-velous peace of God. A-MEN.

Words copyright, 1924. Used by permission of LeRoy P. Percy. Music copyright, 1943, by The Church Pension Fund. Used by permission.

The Steps of Those Whom He Approves 422

From Psalm 37
The Psalter, 1912

DOWNS: C. M.
Lowell Mason, 1832
Har. for this book, 1953

1. The steps of those whom He ap-proves Are or-dered by the Lord;
2. I have not seen, though since my youth Full man - y years have fled,
3. The chil-dren of the mer - ci - ful Find bless-ings kept in store;
4. Wait on the Lord and keep His way, And then, by Him ap - proved,
5. Mark well the per - fect, up-right man, As still his years in - crease;

And though they fall, held by His hand, They yet shall be re - stored.
The saint for-sak - en, nor be-held His chil-dren beg - ging bread.
De - part from e - vil and do good, And live for-ev - er - more.
Thy her - it - age shall still re-main When sin - ners are re - moved.
Be - hold his life, and thou shalt see His jour-ney end in peace. A - MEN.

LIFE IN CHRIST: PEACE

423 Thou Hidden Source of Calm Repose

Charles Wesley, 1749

ST. PETERSBURG: 8. 8. 8. 8. 8. 8.
Dimitri S. Bortniansky, 1825

1. Thou hid - den Source of calm re - pose, Thou all - suf-
2. Thy might - y name sal - va - tion is, And keeps my
3. Je - sus, my All in all Thou art: My rest in
4. In want my plen - ti - ful sup - ply, In weak - ness

fi - cient Love di - vine, My help and ref - uge from my foes,
hap - py soul a - bove: Com - fort it brings, and power, and peace,
toil, my ease in pain, The heal - ing of my bro - ken heart,
my al - might - y power, In bonds my per - fect lib - er - ty,

Se - cure I am while Thou art mine; And lo! from sin, and
And joy, and ev - er - last - ing love: To me, with Thy great
In war my peace, in loss my gain, My smile be - neath the
My light in Sa - tan's dark - est hour, In grief my joy un-

grief, and shame, I hide me, Je - sus, in Thy name.
name, are given Par - don and ho - li - ness and heaven.
ty - rant's frown, In shame my glo - ry and my crown,
speak - a - ble, My life in death: my All in all. A - MEN.

LIFE IN CHRIST: PEACE

[356]

O What Their Joy and Their Glory Must Be 424

Pierre Abélard (1079-1142)
Trans. by John Mason Neale, 1854; alt.

O QUANTA QUALIA: 10. 10. 10. 10.
La Feillée's *Méthode du plain-chant*, 1808

1. O what their joy and their glory must be,
Those end-less Sab-baths the bless-ed ones see;
Crown for the val-iant, to wea-ry ones rest;
God shall be All, and in all ev-er blest.

2. Tru-ly Je-ru-sa-lem name we that shore,
"Vi-sion of Peace," that brings joy ev-er-more;
Wish and ful-fill-ment can sev-ered be ne'er,
Nor the thing prayed for come short of the prayer.

3. We, where no trou-ble dis-trac-tion can bring,
Safe-ly the an-thems of Zi-on shall sing;
While for Thy grace, Lord, their voi-ces of praise
Thy bless-ed peo-ple shall ev-er-more raise.

4. Low be-fore Him with our prais-es we fall,
Of whom, and in whom, and through whom are all;
Of whom, the Fa-ther; and through whom, the Son;
In whom, the Spir-it, with these ev-er One.

A-MEN.

LIFE IN CHRIST: THE LIFE EVERLASTING

[357]

425 For All the Saints Who from Their Labors Rest

(FIRST TUNE)

William Walsham How, 1864

SINE NOMINE: 10. 10. 10. 4.
R. Vaughan Williams, 1906; alt., 1927

In unison

1. For all the saints who from their la-bors rest, Who Thee by faith be-
2. Thou wast their Rock, their For-tress, and their Might; Thou, Lord, their Cap-tain
3. O may Thy sol - diers, faith-ful, true, and bold, Fight as the saints who
4. O blest com-mun - ion, fel - low-ship di - vine! We fee-bly strug - gle,
5. And when the fight is fierce, the war-fare long, Steals on the ear the
6. From earth's wide bounds, from o-cean's far-thest coast, Through gates of pearl streams

fore the world con-fessed, Thy name, O Je - sus, be for - ev - er blest.
in the well-fought fight; Thou, in the dark - ness drear, their one true Light.
no - bly fought of old, And win with them the vic - tor's crown of gold.
they in glo - ry shine; Yet all are one in Thee, for all are Thine.
dis - tant tri-umph song, And hearts are brave a - gain, and arms are strong.
in the count-less host, Sing - ing to Fa - ther, Son, and Ho - ly Ghost,

Al - le - lu - ia! Al - le - lu - ia! A-MEN.

Music from *The Church Hymnary*, Revised Edition. Used by permission of Oxford University Press.
LIFE IN CHRIST: THE LIFE EVERLASTING

For All the Saints Who from Their Labors Rest 425

(SECOND TUNE)

William Walsham How, 1864

SARUM: 10. 10. 10. 4.
Joseph Barnby, 1868

1. For all the saints who from their la-bors rest, Who Thee by
2. Thou wast their Rock, their For-tress, and their Might; Thou, Lord, their
3. O may Thy sol-diers, faith-ful, true, and bold, Fight as the
4. O blest com-mun-ion, fel-low-ship di-vine! We fee-bly
5. And when the fight is fierce, the war-fare long, Steals on the
6. From earth's wide bounds, from o-cean's far-thest coast, Through gates of

faith be-fore the world con-fessed, Thy name, O Je-sus,
Cap-tain in the well-fought fight; Thou, in the dark-ness
saints who no-bly fought of old, And win with them the
strug-gle, they in glo-ry shine; Yet all are one in
ear the dis-tant tri-umph song, And hearts are brave a-
pearl streams in the count-less host, Sing-ing to Fa-ther,

be for-ev-er blest. Al-le-lu-ia! Al-le-lu-ia!
drear, their one true Light. Al-le-lu-ia! Al-le-lu-ia!
vic-tor's crown of gold. Al-le-lu-ia! Al-le-lu-ia!
Thee, for all are Thine. Al-le-lu-ia! Al-le-lu-ia!
gain, and arms are strong. Al-le-lu-ia! Al-le-lu-ia!
Son, and Ho-ly Ghost, Al-le-lu-ia! Al-le-lu-ia! A-MEN.

LIFE IN CHRIST: THE LIFE EVERLASTING

426 Hark! Hark, My Soul!

Frederick W. Faber, 1854; alt.

PILGRIMS (Smart): 11. 10. 11. 10. with Refrain
Henry Smart, 1868

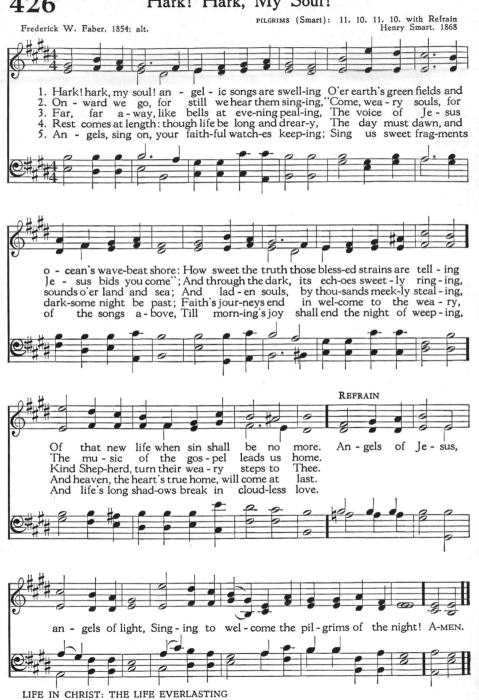

1. Hark! hark, my soul! an - gel - ic songs are swell-ing O'er earth's green fields and
2. On - ward we go, for still we hear them sing-ing, "Come, wea - ry souls, for
3. Far, far a - way, like bells at eve-ning peal-ing, The voice of Je - sus
4. Rest comes at length: though life be long and drear-y, The day must dawn, and
5. An - gels, sing on, your faith-ful watch-es keep-ing; Sing us sweet frag-ments

o - cean's wave-beat shore: How sweet the truth those bless-ed strains are tell - ing
Je - sus bids you come"; And through the dark, its ech-oes sweet-ly ring-ing,
sounds o'er land and sea; And lad - en souls, by thou-sands meek-ly steal-ing,
dark-some night be past; Faith's jour-neys end in wel-come to the wea - ry,
of the songs a - bove, Till morn-ing's joy shall end the night of weep-ing,

REFRAIN

Of that new life when sin shall be no more. An - gels of Je - sus,
The mu - sic of the gos - pel leads us home.
Kind Shep-herd, turn their wea - ry steps to Thee.
And heaven, the heart's true home, will come at last.
And life's long shad-ows break in cloud-less love.

an - gels of light, Sing - ing to wel - come the pil - grims of the night! A-MEN.

LIFE IN CHRIST: THE LIFE EVERLASTING

Ten Thousand Times Ten Thousand

427

Henry Alford, 1867; alt.

ALFORD: 7. 6. 8. 6. D.
John B. Dykes, 1875

1. Ten thou-sand times ten thou-sand In spar-kling rai-ment bright,
2. What rush of al-le-lu-ias Fills all the earth and sky!
3. O then what rap-tured greet-ings On Ca-naan's hap-py shore;
4. Bring near Thy great sal-va-tion, Thou Lamb for sin-ners slain;

The ar-mies of the ran-somed saints Throng up the steeps of light;
What ring-ing of a thou-sand harps Be-speaks the tri-umph nigh!
What meet-ing there of part-ed friends Where part-ings are no more!
Fill up the roll of Thine e-lect, Then take Thy power, and reign;

'Tis fin-ished, all is fin-ished, Their fight with death and sin:
O day, for which cre-a-tion And all its tribes were made;
Then eyes with joy shall spar-kle, That brimmed with tears of late;
Ap-pear, De-sire of na-tions, Thine ex-iles long for home;

Fling o-pen wide the gold-en gates, And let the vic-tors in.
O joy, for all its for-mer woes A thou-sand-fold re-paid!
Or-phans no long-er fa-ther-less, Nor wid-ows des-o-late.
Show in the heaven Thy prom-ised sign; Thou Prince and Sav-iour, come. A-MEN.

LIFE IN CHRIST: THE LIFE EVERLASTING

[361]

428 Jerusalem the Golden

Bernard of Cluny, 12th century
Trans. by John Mason Neale (1818-1866)

EWING: 7. 6. 7. 6. D.
Alexander Ewing, 1853

1. Je - ru - sa - lem the gold - en, With milk and hon - ey blest,
2. They stand, those halls of Zi - on, All ju - bi - lant with song,
3. There is the throne of Da - vid; And there, from care re - leased,
4. O sweet and bless - ed coun - try, The home of God's e - lect!

Be - neath thy con - tem - pla - tion Sink heart and voice op - pressed.
And bright with man - y an an - gel, And all the mar - tyr throng.
The song of them that tri - umph, The shout of them that feast;
O sweet and bless - ed coun - try That ea - ger hearts ex - pect!

I know not, O I know not, What joys a - wait us there;
The Prince is ev - er in them, The day - light is se - rene;
And they who with their Lead - er Have con - quered in the fight,
Je - sus, in mer - cy bring us To that dear land of rest;

What ra - dian - cy of glo - ry, What bliss be - yond com - pare.
The pas - tures of the bless - ed Are decked in glo - rious sheen.
For - ev - er and for - ev - er Are clad in robes of white.
Who art, with God the Fa - ther And Spir - it, ev - er blest. A-MEN.

For Thee, O Dear, Dear Country 429

Bernard of Cluny, 12th century; trans. by John Mason Neale (1818-1866)

1. For thee, O dear, dear country,
   Mine eyes their vigils keep;
   For very love, beholding
   Thy happy name, they weep:
   The mention of thy glory
   Is unction to the breast,
   And medicine in sickness,
   And love, and life, and rest.

2. O one, O only mansion!
   O paradise of joy,
   Where tears are ever banished,
   And smiles have no alloy!

The cross is all thy splendor,
The Crucified thy praise;
His laud and benediction
Thy ransomed people raise.

3. Thou hast no shore, fair ocean!
   Thou hast no time, bright day!
   Dear fountain of refreshment
   To pilgrims far away!
   Upon the Rock of Ages
   They raise the holy tower;
   Thine is the victor's laurel
   And thine the golden dower. AMEN.

This hymn may be sung to the tune "Ewing," on opposite page.

Brief Life Is Here Our Portion 430

Bernard of Cluny, 12th century; trans. by John Mason Neale (1818-1866)

1. Brief life is here our portion,
   Brief sorrow, short-lived care,
   The life that knows no ending,
   The tearless life, is there.
   O happy retribution!
   Short toil, eternal rest;
   For mortals and for sinners
   A mansion with the blest!

2. There grief is turned to pleasure,
   Such pleasure as below
   No human voice can utter,
   No human heart can know.

And now we fight the battle,
But then shall wear the crown
Of full and everlasting
And passionless renown.

3. The morning shall awaken,
   The shadows flee away,
   And each true-hearted servant
   Shall shine as doth the day.
   There God, our King and portion,
   In fullness of His grace,
   We then shall see forever,
   And worship face to face. AMEN.

This hymn may be sung to the tune "Ewing," on opposite page.

LIFE IN CHRIST: THE LIFE EVERLASTING

O Where Are Kings and Empires Now 431

ST. ANNE: C. M.
Ascribed to William Croft
Supplement to the New Version, 1708

Arthur Cleveland Coxe, 1839

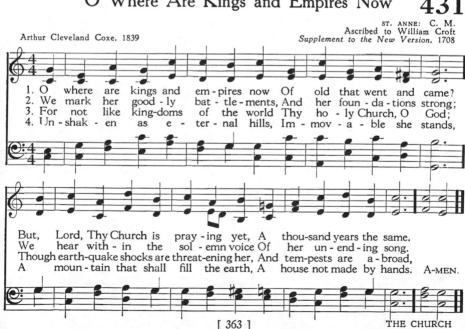

1. O where are kings and em-pires now Of old that went and came?
2. We mark her good-ly bat-tle-ments, And her foun-da-tions strong;
3. For not like king-doms of the world Thy ho-ly Church, O God;
4. Un-shak-en as e-ter-nal hills, Im-mov-a-ble she stands,

But, Lord, Thy Church is pray-ing yet, A thou-sand years the same.
We hear with-in the sol-emn voice Of her un-end-ing song.
Though earth-quake shocks are threat-ening her, And tem-pests are a-broad,
A moun-tain that shall fill the earth, A house not made by hands. A-MEN.

THE CHURCH

432 Built on the Rock

Nicolai F. S. Grundtvig, 1837
Trans. by Carl Doving, 1909

BUILT ON THE ROCK: 8. 8. 8. 8. 8. 8. 8. 8.
Ludvig M. Lindeman (1812-1887)

1. Built on the Rock the Church doth stand, E - ven when stee - ples are
2. Sure - ly in tem - ples made with hands, God, the Most High, is not
3. We are God's house of liv - ing stones, Build-ed for His hab - i -
4. Now we may gath - er with our King; E'en in the low - li - est
5. Still we our earth - ly tem - ples rear, That we may her - ald His

fall - ing; Crum-bled have spires in ev - ery land, Bells still are chim-ing and
dwell - ing, High a - bove earth His tem - ple stands, All earth-ly tem-ples ex -
ta - tion; He through bap-tis - mal grace us owns, Heirs of His won-drous sal -
dwell - ing; Prais - es to Him we there may bring, His won-drous mer-cy forth-
prais - es; They are the homes where He draws near And lit - tle chil-dren em -

call - ing; Call - ing the young and old to rest, But a - bove
cell - ing; Yet He whom heavens can - not con - tain Chose to a -
va - tion; Were we but two His name to tell, Yet He would
tell - ing; Je - sus His grace to us ac - cords, Spir - it and
brac - es, Beau - ti - ful things in them are said, God there with

all the soul dis - tressed, Long-ing for rest ev - er - last - ing.
bide on earth with men, Built in our bod - ies His tem - ple.
deign with us to dwell, With all His grace and His fa - vor.
life are all His words, His truth doth hal-low the tem - ple.
us His cov-enant made, Mak-ing us heirs of His King - dom. A - MEN.

Words and music from *The Lutheran Hymnary*. Used by permission of Augsburg Publishing House, Min-
neapolis, Minnesota.

THE CHURCH

Christ Is Made the Sure Foundation

Latin, 7th century
Trans. by John Mason Neale, 1851

REGENT SQUARE: 8. 7. 8. 7. 8. 7.
Henry Smart, 1867

433

1. Christ is made the sure Foun - da - tion, Christ the Head and
2. To this tem - ple, where we call Thee, Come, O Lord of
3. Here vouch - safe to all Thy serv - ants What they ask of
4. Laud and hon - or to the Fa - ther, Laud and hon - or

Cor - ner - stone, Cho - sen of the Lord and pre - cious,
Hosts, to - day: With Thy wont - ed lov - ing - kind - ness
Thee to gain, What they gain from Thee for - ev - er
to the Son, Laud and hon - or to the Spir - it,

Bind - ing all the Church in one; Ho - ly Zi - on's
Hear Thy peo - ple as they pray; And Thy full - est
With the bless - ed to re - tain, And here - aft - er
Ev - er Three and ev - er One, One in might, and

help for - ev - er, And her con - fi - dence a - lone.
ben - e - dic - tion Shed with - in its walls al - way.
in Thy glo - ry Ev - er - more with Thee to reign.
One in glo - ry, While un - end - ing a - ges run! A - MEN.

[365]

THE CHURCH

434 Glorious Things of Thee Are Spoken

From Psalm 87
John Newton, 1779

AUSTRIAN HYMN: 8. 7. 8. 7. D.
Franz Joseph Haydn, 1797

1. Glorious things of thee are spoken, Zion, city of our God;
He whose word cannot be broken Formed thee for His own abode:
On the Rock of Ages founded, What can shake thy sure repose?
With salvation's walls surrounded, Thou mayst smile at all thy foes.

2. See, the streams of living waters, Springing from eternal Love,
Well supply thy sons and daughters, And all fear of want remove:
Who can faint, while such a river Ever flows their thirst to assuage;
Grace, which, like the Lord the Giver, Never fails from age to age?

3. Round each habitation hovering, See the cloud and fire appear
For a glory and a covering, Showing that the Lord is near:
Thus deriving from their banner Light by night and shade by day,
Safe they feed upon the manna Which He gives them when they pray. A-MEN.

THE CHURCH

[366]

I Love Thy Kingdom, Lord

435

From Psalm 137
Timothy Dwight, 1800

ST. THOMAS: S. M.
Williams' Psalmody, 1770

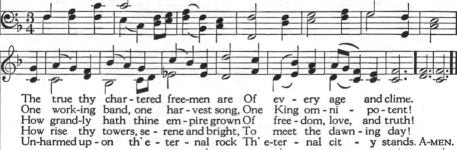

1. I love Thy King - dom, Lord, The house of Thine a - bode,
2. I love Thy Church, O God: Her walls be - fore Thee stand,
3. For her my tears shall fall, For her my prayers as - cend;
4. Be - yond my high - est joy I prize her heaven - ly ways,
5. Sure as Thy truth shall last, To Zi - on shall be given

The Church our blest Re - deem - er saved With His own pre - cious blood.
Dear as the ap - ple of Thine eye, And grav - en on Thy hand.
To her my cares and toils be given, Till toils and cares shall end.
Her sweet com - mun - ion, sol - emn vows, Her hymns of love and praise.
The bright - est glo - ries earth can yield, And bright - er bliss of heaven. A-MEN.

City of God

436

RICHMOND: C. M.

Samuel Johnson, 1860

Thomas Haweis, 1792, Arr. by S. Webbe, the younger (1770-1843)

1. Cit - y of God, how broad and far Out - spread thy walls sub - lime!
2. One ho - ly Church, one ar - my strong, One stead - fast high in - tent,
3. How pure - ly hath thy speech come down From man's pri - me - val youth;
4. How gleam thy watch-fires through the night With nev - er - faint - ing ray!
5. In vain the sur - ge's an - gry shock, In vain the drift - ing sands:

The true thy char - tered free - men are Of ev - ery age and clime.
One work - ing band, one har - vest song, One King om - ni - po - tent!
How grand - ly hath thine em - pire grown Of free - dom, love, and truth!
How rise thy towers, se - rene and bright, To meet the dawn - ing day!
Un - harmed up - on th' e - ter - nal rock Th' e - ter - nal cit - y stands. A-MEN.

Alternative tune, "Gräfenburg," Hymn 243.   [367]   THE CHURCH

437
The Church's One Foundation

AURELIA: 7. 6. 7. 6. D.

Samuel J. Stone, 1866

Samuel S. Wesley, 1864

1. The Church's one Foun-da-tion Is Je-sus Christ her Lord;
2. E-lect from ev-ery na-tion, Yet one o'er all the earth,
3. Mid toil and trib-u-la-tion, And tu-mult of her war,
4. Yet she on earth hath un-ion With God the Three in One,

She is His new cre-a-tion By wa-ter and the word:
Her char-ter of sal-va-tion One Lord, one faith, one birth;
She waits the con-sum-ma-tion Of peace for-ev-er-more;
And mys-tic sweet com-mun-ion With those whose rest is won:

From heaven He came and sought her To be His ho-ly Bride;
One ho-ly name she bless-es, Par-takes one ho-ly food,
Till with the vi-sion glo-rious, Her long-ing eyes are blest,
O hap-py ones and ho-ly! Lord, give us grace that we,

With His own blood He bought her, And for her life He died.
And to one hope she press-es, With ev-ery grace en-dued.
And the great Church vic-to-rious Shall be the Church at rest.
Like them, the meek and low-ly, On high may dwell with Thee. A-MEN.

THE CHURCH

[368]

The Church's One Foundation

ALTERNATIVE HARMONIZATION

AURELIA: 7. 6. 7. 6. D.
Samuel S. Wesley, 1864, Har. by Eric Thiman, 1937

437

From *Varied Accompaniments to Thirty-four Well-known Hymn Tunes.* Used by permission of Oxford University Press.
This version may be used for one or more stanzas, the congregation and the choir singing the melody.

Within Thy Temple's Sacred Courts

438

From Psalm 48
The Psalter, 1912

ST. JOHN'S HIGHLANDS: L. M.
Source unknown; alt., 1953

1. With-in Thy tem-ple's sa-cred courts, With lov-ing and a-dor-ing thought,
2. Wher-e'er Thy name, O God, is known, Wher-e'er Thy glo-rious fame ex-tends,
3. This might-y God for-ev-er lives Our God and Sav-iour to a-bide,

We con-tem-plate Thy grace, O God, And all Thy deeds with mer-cy fraught.
There al-so is Thy praise pro-claimed, Far as the earth's re-mot-est ends.
And till our pil-grim days shall end Will ev-er be our faith-ful guide. A-MEN.

[369]

THE CHURCH

439 With Joy I Heard My Friends Exclaim

From Psalm 122
The Psalter, 1912

MORNING HYMN (Boyce): L. M.
William Boyce (1710-1779)

1. With joy I heard my friends ex-claim, "Come, let us in God's tem-ple meet;
2. How beau-ti-ful doth Zi-on stand, A cit-y built com-pact and fair;
3. They come to learn the will of God, To pay their vows, His grace to own,
4. For Zi-on's peace let prayer be made; May all that love thee pros-per well;
5. For sake of friends and kin-dred dear, My heart's de-sire is Zi-on's peace,

With-in thy gates, O Zi-on blest, Shall ev-er stand our will-ing feet."
The peo-ple of the Lord u-nite With joy and praise to wor-ship there.
For there is judg-ment's roy-al seat, Mes-si-ah's sure and last-ing throne.
With-in thy walls let peace a-bide, And glad-ness with thy chil-dren dwell.
And for the house of God, the Lord, My lov-ing care shall nev-er cease. A-MEN.

440 How Dear to Me, O Lord of Hosts

IRISH: C. M.

From Psalm 84 *The Psalter*, 1912   Melody from *A Collection of Hymns and Sacred Poems*, Dublin, 1749

1. How dear to me, O Lord of Hosts, The place where Thou dost dwell;
2. My spir-it longs, yea, e-ven faints, Thy sa-cred courts to see;
3. Be-neath Thy care the spar-row finds A place of peace-ful rest;
4. Then, Lord of Hosts, my King, my God, Thy love will shel-ter me;
5. Blest they who dwell with-in Thy house, Their per-fect strength Thou art;
6. Their tears of grief, like ear-ly rain, Sweet springs of joy shall fill;

The tab-er-nac-les of Thy grace In pleas-ant-ness ex-cel.
My thirst-ing heart and flesh cry out, O liv-ing God, for Thee.
Where she may safe-ly lay her young The swal-low finds a nest;
Be-neath Thy al-tar's peace-ful shade My dwell-ing place shall be.
Their joy-ful praise shall nev-er cease, Thy ways are in their heart.
With strength re-newed they jour-ney safe To Zi-on's ho-ly hill. A-MEN.

Pleasant Are Thy Courts Above

From Psalm 84
Henry Francis Lyte, 1834

MAIDSTONE: 7. 7. 7. 7. D.
Walter B. Gilbert, 1862

1. Pleas-ant are Thy courts a-bove In the land of light and love;
2. Hap-py birds that sing and fly Round Thy al - tars, O Most High;
3. Hap-py souls, their prais-es flow E - ven in this vale of woe;
4. Lord, be mine this prize to win; Guide me through a world of sin;

Pleas-ant are Thy courts be-low In this land of sin and woe.
Hap-pier souls that find a rest In a heaven-ly Fa-ther's breast!
Wa-ters in the des-ert rise, Man-na feeds them from the skies:
Keep me by Thy sav-ing grace; Give me at Thy side a place.

O my spir-it longs and faints For the con-verse of Thy saints, For the
Like the wan-dering dove that found No re-pose on earth a-round, They can
On they go from strength to strength Till they reach Thy throne at length, At Thy
Sun and shield a-like Thou art; Guide and guard my err-ing heart. Grace and

bright-ness of Thy face, For Thy full-ness, God of grace.
to their ark re-pair And en-joy it ev-er there.
feet a-dor-ing fall, Who hast led them safe through all.
glo-ry flow from Thee; Shower, O shower them, Lord, on me. A-MEN.

Music used by permission of Novello & Co., Ltd.

[371]

THE CHURCH

442 Here, O My Lord, I See Thee Face to Face

Horatius Bonar, 1855

MORECAMBE: 10. 10. 10. 10.
Frederick C. Atkinson, 1870

1. Here, O my Lord, I see Thee face to face;
2. Here would I feed upon the bread of God,
3. This is the hour of ban - quet and of song;
4. I have no help but Thine, nor do I need

Here would I touch and han - dle things un - seen,
Here drink with Thee the roy - al wine of heaven;
This is the heaven - ly Ta - ble spread for me:
An - oth - er arm save Thine to lean up - on:

Here grasp with firm - er hand e - ter - nal grace,
Here would I lay a - side each earth - ly load,
Here let me feast, and, feast - ing, still pro - long
It is e - nough, my Lord, e - nough in - deed;

And all my wea - ri - ness up - on Thee lean.
Here taste a - fresh the calm of sin for - given.
The brief, bright hour of fel - low - ship with Thee.
My strength is in Thy might, Thy might a - lone. A-MEN.

THE CHURCH: THE LORD'S SUPPER

A Parting Hymn We Sing

443

Aaron R. Wolfe, 1858

SCHUMANN: S. M.
Mason and Webb's *Cantica Laudis*, 1850

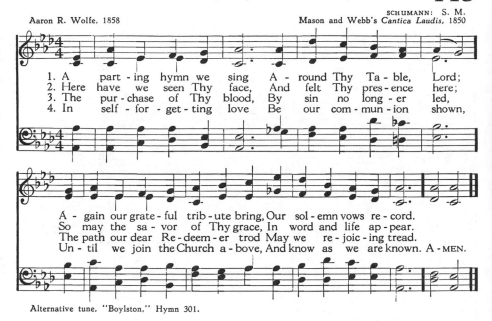

1. A parting hymn we sing A - round Thy Ta - ble, Lord;
2. Here have we seen Thy face, And felt Thy pres - ence here;
3. The pur - chase of Thy blood, By sin no long - er led,
4. In self - for - get - ting love Be our com - mun - ion shown,

A - gain our grate - ful trib - ute bring, Our sol - emn vows re - cord.
So may the sa - vor of Thy grace, In word and life ap - pear.
The path our dear Re - deem - er trod May we re - joic - ing tread.
Un - til we join the Church a - bove, And know as we are known. A - MEN.

Alternative tune, "Boylston," Hymn 301.

According to Thy Gracious Word

444

James Montgomery, 1825

DALEHURST: C. M.
Arthur Cottman, 1874

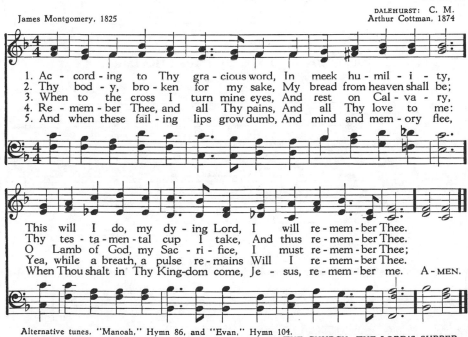

1. Ac - cord - ing to Thy gra - cious word, In meek hu - mil - i - ty,
2. Thy bod - y, bro - ken for my sake, My bread from heaven shall be;
3. When to the cross I turn mine eyes, And rest on Cal - va - ry,
4. Re - mem - ber Thee, and all Thy pains, And all Thy love to me:
5. And when these fail - ing lips grow dumb, And mind and mem - ory flee,

This will I do, my dy - ing Lord, I will re - mem - ber Thee.
Thy tes - ta - men - tal cup I take, And thus re - mem - ber Thee.
O Lamb of God, my Sac - ri - fice, I must re - mem - ber Thee;
Yea, while a breath, a pulse re - mains Will I re - mem - ber Thee.
When Thou shalt in Thy King-dom come, Je - sus, re - mem - ber me. A - MEN.

Alternative tunes, "Manoah," Hymn 86, and "Evan," Hymn 104.

THE CHURCH: THE LORD'S SUPPER

445 Bread of the World in Mercy Broken

Reginald Heber, 1827

EUCHARISTIC HYMN: 9. 8. 9. 8.
John S. B. Hodges, 1868

1. Bread of the world in mer - cy bro-ken, Wine of the soul in
2. Look on the heart by sor - row bro-ken, Look on the tears by

mer - cy shed, By whom the words of life were spo - ken,
sin - ners shed; And be Thy feast to us the to - ken

And in whose death our sins are dead:
That by Thy grace our souls are fed. A - MEN.

446 Be Known to Us in Breaking Bread

James Montgomery, 1825

ST. FLAVIAN: C. M.
Day's Psalter, 1563

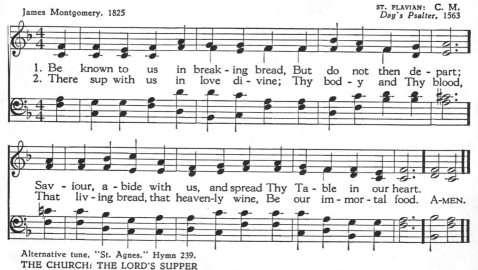

1. Be known to us in break - ing bread, But do not then de - part;
2. There sup with us in love di - vine; Thy bod - y and Thy blood,

Sav - iour, a - bide with us, and spread Thy Ta - ble in our heart.
That liv - ing bread, that heaven-ly wine, Be our im - mor - tal food. A-MEN.

Alternative tune, "St. Agnes," Hymn 239.
THE CHURCH: THE LORD'S SUPPER

Let Us Break Bread Together

447

COMMUNION SPIRITUAL: 7. 3. 7. 3. with Refrain
Calhoun melody
Har. for this book, 1953

Negro spiritual

1. Let us break bread to-geth-er, On our knees, on our knees;
2. Let us drink wine to-geth-er, On our knees, on our knees;
3. Let us praise God to-geth-er, On our knees, on our knees;

Let us break bread to-geth-er on our knees, on our knees.
Let us drink wine to-geth-er on our knees, on our knees.
Let us praise God to-geth-er on our knees, on our knees.

REFRAIN

When I fall on my knees, with my face to the ris-ing

sun, O Lord, have mer-cy on me. A - MEN.

THE CHURCH: THE LORD'S SUPPER

448
'Twas on That Night

John Morison
Scottish Paraphrases, 1781

ROCKINGHAM OLD: L. M.
Source unknown
Adapted by Edward Miller, 1790

1. 'Twas on that night when doomed to know The ea - ger
2. And, aft - er thanks and glo - ry given To Him that
3. "My bro - ken bod - y thus I give For you, for
4. Then in His hands the cup He raised, And God a -
5. "My blood I thus pour forth," He cries, "To cleanse the
6. "With love to man this cup is fraught; Let all par -

rage of ev - ery foe, That night in which He
rules in earth and heaven, That sym - bol of His
new He thanked and praised, While kind - ness in His
soul in sin that lies; In this the cov - e -
take the sa - cred draught; Through lat - est a - ges

was be - trayed, The Sav - iour of the world took bread;
flesh He broke, And thus to all His fol - lowers spoke:
rite re - new That brings my sav - ing love to view."
bos - om glowed, And from His lips sal - va - tion flowed.
nant is sealed, And heaven's e - ter - nal grace re - vealed.
let it pour, In mem - ory of my dy - ing hour." A - MEN.

449
For the Bread, Which Thou Hast Broken

Louis F. Benson, 1924

CROSS OF JESUS: 8. 7. 8. 7.
John Stainer, 1887

1. For the bread, which Thou hast bro - ken; For the wine, which Thou hast poured;
2. By this pledge that Thou dost love us, By Thy gift of peace re - stored,
3. With our saint - ed ones in glo - ry Seat - ed at our Fa - ther's board,
4. In Thy serv - ice, Lord, de - fend us, In our hearts keep watch and ward,

THE CHURCH: THE LORD'S SUPPER

[376]

For the Bread, Which Thou Hast Broken

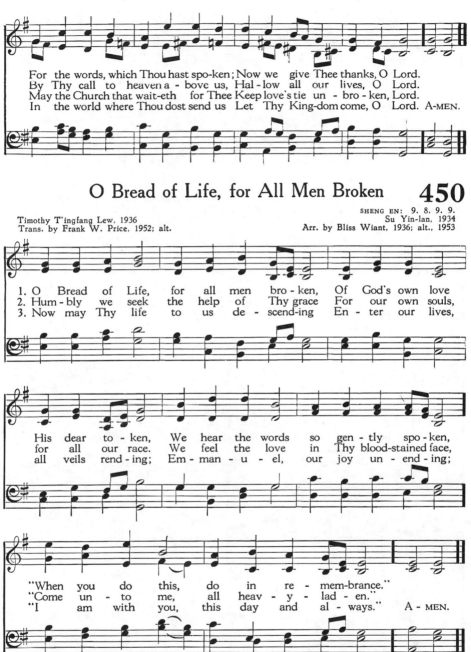

For the words, which Thou hast spo-ken; Now we give Thee thanks, O Lord.
By Thy call to heaven a - bove us, Hal - low all our lives, O Lord.
May the Church that wait-eth for Thee Keep love's tie un - bro - ken, Lord.
In the world where Thou dost send us Let Thy King-dom come, O Lord. A-MEN.

O Bread of Life, for All Men Broken 450

SHENG EN: 9. 8. 9. 9.

Timothy T'ingfang Lew, 1936
Trans. by Frank W. Price, 1952; alt.

Su Yin-lan, 1934
Arr. by Bliss Wiant, 1936; alt., 1953

1. O Bread of Life, for all men bro - ken, Of God's own love
2. Hum - bly we seek the help of Thy grace For our own souls,
3. Now may Thy life to us de - scend-ing En - ter our lives,

His dear to - ken, We hear the words so gen - tly spo-ken,
for all our race. We feel the love in Thy blood-stained face,
all veils rend - ing; Em - man - u - el, our joy un - end-ing;

"When you do this, do in re - mem-brance."
"Come un - to me, all heav - y - lad - en."
"I am with you, this day and al - ways." A - MEN.

Translation copyright, 1953, by Frank W. Price. Used by permission. Music from *Hymns of Universal Praise*. Used by permission.

THE CHURCH: THE LORD'S SUPPER

451 Jesus, Friend, So Kind and Gentle

Philip E. Gregory. 1948

SICILIAN MARINERS: 8. 7. 8. 7. 8. 7.
Arr. from a Sicilian melody

1. Je - sus, Friend, so kind and gen - tle, Lit - tle ones we bring to Thee; Grant to them Thy dear - est bless - ing, Let Thine arms a - round them be; Now en - fold them in Thy good - ness, From all dan - ger keep them free.

2. Thou who didst re - ceive the chil - dren To Thy - self so ten - der - ly, Give to all who teach and guide them, Wis - dom and hu - mil - i - ty; Vi - sion true to keep them no - ble, Love to serve them faith - ful - ly.

3. Grant to us a deep com - pas - sion For Thy chil - dren ev - ery - where. May we see our hu - man fam - i - ly Free from sor - row and de - spair, And be - hold Thy King - dom glo - rious, In our world so bright and fair. A - MEN.

Words used by permission of the author.
THE CHURCH: HOLY BAPTISM

[378]

O Jesus Christ, Our Lord Most Dear 452

Heinrich von Laufenberg (c. 1385-1460)
Trans. by Catherine Winkworth, 1869; alt.

VOM HIMMEL HOCH: L. M.
Geistliche Lieder, Leipzig, 1539

1. O Je - sus Christ, our Lord most dear,
2. As in Thy heaven - ly King - dom, Lord,
3. Their watch let an - gels round him keep

As Thou wast once an in - fant here,
All things o - bey Thy sa - cred word,
Wher - e'er he be, a - wake, a - sleep;

So give this child of Thine, we pray,
Do Thou Thy child might - y suc - cor give,
Thy ho - ly cross now let him bear,

Thy grace and bless - ing day by day.
And shield this child by morn and eve.
That he Thy crown with saints may wear. A - MEN.

THE CHURCH: HOLY BAPTISM

453 O Perfect Love, All Human Thought Transcending

Dorothy Frances Gurney, 1883

PERFECT LOVE: 11. 10. 11. 10.
Joseph Barnby, 1889

1. O per - fect Love, all hu - man thought tran - scend - ing,
2. O per - fect Life, be Thou their full as - sur - ance
3. Grant them the joy which bright - ens earth - ly sor - row;

Low - ly we kneel in prayer be - fore Thy throne,
Of ten - der char - i - ty and stead - fast faith,
Grant them the peace which calms all earth - ly strife,

That theirs may be the love which knows no end - ing,
Of pa - tient hope, and qui - et, brave en - dur - ance,
And to life's day the glo - rious un - known mor - row

Whom Thou for - ev - er - more dost join in one.
With child - like trust that fears nor pain nor death.
That dawns up - on e - ter - nal love and life. A-MEN.

Words copyright. Used by permission of Oxford University Press.
THE CHURCH: MARRIAGE

O Love Divine and Golden

John S. B. Monsell, 1866

BLAIRGOWRIE: 7. 6. 7. 6. D.
John B. Dykes, 1872

454

1. O Love di - vine and gold - en, Mys - te - rious depth and height,
2. O Love di - vine and ten - der, That through our homes dost move,
3. God bless these hands u - nit - ed; God bless these hearts made one!

To Thee the world be - hold - en Looks up for life and light;
Veiled in the sof - tened splen - dor Of ho - ly house - hold love,
Un - sev - ered and un - blight - ed May they through life go on,

O Love di - vine and gen - tle, The Bless - er and the Blest,
A throne with - out Thy bless - ing Were la - bor with - out rest,
Here in earth's home pre - par - ing For the bright home a - bove,

Be - neath Thy care pa - ren - tal The world lies down in rest.
And cot - ta - ges pos - sess - ing Thy bless - ed - ness are blest.
And there for - ev - er shar - ing Its joy where God is Love. A-MEN.

THE CHURCH: THE CHRISTIAN HOME

455 O Happy Home, Where Thou Art Loved

Karl J. P. Spitta. 1833
Trans. by Sarah B. Findlater. 1858; alt.

CONSOLATION (Mendelssohn): 11. 10. 11. 10.
Felix Mendelssohn (1809-1847)

1. O hap - py home, where Thou art loved the dear - est,
2. O hap - py home, where each one serves Thee, low - ly,
3. O hap - py home, where Thou art not for - got - ten
4. Un - til at last, when earth's day's work is end - ed,

Thou lov - ing Friend and Sav - iour of our race,
What - ev - er his ap - point - ed work may be,
When joy is o - ver - flow - ing, full, and free;
All meet Thee in the bless - ed home a - bove,

And where a - mong the guests there nev - er com - eth
Till ev - ery com - mon task seems great and ho - ly,
O hap - py home, where ev - ery wound - ed spir - it
From whence Thou cam - est, where Thou hast as - cend - ed,

One who can hold such high and hon - ored place.
When it is done, O Lord, as un - to Thee.
Is brought, Phy - si - cian, Com - fort - er, to Thee,
Thy ev - er - last - ing home of peace and love! A - MEN.

Words used by permission of Thomas Nelson & Sons, Ltd.
THE CHURCH: THE CHRISTIAN HOME

All Things Bright and Beautiful

456

Cecil Frances Alexander, 1848
In unison
Stanza 1 to be sung as refrain after stanzas 2 to 5

ROYAL OAK: 7. 6. 7. 6. with Refrain
Traditional English melody
Har. for this book, 1953

1. All things bright and beau-ti-ful, All crea-tures great and small,

Fine

All things wise and won-der-ful: The Lord God made them all.

2. Each lit-tle flower that o-pens, Each lit-tle bird that sings:
3. The pur-ple-head-ed moun-tain, The riv-er run-ning by,
4. The cold wind in the win-ter, The pleas-ant sum-mer sun,
5. He gave us eyes to see them, And lips that we might tell

He made their glow-ing col-ors, He made their ti-ny wings.
The sun-set, and the morn-ing That bright-ens up the sky,
The ripe fruits in the gar-den: He made them ev-ery one.
How great is God Al-might-y, Who has made all things well. A-MEN.

457

Saviour, Teach Me, Day by Day

ORIENTIS PARTIBUS: 7. 7. 7. 7.
Attributed to Pierre de Corbeil (?-1222)
Har. by R. Vaughan Williams, 1906

Jane E. Leeson, 1842

1. Sav - iour, teach me, day by day, Love's sweet les - son, to o - bey;
2. With a child's glad heart of love, At Thy bid - ding may I move,
3. Teach me thus Thy steps to trace, Strong to fol - low in Thy grace,
4. Love in lov - ing finds em - ploy, In o - be - dience all her joy;

Sweet - er les - son can - not be, Lov - ing Him who first loved me.
Prompt to serve and fol - low Thee, Lov - ing Him who first loved me.
Learn - ing how to love from Thee, Lov - ing Him who first loved me.
Ev - er new that joy will be, Lov - ing Him who first loved me. A - MEN.

Music adapted from *The English Hymnal* by permission of Oxford University Press.
Alternative tune, "Posen," below.

458

Father, Lead Me Day by Day

POSEN: 7. 7. 7. 7.
Georg C. Strattner, 1691

John Page Hopps, 1877

1. Fa - ther, lead me day by day, Ev - er in Thine own sweet way;
2. When in dan - ger, make me brave, Make me know that Thou canst save;
3. When I'm tempt - ed to do wrong, Make me stead-fast, wise, and strong;
4. May I do the good I know, Serv - ing glad - ly here be - low,

Teach me to be pure and true; Show me what I ought to do.
Keep me safe by Thy dear side; Let me in Thy love a - bide.
And when all a - lone I stand, Shield me with Thy might-y hand.
Then at last go home to Thee, Ev - er - more Thine own to be. A - MEN.

Alternative tune, "Orientis partibus," above.
THE CHURCH: HYMNS FOR THE YOUNG

Tell Me the Stories of Jesus

William H. Parker, 1885
Unison or duet

STORIES OF JESUS: 8. 4. 8. 4. 5. 4. 5. 4.
Frederic A. Challinor, 1905

1. Tell me the sto - ries of Je - sus I love to hear;
2. First let me hear how the chil - dren Stood round His knee,
3. In - to the cit - y I'd fol - low The chil - dren's band,

Things I would ask Him to tell me If He were here:
And I shall fan - cy His bless - ing Rest - ing on me;
Wav - ing a branch of the palm tree High in my hand;

Scenes by the way - side, Tales of the sea,
Words full of kind - ness, Deeds full of grace,
One of His her - alds, Yes, I would sing

Sto - ries of Je - sus, Tell them to me.
All in the love - light Of Je - sus' face.
Loud - est ho - san - nas, "Je - sus is King!" A - MEN.

Words and music copyright by The National Sunday School Union. Used by permission.

THE CHURCH: HYMNS FOR THE YOUNG

460 I Think When I Read That Sweet Story of Old

LUKE (SWEET STORY): Irregular
Greek melody
Arr. by William B. Bradbury, 1859
Har. by Charles Winfred Douglas, 1918

Jemima Luke, 1841; alt.

In unison

1. I think when I read that sweet sto - ry of old, When
2. I wish that His hands had been placed on my head, That His
3. Yet still to His foot - stool in prayer I may go, And

Je - sus was here a - mong men, How He called lit - tle chil - dren as
arms had been thrown a - round me, And that I might have seen His kind
know that I share in His love; And if I now ear - nest - ly

lambs to His fold: I should like to have been with them then.
look when He said, "Let the lit - tle ones come un - to Me."
serve Him be - low, I shall see Him and serve Him a - bove. A - MEN.

Music used by permission of The Church Pension Fund.

461 It Fell Upon a Summer Day

CHILDHOOD: 8. 8. 8. 6.
University of Wales, 1923

Stopford Augustus Brooke, 1881

1. It fell up - on a sum-mer day, When Je - sus walked in Gal - i - lee,
2. He took them in His arms, and laid His hands on each re-mem-bered head;
3. "For-bid them not; un - less ye bear The child-like heart your hearts with-in,
4. O Fa - ther, grant this child-like heart, That I may come to Christ, and feel

THE CHURCH: HYMNS FOR THE YOUNG

[386]

It Fell Upon a Summer Day

The moth-ers from a vil-lage brought Their chil-dren to His knee.
"Suf-fer these lit-tle ones to come To Me," He gen-tly said.
Un-to My King-dom ye may come, But may not en-ter in."
His hands on me in bless-ing laid, Love-giv-ing, strong to heal. A-MEN.

Music from *A Students' Hymnal*. Used by permission of Oxford University Press.
Words copyright. Used by permission of Oxford University Press.

Once in Royal David's City   462

IRBY: 8. 7. 8. 7. 8. 7.

Cecil Frances Alexander, 1848

Henry J. Gauntlett, 1849

1. Once in roy - al Da - vid's cit - y Stood a low - ly cat - tle shed,
2. He came down to earth from heav - en Who is God and Lord of all,
3. Je - sus is our child - hood's pat - tern, Day by day like us He grew;
4. And our eyes at last shall see Him, Through His own re - deem - ing love;

Where a moth - er laid her Ba - by In a man - ger for His bed:
And His shel - ter was a sta - ble, And His cra - dle was a stall:
He was lit - tle, weak, and help-less, Tears and smiles like us He knew:
For that Child so dear and gen - tle Is our Lord in heav - en a - bove,

Mar - y was that moth-er mild, Je - sus Christ, her lit - tle Child.
With the poor, and mean, and low-ly, Lived on earth our Sav - iour ho - ly.
And He feel - eth for our sad-ness, And He shar - eth in our glad-ness.
And He leads His chil-dren on To the place where He is gone. A-MEN.

THE CHURCH: HYMNS FOR THE YOUNG

463 With Happy Voices Ringing

William George Tarrant, 1888

TOURS: 7. 6. 7. 6. D.
Berthold Tours, 1872

1. With hap-py voi-ces ring-ing, Thy chil-dren, Lord, ap-pear;
2. What though no eye be-holds Thee, No hand Thy hand may feel,
3. And shall we not a-dore Thee, With more than joy-ous song,

Their joy-ous prais-es bring-ing In an-thems sweet and clear.
Thy u-ni-verse un-folds Thee, Thy star-ry heavens re-veal;
And live in truth be-fore Thee, All beau-ti-ful and strong?

For skies of gold-en splen-dor, For az-ure roll-ing sea,
The earth and all its glo-ry, Our homes and all we love,
Lord, bless our souls' en-deav-or Thy serv-ants true to be,

For blos-soms sweet and ten-der, O Lord, we wor-ship Thee.
Tell forth the won-drous sto-ry Of One who reigns a-bove.
And through all life, for-ev-er, To live our praise to Thee. A-MEN.

Words used by permission of Dorothy Tarrant.
THE CHURCH: HYMNS FOR THE YOUNG

Morning Has Broken

Eleanor Farjeon, 1931

BUNESSAN: 5. 5. 5. 4. D.
Gaelic melody
Har. by David Evans, 1927

In unison

1. Morn-ing has bro - ken Like the first morn - ing, Black-bird has
2. Sweet the rain's new fall Sun - lit from heav - en, Like the first
3. Mine is the sun - light! Mine is the morn - ing Born of the

spo - ken Like the first bird. Praise for the sing - ing!
dew - fall On the first grass. Praise for the sweet - ness
one light E - den saw play! Praise with e - la - tion,

Praise for the morn - ing! Praise for them, spring-ing Fresh from the Word!
Of the wet gar - den, Sprung in com-plete - ness Where His feet pass.
Praise ev-ery morn - ing, God's re-cre-a - tion Of the new day! A-MEN.

Words copyright by Eleanor Farjeon. Used by permission. Music from *The Church Hymnary*, Revised Edition. Used by permission of Oxford University Press.

THE CHURCH: HYMNS FOR THE YOUNG

465 Jesus Loves Me! This I Know

WARNER: 7. 7. 7. 7. 5. 5. 5. 6.
William B. Bradbury, 1861
Har. for this book, 1953

Anna Warner, 1859

Je - sus loves me! this I know, For the Bi - ble tells me so. Lit - tle

ones to Him be - long; They are weak but He is strong. Yes, Je - sus loves me,

Yes, Je - sus loves me, Yes, Je - sus loves me, The Bi-ble tells me so. A-MEN.

466 God Who Made the Earth

CURA DEI: 5. 6. 6. 4.
Donald S. Barrows, 1941

Sarah Betts Rhodes, 1870
In unison

1. God who made the earth, The air, the sky, the sea,
2. God who made the grass, The flower, the fruit, the tree,
3. God who made the sun, The moon, the stars, is He

Who gave the light its birth, Car - eth for me.
The day and night to pass, Car - eth for me.
Who, when life's clouds come on, Car - eth for me. A - MEN.

Music copyright, 1942, by The Church Pension Fund. Used by permission.
THE CHURCH: HYMNS FOR THE YOUNG

Father, We Thank Thee for the Night 467

Ascribed to Rebecca J. Weston, 1885

ONSLOW: L. M.
Daniel Batchellor, 1885
Har. by Austin C. Lovelace, 1953

In unison

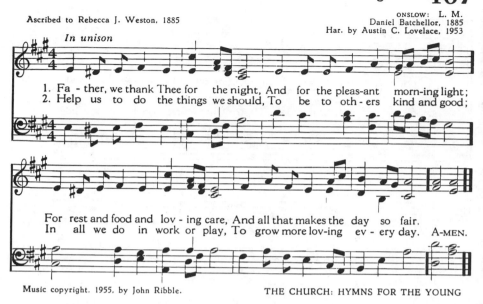

1. Fa - ther, we thank Thee for the night, And for the pleas-ant morn-ing light;
2. Help us to do the things we should, To be to oth - ers kind and good;

For rest and food and lov - ing care, And all that makes the day so fair.
In all we do in work or play, To grow more lov-ing ev - ery day. A-MEN.

Music copyright. 1955. by John Ribble.

THE CHURCH: HYMNS FOR THE YOUNG

O Thou Whose Feet Have Climbed Life's Hill 468

Louis F. Benson, 1894, 1911

ST. MAGNUS: C. M.
Jeremiah Clark, 1709

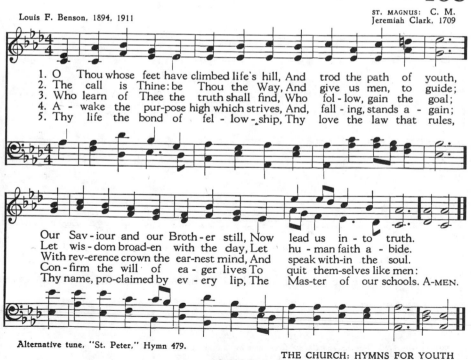

1. O Thou whose feet have climbed life's hill, And trod the path of youth,
2. The call is Thine: be Thou the Way, And give us men, to guide;
3. Who learn of Thee the truth shall find, Who fol - low, gain the goal;
4. A - wake the pur-pose high which strives, And, fall - ing, stands a - gain;
5. Thy life the bond of fel - low - ship, Thy love the law that rules,

Our Sav - iour and our Broth - er still, Now lead us in - to truth.
Let wis - dom broad-en with the day, Let hu - man faith a - bide.
With rev-erence crown the ear-nest mind, And speak with-in the soul.
Con - firm the will of ea - ger lives To quit them-selves like men:
Thy name, pro-claimed by ev - ery lip, The Mas-ter of our schools. A-MEN.

Alternative tune, "St. Peter," Hymn 479.

THE CHURCH: HYMNS FOR YOUTH

469 Now in the Days of Youth

DIADEMATA: S. M. D.

Walter J. Mathams, 1913

George J. Elvey, 1868

1. Now in the days of youth, When life flows fresh and free,
2. Teach us, wher-e'er we live, To act as in Thy sight,
3. Teach us to love the true, The beau-ti-ful and pure,
4. Spir-it of Christ, do Thou Our first bright days in-spire,

Thou Lord of all our hearts and lives, We give our-selves to Thee;
And do what Thou wouldst have us do With ra-di-ant de-light;
And let us not for one short hour An e-vil thought en-dure.
That we may live the life of love And loft-i-est de-sire;

Our fer-vent gift re-ceive, And fit us to ful-fill,
Not choos-ing what is great, Nor spurn-ing what is small,
But give us grace to stand De-cid-ed, brave and strong,
And be by Thee pre-pared For larg-er years to come,

Through all our days, in all our ways, Our Heaven-ly Fa-ther's will.
But take as from Thy hands our tasks, And glo-ri-fy them all.
The lov-ers of all ho-ly things, The foes of all things wrong.
And for the life in-ef-fa-ble With-in the Fa-ther's home. A-MEN.

Words from *New Worship and Song*. Copyright by The Pilgrim Press. Used by permission.
THE CHURCH: HYMNS FOR YOUTH

We Would Be Building

FINLANDIA: 10. 10. 10. 10. 10. 10.
Jean Sibelius, 1899
Arr. for *The Hymnal*, 1933

Purd E. Deitz, 1935

1. We would be build - ing; tem-ples still un - done O'er crum-bling walls their
2. Teach us to build; up - on the sol - id rock We set the dream that
3. O keep us build - ing, Mas-ter; may our hands Ne'er fal - ter when the

cross - es scarce-ly lift; Wait-ing till love can raise the bro - ken stone,
hard - ens in - to deed, Ribbed with the steel that time and change doth mock,
dream is in our hearts, When to our ears there come di - vine com - mands

And hearts cre - a - tive bridge the hu - man rift; We would be build - ing;
Th' un-fail - ing pur - pose of our no - blest creed; Teach us to build; O
And all the pride of sin - ful will de - parts; We build with Thee; O

Mas - ter, let Thy plan Re - veal the life that God would give to man.
Mas - ter, lend us sight To see the tow - ers gleam-ing in the light.
grant en - dur - ing worth Un - til the Heaven-ly King-dom comes on earth. A-MEN.

Words copyright, 1936, by Purd E. Deitz; used by permission. Melody used by permission of Breitkopf & Härtel, Wiesbaden; all rights reserved. Arrangement copyright, 1933, by the Presbyterian Board of Christian Education; used by permission.

THE CHURCH: HYMNS FOR YOUTH

471 Shepherd of Eager Youth

Ascribed to Clement of Alexandria, c. 200
Trans. by Henry M. Dexter, 1846; alt.

HINMAN: 6. 6. 4. 6. 6. 6. 4.
Austin C. Lovelace, 1953

In unison

1. Shep-herd of ea - ger youth, Guid-ing in love and truth Through de-vious ways,
2. Thou art our ho - ly Lord, The all - sub - du - ing Word, Heal - er of strife;
3. Ev - er be Thou our Guide, Our Shep-herd and our Pride, Our Staff and Song;
4. So now, and till we die, Sound we Thy prais - es high, And joy-ful sing;

Christ, our tri - um - phant King, We come Thy name to sing,
Thou didst Thy - self a - base, That from sin's deep dis - grace
Je - sus, Thou Christ of God, By Thy per - en - nial Word,
Let all the ho - ly throng Who to Thy Church be - long

Hith - er our chil - dren bring To shout Thy praise.
Thou might - est save our race, And give us life.
Lead us where Thou hast trod, Make our faith strong.
U - nite and swell the song To Christ our King! A - MEN.

Music copyright, 1955, by John Ribble.
THE CHURCH: HYMNS FOR YOUTH

Just as I Am, Thine Own to Be

472

Marianne Hearn, 1887

JUST AS I AM: 8. 8. 8. 6.
Joseph Barnby, 1893

1. Just as I am, Thine own to be, Friend of the young, who lov-est me,
2. In the glad morn-ing of my day, My life to give, my vows to pay,
3. I would live ev - er in the light, I would work ev - er for the right,
4. Just as I am, young, strong, and free, To be the best that I can be

To con - se - crate my - self to Thee, O Je - sus Christ, I come.
With no re - serve and no de - lay, With all my heart I come.
I would serve Thee with all my might; There-fore, to Thee I come.
For truth, and right-eous-ness, and Thee, Lord of my life, I come. A-MEN.

Words used by permission of James Clarke & Co., Ltd.

THE CHURCH: HYMNS FOR YOUTH

Blest Be the Tie That Binds

473

DENNIS: S. M.
Hans G. Nägeli (1773-1836)
Arr. by Lowell Mason, 1845

John Fawcett, 1782

1. Blest be the tie that binds Our hearts in Chris - tian love:
2. Be - fore our Fa - ther's throne We pour our ar - dent prayers;
3. We share our mu - tual woes, Our mu - tual bur - dens bear,
4. From sor - row, toil, and pain, And sin, we shall be free;

The fel - low - ship of kin - dred minds Is like to that a - bove.
Our fears, our hopes, our aims, are one, Our com - forts and our cares.
And of - ten for each oth - er flows The sym - pa - thiz - ing tear.
And per - fect love and friend-ship reign Through all e - ter - ni - ty. A-MEN.

Alternative tune, "Boylston," Hymn 301.

THE CHURCH: CHRISTIAN FELLOWSHIP

474 O Brother Man

John Greenleaf Whittier, 1848

WELWYN: 11. 10. 11. 10.
Alfred Scott-Gatty, 1902

1. O broth-er man, fold to thy heart thy broth-er;
2. For he whom Je - sus loved has tru - ly spo - ken:
3. Fol - low with rev - erent steps the great ex - am - ple
4. Then shall all shack - les fall; the storm - y clang - or

Where pit - y dwells, the peace of God is there;
The ho - lier wor - ship which He deigns to bless
Of Him whose ho - ly work was do - ing good;
Of wild war mu - sic o'er the earth shall cease;

To wor - ship right - ly is to love each oth - er,
Re - stores the lost, and binds the spir - it bro - ken,
So shall the wide earth seem our Fa - ther's tem - ple,
Love shall tread out the bale - ful fire of an - ger,

Each smile a hymn, each kind - ly deed a prayer.
And feeds the wid - ow and the fa - ther - less.
Each lov - ing life a psalm of grat - i - tude.
And in its ash - es plant the tree of peace. A-MEN.

Words used by permission of Houghton Mifflin Company, authorized publishers. Music used by permission of Mrs. Denis Hyde and the Abbot of Downside.

THE CHURCH: CHRISTIAN FELLOWSHIP

[396]

Through the Night of Doubt and Sorrow 475

Bernhardt S. Ingemann, 1825
Trans. by Sabine Baring-Gould, 1867, 1875

ST. ASAPH: 8. 7. 8. 7. D.
William S. Bambridge, 1872

1. Through the night of doubt and sor-row On-ward goes the pil-grim band,
2. One the light of God's own pres-ence O'er His ran-somed peo-ple shed,
3. One the strain that lips of thou-sands Lift as from the heart of one,
4. On-ward, there-fore, pil-grim broth-ers, On-ward, with the cross our aid;

Sing-ing songs of ex-pec-ta-tion, March-ing to the Prom-ised Land:
Chas-ing far the gloom and ter-ror, Bright-ening all the path we tread;
One the con-flict, one the per-il, One the march in God be-gun;
Bear its shame, and fight its bat-tle, Till we rest be-neath its shade;

Clear be-fore us through the dark-ness Gleams and burns the guid-ing Light;
One the ob-ject of our jour-ney, One the faith which nev-er tires,
One the glad-ness of re-joic-ing On the far e-ter-nal shore,
Soon shall come the great a-wak-ing, Soon the rend-ing of the tomb,

Broth-er clasps the hand of broth-er, Step-ping fear-less through the night.
One the ear-nest look-ing for-ward, One the hope our God in-spires,
Where the One Al-might-y Fa-ther Reigns in love for-ev-er-more.
Then the scat-tering of all shad-ows And the end of toil and gloom. A-MEN.

Words copyright by J. Curwen & Sons, Ltd. Used by permission. Music used by permission of Marl-borough College.

THE CHURCH: CHRISTIAN FELLOWSHIP

476 Forgive, O Lord, Our Severing Ways

O MENSCH SIEH: 8. 8. 8.

John Greenleaf Whittier, 1883; alt.

Bohemian Brethren's *Gesangbuch*, 1566

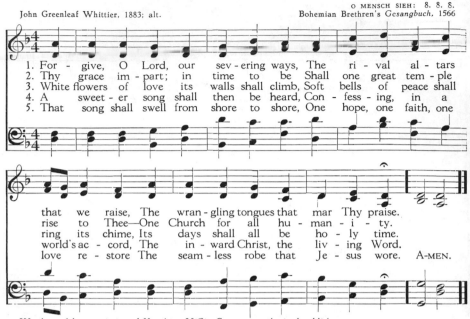

1. For - give, O Lord, our sev - ering ways, The ri - val al - tars
2. Thy grace im - part; in time to be Shall one great tem - ple
3. White flowers of love its walls shall climb, Soft bells of peace shall
4. A sweet - er song shall then be heard, Con - fess - ing, in a
5. That song shall swell from shore to shore, One hope, one faith, one

that we raise, The wran - gling tongues that mar Thy praise.
rise to Thee—One Church for all hu - man - i - ty.
ring its chime, Its days shall all be ho - ly time.
world's ac - cord, The in - ward Christ, the liv - ing Word.
love re - store The seam - less robe that Je - sus wore. A-MEN.

Words used by permission of Houghton Mifflin Company, authorized publishers.

477 Put Forth, O God, Thy Spirit's Might

DUNDEE (FRENCH): C. M.

Howard Chandler Robbins, 1937

Scottish Psalter, 1615

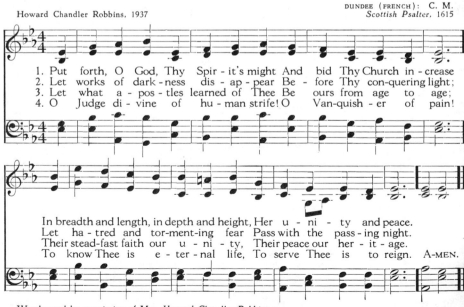

1. Put forth, O God, Thy Spir - it's might And bid Thy Church in - crease
2. Let works of dark - ness dis - ap - pear Be - fore Thy con-quering light;
3. Let what a - pos - tles learned of Thee Be ours from age to age;
4. O Judge di - vine of hu - man strife! O Van-quish - er of pain!

In breadth and length, in depth and height, Her u - ni - ty and peace.
Let ha - tred and tor-ment-ing fear Pass with the pass-ing night.
Their stead-fast faith our u - ni - ty, Their peace our her - it - age.
To know Thee is e - ter - nal life, To serve Thee is to reign. A-MEN.

Words used by permission of Mrs. Howard Chandler Robbins.

THE CHURCH: CHRISTIAN FELLOWSHIP

Hills of the North, Rejoice

Charles E. Oakley, 1870

LITTLE CORNARD: 6. 6. 6. 6. 8. 8.
Martin Shaw, 1915

1. Hills of the North, re - joice; Riv - er and moun - tain - spring,
2. Isles of the South - ern seas, Deep in your cor - al caves
3. Lands of the East, a - wake, Soon shall your sons be free;
4. Shores of the ut - most West, Ye that have wait - ed long,
5. Shout, while ye jour - ney home; Songs be in ev - ery mouth;

Hark to the ad - vent voice; Val - ley and low - land, sing; Though
Pent be each war - ring breeze, Lulled be your rest - less waves: He
The sleep of a - ges break, And rise to lib - er - ty. On
Un - vis - it - ed, un - blest, Break forth to swell - ing song; High
Lo, from the North we come, From East, and West, and South. Ci -

ab - sent long, your Lord is nigh; He judg - ment brings and vic - to - ry.
comes to reign with bound - less sway, And makes your wastes His great high - way.
your far hills, long cold and gray, Has dawned the ev - er - last - ing day.
raise the note, that Je - sus died, Yet lives and reigns, the Cru - ci - fied.
ty of God, the bond are free, We come to live and reign in thee! A - MEN.

Music copyright, 1915, by J. Curwen & Sons, Ltd. Used by permission.

THE KINGDOM OF GOD ON EARTH: BROTHERHOOD

479 In Christ There Is No East or West

(FIRST TUNE)

John Oxenham, 1908

ST. PETER: C. M.
Alexander R. Reinagle, c. 1830

1. In Christ there is no East or West, In Him no South or North;
2. In Him shall true hearts ev-ery-where Their high com-mun - ion find;
3. Join hands, then, broth-ers of the faith, What - e'er your race may be!
4. In Christ now meet both East and West, In Him meet South and North;

But one great fel - low - ship of love Through-out the whole wide earth.
His serv - ice is the gold - en cord Close - bind - ing all man-kind.
Who serves my Fa - ther as a son Is sure - ly kin to me.
All Christ - ly souls are one in Him Through-out the whole wide earth. A-MEN.

Words from *Bees in Amber*, by John Oxenham. Used by permission.

479 In Christ There Is No East or West

(SECOND TUNE)

John Oxenham, 1908

McKEE: C. M.
Negro melody
Adapted by Harry T. Burleigh, 1939

1. In Christ there is no East or West, In Him no South or North;
2. In Him shall true hearts ev - ery-where Their high com - mun - ion find;
3. Join hands, then, broth-ers of the faith, What-e'er your race may be!
4. In Christ now meet both East and West, In Him meet South and North;

But one great fel - low - ship of love Through-out the whole wide earth.
His serv - ice is the gold-en cord Close - bind - ing all man - kind.
Who serves my Fa-ther as a son Is sure - ly kin to me.
All Christ - ly souls are one in Him Through-out the whole wide earth. A-MEN.

Words from *Bees in Amber*, by John Oxenham. Used by permission. Music copyright, 1940, by Harry T. Burleigh. Used by permission.

THE KINGDOM OF GOD ON EARTH: BROTHERHOOD

Let There Be Light, Lord God of Hosts 480

William Merrill Vories, 1908

PENTECOST: L. M.
William Boyd, c. 1864

1. Let there be light, Lord God of Hosts, Let there be wis-dom on the earth;
2. With-in our pas-sioned hearts in-still The calm that end-eth strain and strife;
3. Give us the peace of vi-sion clear To see our broth-ers' good our own,
4. Let woe and waste of war-fare cease, That use-ful la-bor yet may build

Let broad hu-man-i-ty have birth, Let there be deeds, in-stead of boasts.
Make us Thy min-is-ters of life; Purge us from lusts that curse and kill.
To joy and suf-fer not a-lone—The love that cast-eth out all fear.
Its homes with love and laugh-ter filled; God, give Thy way-ward chil-dren peace. A-MEN.

Words used by permission of The American Peace Society. Music used by permission of Novello & Co., Ltd.

Lift Up Our Hearts, O King of Kings 481

John H. B. Masterman (1867-1933); alt.

TRURO: L. M.
T. Williams' *Psalmodia Evangelica*, 1789

1. Lift up our hearts, O King of Kings, To bright-er hopes and kind-lier things;
2. Thy world is wea-ry of its pain, Of sel-fish greed and fruit-less gain,
3. Al-might-y Fa-ther, who dost give The gift of life to all who live,

To vi-sions of a larg-er good, And ho-lier dreams of broth-er-hood.
Of tar-nished hon-or, false-ly strong, And all its an-cient deeds of wrong.
Look down on all earth's sin and strife, And lift us to a ho-lier life. A-MEN.

Words copyright by the Proprietors of *Hymns Ancient and Modern*. Used by permission.

THE KINGDOM OF GOD ON EARTH: BROTHERHOOD

482   The Light of God Is Falling

Louis F. Benson, 1910

GREENLAND: 7. 6. 7. 6. D.
Ascribed to J. Michael Haydn (1737-1806)

1. The light of God is fall - ing Up - on life's com - mon way;
2. Who shares his life's pure pleas - ures, And walks the hon - est road,
3. Where hu - man lives are throng - ing In toil and pain and sin,
4. Thy ran - somed host in glo - ry, All souls that sin and pray,

The Mas - ter's voice still call - ing, "Come, walk with Me to - day";
Who trades with heap - ing meas - ures, And lifts his broth - er's load,
While clois-tered hearts are long - ing To bring the King - dom in,
Turn toward the cross that bore Thee; "Be - hold the Man!" they say;

No du - ty can seem low - ly To him who lives with Thee,
Who turns the wrong down blunt - ly, And lends the right a hand,
O Christ, the Eld - er Broth - er Of proud and beat - en men,
And while Thy Church is plead - ing For all who would do good,

And all of life grows ho - ly, O Christ of Gal - i - lee!
He dwells in God's own coun - try, He tills the Ho - ly Land.
When they have found each oth - er, Thy King-dom will come then!
We hear Thy true voice lead - ing Our song of broth - er - hood. A-MEN.

THE KINGDOM OF GOD ON EARTH: BROTHERHOOD

O God of Love, O King of Peace

483

Henry W. Baker, 1861

QUEBEC: L. M.
Henry Baker, 1854

1. O God of love, O King of peace, Make wars through-out the world to cease;
2. Re - mem-ber, Lord, Thy works of old, The won-ders that our fa - thers told;
3. Whom shall we trust but Thee, O Lord? Where rest but on Thy faith-ful word?
4. Where saints and an - gels dwell a - bove, All hearts are knit in ho - ly love;

The wrath of sin - ful man re-strain: Give peace, O God, give peace a - gain!
Re - mem-ber not our sin's dark stain: Give peace, O God, give peace a - gain!
None ev - er called on Thee in vain: Give peace, O God, give peace a - gain!
O bind us in that heaven-ly chain: Give peace, O God, give peace a - gain! A-MEN.

Music copyright by W. Garrett Horder. Used by permission.

"Thy Kingdom Come," on Bended Knee

484

ST. FLAVIAN: C. M.
Day's Psalter, 1563

Frederick Lucian Hosmer, 1891

1. "Thy King-dom come," on bend - ed knee The pass-ing a - ges pray;
2. But the slow watch - es of the night Not less to God be - long;
3. And lo! al - read - y on the hills The flags of dawn ap - pear;
4. The day in whose clear-shin - ing light All wrong shall stand re - vealed;
5. When knowl-edge, hand in hand with peace, Shall walk the earth a - broad;

And faith-ful souls have yearned to see On earth that King-dom's day.
And for the ev - er - last - ing right The si - lent stars are strong.
Gird up your loins, ye proph - et souls, Pro-claim the day is near:
When jus - tice shall be clothed with might, And ev - ery hurt be healed.
The day of per - fect right-eous - ness, The prom-ised day of God. A-MEN.

THE KINGDOM OF GOD ON EARTH: WORLD FRIENDSHIP AND PEACE

[403]

485 Eternal God, Whose Power Upholds

Henry Hallam Tweedy, 1929

FOREST GREEN: C. M. D.
Traditional English melody
Arr. by R. Vaughan Williams, 1906

1. E - ter - nal God, whose power up - holds Both flower and flam - ing star,
2. O God of love, whose spir - it wakes In ev - ery hu - man breast,
3. O God of truth, whom sci - ence seeks And rev - erent souls a - dore,
4. O God of beau - ty, oft re - vealed In dreams of hu - man art,
5. O God of right-eous - ness and grace, Seen in the Christ, Thy Son,

To whom there is no here nor there, No time, no near nor far,
Whom love, and love a - lone, can know, In whom all hearts find rest:
Who light - est ev - ery ear - nest mind Of ev - ery clime and shore:
In speech that flows to mel - o - dy, In ho - li - ness of heart:
Whose life and death re - veal Thy face, By whom Thy will was done:

No a - lien race, no for - eign shore, No child un-sought, un-known:
Help us to spread Thy gra - cious reign Till greed and hate shall cease,
Dis - pel the gloom of er - ror's night, Of ig - no-rance and fear,
Teach us to ban all ug - li - ness That blinds our eyes to Thee,
In - spire Thy her - alds of good news To live Thy life di - vine,

O send us forth, Thy proph-ets true, To make all lands Thine own!
And kind-ness dwell in hu-man hearts, And all the earth find peace!
Un - til true wis - dom from a - bove Shall make life's path-way clear!
Till all shall know the love - li - ness Of lives made fair and free!
Till Christ is formed in all man-kind And ev - ery land is Thine! A-MEN.

Words copyright. 1929. by The Hymn Society of America. Used by permission. Music from *The English Hymnal.* Used by permission of Oxford University Press.
Alternative tune, "Materna." Hymn 510.

THE KINGDOM OF GOD ON EARTH: WORLD FRIENDSHIP AND PEACE

Father Eternal, Ruler of Creation

486

LANGHAM: 11. 10. 11. 10. 10.

Laurence Housman, 1919
Geoffrey Shaw, 1921

In unison

1. Fa - ther e - ter - nal, Rul - er of cre - a - tion, Spir - it of life, which moved ere form was made; Through the thick dark - ness cov - ering ev - ery na - tion, Light to man's blind - ness, O be Thou our aid: Thy King-dom come, O Lord, Thy will be done.

2. Ra - ces and peo - ples, lo! we stand di - vid - ed, And shar - ing not our griefs, no joy can share; By wars and tu - mults Love is mocked, de - rid - ed, His con-quering cross no king-dom wills to bear: Thy King-dom come, O Lord, Thy will be done.

3. En - vious of heart, blind - eyed, with tongues con-found-ed, Na - tion by na - tion still goes un - for - given; In wrath and fear, by jeal - ous - ies sur-round - ed, Build - ing proud towers which shall not reach to heaven: Thy King-dom come, O Lord, Thy will be done.

4. How shall we love Thee, ho - ly, hid - den Be - ing, If we love not the world which Thou hast made? O give us broth - er love for bet - ter see - ing Thy Word made flesh, and in a man-ger laid: Thy King-dom come, O Lord, Thy will be done. A - MEN.

Words from *Songs of Praise*, Enlarged Edition. Used by permission of Oxford University Press. Music used by permission of the League of Nations Union.

THE KINGDOM OF GOD ON EARTH: WORLD FRIENDSHIP AND PEACE

487 God the Omnipotent!

Stanzas 1. 2. Henry F. Chorley. 1842. alt.
Stanzas 3. 4. John Ellerton. 1870; alt.

RUSSIAN HYMN: 11. 10. 11. 9.
Alexis Lwoff, 1833

1. God the Om - nip - o - tent! King, who or - dain - est Thun - der Thy
2. God the All - mer - ci - ful! earth hath for - sak - en Thy ways all -
3. God the All - right - eous One! man hath de - fied Thee; Yet to e -
4. God the All - prov - i - dent! earth by Thy chas-tening, Yet shall to

clar - ion, the light - ning Thy sword; Show forth Thy pit - y on
ho - ly, and slight - ed Thy word; Bid not Thy wrath in its
ter - ni - ty stand - eth Thy word; False-hood and wrong shall not
free - dom and truth be re - stored; Through the thick dark - ness Thy

high where Thou reign-est: Give to us peace in our time, O Lord.
ter - rors a - wak - en: Give to us peace in our time, O Lord.
tar - ry be - side Thee: Give to us peace in our time, O Lord.
King - dom is has-tening: Thou wilt give peace in Thy time, O Lord. A-MEN.

488 Thy Kingdom Come, O Lord

Frederick Lucian Hosmer, 1891

ST. CECILIA: 6. 6. 6. 6.
Leighton G. Hayne, 1863

1. Thy King - dom come, O Lord, Wide - cir - cling as the sun;
2. One in the bond of peace, The serv - ice glad and free
3. Speed, speed the longed - for time Fore - told by rap - tured seers—
4. Till rise at last, to span Its firm foun - da - tions broad,

THE KINGDOM OF GOD ON EARTH: WORLD FRIENDSHIP AND PEACE

Thy Kingdom Come, O Lord

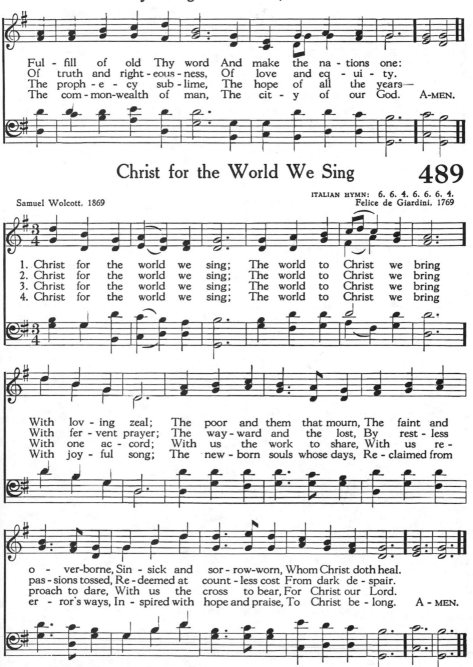

Ful - fill of old Thy word And make the na - tions one:
Of truth and right - eous - ness, Of love and eq - ui - ty.
The proph - e - cy sub - lime, The hope of all the years—
The com - mon-wealth of man, The cit - y of our God. A-MEN.

Christ for the World We Sing

489

ITALIAN HYMN: 6. 6. 4. 6. 6. 6. 4.

Samuel Wolcott, 1869

Felice de Giardini, 1769

1. Christ for the world we sing; The world to Christ we bring
2. Christ for the world we sing; The world to Christ we bring
3. Christ for the world we sing; The world to Christ we bring
4. Christ for the world we sing; The world to Christ we bring

With lov - ing zeal; The poor and them that mourn, The faint and
With fer - vent prayer; The way - ward and the lost, By rest - less
With one ac - cord; With us the work to share, With us re -
With joy - ful song; The new - born souls whose days, Re - claimed from

o - ver-borne, Sin - sick and sor - row-worn, Whom Christ doth heal.
pas - sions tossed, Re - deemed at count - less cost From dark de - spair.
proach to dare, With us the cross to bear, For Christ our Lord.
er - ror's ways, In - spired with hope and praise, To Christ be - long. A - MEN.

Alternative tune, "Hinman," Hymn 471.

THE KINGDOM OF GOD ON EARTH: WORLD FRIENDSHIP AND PEACE

[407]

490 Turn Back, O Man, Forswear Thy Foolish Ways

Clifford Bax, 1916

OLD 124TH: 10. 10. 10. 10. 10.
Genevan Psalter, 1551

1. Turn back, O man, for-swear thy fool-ish ways. Old now is earth, and none may count her days, Yet thou, her child, whose head is crowned with flame, Still wilt not hear thine in-ner God pro-claim— "Turn back, O man, for-swear thy fool-ish ways."

2. Earth might be fair and all men glad and wise. Age aft-er age their trag-ic em-pires rise, Built while they dream, and in that dream-ing weep: Would man but wake from out his haunt-ed sleep, Earth might be fair and all men glad and wise.

3. Earth shall be fair, and all her peo-ple one: Nor till that hour shall God's whole will be done. Now, e-ven now, once more from earth to sky, Peals forth in joy man's old, un-daunt-ed cry— "Earth shall be fair, and all her folk be one!" A-MEN.

Words used by permission of A. D. Peters.
THE KINGDOM OF GOD ON EARTH: WORLD FRIENDSHIP AND PEACE

[408]

O Zion, Haste, Thy Mission High Fulfilling 491

Mary Ann Thomson, 1868

TIDINGS: 11. 10. 11. 10. with Refrain
James Walch, 1875

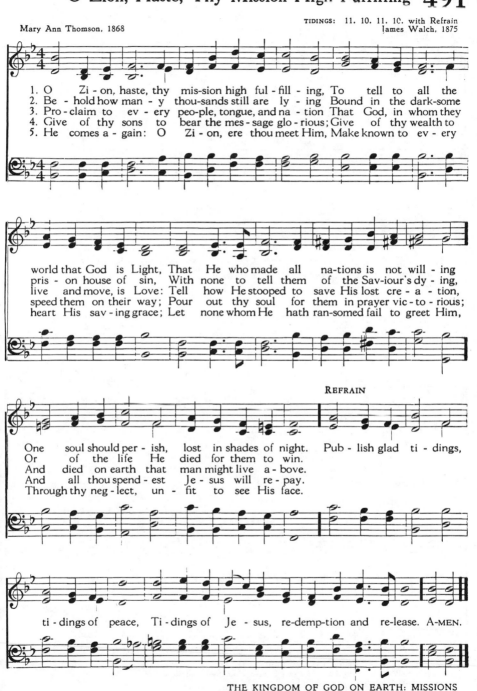

1. O Zi - on, haste, thy mis-sion high ful-fill - ing, To tell to all the
2. Be - hold how man - y thou-sands still are ly - ing Bound in the dark-some
3. Pro - claim to ev - ery peo-ple, tongue, and na - tion That God, in whom they
4. Give of thy sons to bear the mes - sage glo - rious; Give of thy wealth to
5. He comes a - gain: O Zi - on, ere thou meet Him, Make known to ev - ery

world that God is Light, That He who made all na-tions is not will - ing
pris - on house of sin, With none to tell them of the Sav-iour's dy - ing,
live and move, is Love: Tell how He stooped to save His lost cre - a - tion,
speed them on their way; Pour out thy soul for them in prayer vic - to - rious;
heart His sav - ing grace; Let none whom He hath ran-somed fail to greet Him,

REFRAIN

One soul should per - ish, lost in shades of night. Pub - lish glad ti - dings,
Or of the life He died for them to win.
And died on earth that man might live a - bove.
And all thou spend - est Je - sus will re - pay.
Through thy neg - lect, un - fit to see His face.

ti - dings of peace, Ti - dings of Je - sus, re-demp-tion and re-lease. A-MEN.

THE KINGDOM OF GOD ON EARTH: MISSIONS

492 Christ Is the World's True Light

George Wallace Briggs, 1931

ST. JOAN: 6. 7. 6. 7. 6. 6. 6. 6.
Percy E. B. Coller, 1941

1. Christ is the world's true Light, Its Cap-tain of sal - va - tion,
2. In Christ all ra - ces meet, Their an-cient feuds for - get - ting,
3. One Lord, in one great name U - nite us all who own Thee;

The Day-star clear and bright Of ev - ery man and na - tion;
The whole round world com - plete, From sun-rise to its set - ting:
Cast out our pride and shame That hin-der to en - throne Thee;

New life, new hope a - wakes, Wher - e'er men own His sway:
When Christ is throned as Lord, Men shall for - sake their fear,
The world has wait - ed long, Has trav - ailed long in pain;

Free-dom her bond - age breaks, And night is turned to day.
To plow-share beat the sword, To prun-ing hook the spear.
To heal its an - cient wrong, Come, Prince of Peace, and reign. A - MEN.

Words from *Songs of Praise*, Enlarged Edition. Used by permission of Oxford University Press. Music copyright, 1942, by The Church Pension Fund. Used by permission.

THE KINGDOM OF GOD ON EARTH: MISSIONS

Lord, Bless and Pity Us

493

From Psalm 67
The Psalter, 1912

ST. MICHAEL: S. M.
Melody by Louis Bourgeois, 1551
Adapted by William Crotch, 1836

1. Lord, bless and pit-y us, Shine on us with Thy face,
2. Thy praise, O gra-cious God, Let all the na-tions sing;
3. The na-tions Thou wilt judge And lead them in Thy ways;
4. The earth her fruit shall yield, For God, our God, will bless;

That all the earth Thy way may know And men may see Thy grace.
Let all men wor-ship Thee with joy And songs of glad-ness bring.
Let all men praise Thy name, O God, Let all the peo-ple praise.
We shall be blest, and all the world His glo-ry shall con-fess. A-MEN.

Ye Christian Heralds, Go Proclaim

494

Bourne Hall Draper, 1803; alt.

MISSIONARY CHANT: L. M.
Heinrich Christoph Zeuner, 1832

1. Ye Chris-tian her-alds, go pro-claim Sal-va-tion through Em-man-uel's name;
2. God shield you with a wall of fire, With ho-ly zeal your hearts in-spire,
3. And when our la-bors all are o'er, Then we shall meet to part no more;

To dis-tant climes the ti-dings bear, And plant the Rose of Shar-on there.
Bid rag-ing winds their fu-ry cease, And calm the tem-pests in-to peace.
Meet with the ran-somed throng to fall, And crown our Sav-iour Lord of all. A-MEN.

THE KINGDOM OF GOD ON EARTH: MISSIONS

495 Remember All the People

Percy Dearmer, 1929, 1931

FAR-OFF LANDS: 7. 6. 7. 6. D.
Melody in *Hemmets Koralbok*, 1921
Arr. by Charles Winfred Douglas, 1943

In unison

1. Re - mem - ber all the peo - ple Who live in far - off lands,
2. Some work in sul - try for - ests Where apes swing to and fro,
3. God bless the men and wom - en Who serve Him o - ver - sea;

In strange and love - ly cit - ies, Or roam the des - ert sands,
Some fish in might - y riv - ers, Some hunt a - cross the snow.
God raise up more to help them To set the na - tions free,

Or farm the moun - tain pas - tures, Or till the end - less plains
Re - mem - ber all God's chil - dren Who yet have nev - er heard
Till all the dis - tant peo - ple In ev - ery for - eign place

Where chil - dren wade through rice fields And watch the cam - el trains.
The truth that comes from Je - sus, The glo - ry of His Word.
Shall un - der - stand His King - dom And come in - to His grace. A-MEN.

Words from *Songs of Praise*, Enlarged Edition. Used by permission of Oxford University Press. Music used by permission of The Church Pension Fund.

THE KINGDOM OF GOD ON EARTH: MISSIONS

Jesus Shall Reign Where'er the Sun

496

From Psalm 72
Isaac Watts, 1719

DUKE STREET: L. M.
John Hatton, d. 1793

1. Je - sus shall reign wher-e'er the sun Does his suc-ces-sive jour-neys run;
2. For Him shall end-less prayer be made, And prais-es throng to crown His head;
3. Peo - ple and realms of ev - ery tongue Dwell on His love with sweet-est song;
4. Bless-ings a - bound wher-e'er He reigns; The pris-oner leaps to lose his chains,
5. Let ev-ery crea-ture rise and bring Pe - cu - liar hon-ors to our King;

His King-dom stretch from shore to shore, Till moons shall wax and wane no more.
His name, like sweet per - fume, shall rise With ev-ery morn - ing sac-ri - fice.
And in-fant voi - ces shall pro-claim Their ear - ly bless-ings on His name.
The wea-ry find e - ter - nal rest, And all the sons of want are blest.
An - gels de - scend with songs a - gain, And earth re - peat the loud A - men! A-MEN.

Arm of the Lord, Awake!

497

William Shrubsole (1759-1829)

CHURCH TRIUMPHANT: L. M.
James W. Elliott, 1874

1. Arm of the Lord, a - wake, a - wake! Put on Thy strength, the na-tions shake,
2. Say to the hea-then from Thy throne, "I am Je - ho - vah, God a - lone";
3. Let Zi - on's time of fa - vor come; O bring the tribes of Is - rael home;
4. Al - might - y God, Thy grace pro-claim In ev - ery clime of ev - ery name;

And let the world, a - dor - ing, see Tri-umphs of mer-cy wrought by Thee.
Thy voice their i-dols shall con-found, And cast their al - tars to the ground.
And let our won-dering eyes be-hold Gen - tiles and Jews in Je - sus' fold.
Let ad-verse powers be-fore Thee fall, And crown the Sav-iour Lord of all. A-MEN.

Music used by permission of Novello & Co., Ltd.

THE KINGDOM OF GOD ON EARTH: MISSIONS

498 Heralds of Christ, Who Bear the King's Commands

Laura S. Copenhaver(1868-1940)

NATIONAL HYMN: 10. 10. 10. 10.
George William Warren, 1894

*Trumpets, before
each stanza
(Optional)*

1. Her - alds of Christ, who bear the King's com-mands,
2. Through des-ert ways, dark fen, and deep mo - rass,
3. Where once the crook - ed trail in dark-ness wound
4. Lord, give us faith and strength the road to build,

Im - mor - tal ti - dings in your mor - tal hands,
Through jun - gles, slug - gish seas, and moun - tain pass,
Let march - ing feet and joy - ous song re - sound,
To see the prom - ise of the day ful - filled,

Pass on and car - ry swift the news ye bring:
Build ye the road, and fal - ter not, nor stay;
Where burn the fu - neral pyres, and cen - sers swing,
When war shall be no more and strife shall cease

Make straight, make straight the high - way of the King.
Pre - pare a - cross the earth the King's high - way.
Make straight, make straight the high - way of the King.
Up - on the high - way of the Prince of Peace. A - MEN.

Words used by permission of The Women's Missionary Society of the United Lutheran Church in America.
For lower key, see Hymn 515.
THE KINGDOM OF GOD ON EARTH: MISSIONS

[414]

The Morning Light Is Breaking

Samuel F. Smith, 1832; alt.

WEBB: 7. 6. 7. 6. D.
George J. Webb, 1837

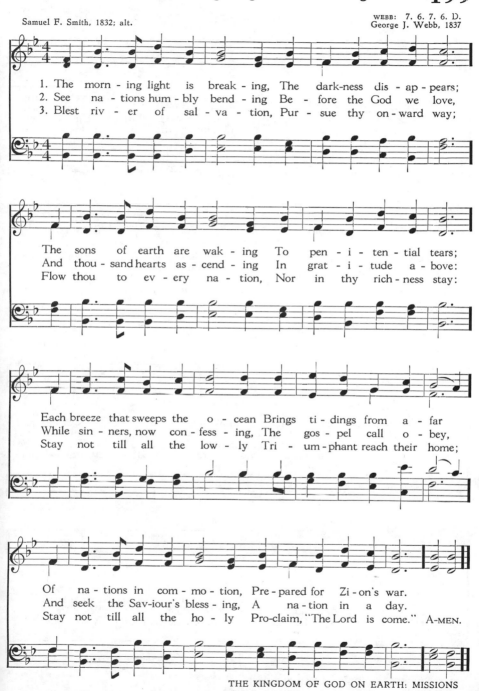

1. The morn-ing light is break-ing, The dark-ness dis-ap-pears;
2. See na-tions hum-bly bend-ing Be-fore the God we love,
3. Blest riv-er of sal-va-tion, Pur-sue thy on-ward way;

The sons of earth are wak-ing To pen-i-ten-tial tears;
And thou-sand hearts as-cend-ing In grat-i-tude a-bove:
Flow thou to ev-ery na-tion, Nor in thy rich-ness stay:

Each breeze that sweeps the o-cean Brings ti-dings from a-far
While sin-ners, now con-fess-ing, The gos-pel call o-bey,
Stay not till all the low-ly Tri-um-phant reach their home;

Of na-tions in com-mo-tion, Pre-pared for Zi-on's war.
And seek the Sav-iour's bless-ing, A na-tion in a day.
Stay not till all the ho-ly Pro-claim, "The Lord is come." A-MEN.

THE KINGDOM OF GOD ON EARTH: MISSIONS

500 God Is Working His Purpose Out

Arthur Campbell Ainger, 1894

PURPOSE: Irregular
Martin Shaw, 1931

In unison

1. God is work-ing His pur-pose out As year suc-
2. From ut-most east to ut-most west, Wher-e'er man's
3. March we forth in the strength of God, With the ban-ner of
4. All we can do is noth-ing worth Un-less God

ceeds to year: . . . . . God is work-ing His
foot hath trod, By the mouth of man-y
Christ un-furled, That the light of the glo-rious
bless-es the deed; . . . . . Vain-ly we hope for the

pur-pose out, And the time is draw-ing near; Near-er and
mes-sen-gers Goes forth the voice of God: "Give ear to
gos-pel of truth May shine through-out the world: Fight we the
har-vest-tide Till God gives life to the seed; Yet near-er and

near-er draws the time, The time that shall sure-ly be,
Me, ye con-ti-nents, Ye isles, give ear to Me,
fight with sor-row and sin To set their cap-tives free,
near-er draws the time, The time that shall sure-ly be,

THE KINGDOM OF GOD ON EARTH: MISSIONS

God Is Working His Purpose Out

When the earth shall be filled with the glo - ry of God
That the earth may be filled with the glo - ry of God
That the earth may be filled with the glo - ry of God
When the earth shall be filled with the glo - ry of God

St. 1, 2, 3   *St. 4*

As the wa - ters cov - er the sea.
As the wa - ters cov - er the sea.
As the wa - ters cov - er the sea.
As the wa - ters cov - er the sea. . . . . . A-MEN.

Words copyright by the author's heirs. Music copyright; reprinted from *Songs of Praise*. Enlarged Edition, by permission of Oxford University Press.

The Ends of All the Earth Shall Hear 501

From Psalm 22
The Psalter, 1912

VISION: L. M.
William H. Doane, 1873
Har. for this book, 1955

1. The ends of all the earth shall hear And turn un - to the Lord in fear;
2. For His the King-dom, His of right, He rules the na - tions by His might;
3. Both rich and poor, the bond and free, Shall wor-ship Him on bend - ed knee,

All kin-dreds of the earth shall own And wor-ship Him as God a - lone.
All earth to Him her hom-age brings, The Lord of Lords, the King of Kings.
And chil-dren's chil-dren shall pro-claim The glo-rious hon - or of His name. A-MEN.

Music copyright, 1955, by John Ribble.
THE KINGDOM OF GOD ON EARTH: MISSIONS

502 Christ Shall Have Dominion

ARMAGEDDON: 6. 5. 6. 5. D. with Refrain

From Psalm 72
The Psalter, 1912

German melody
Adapted by John Goss, 1871

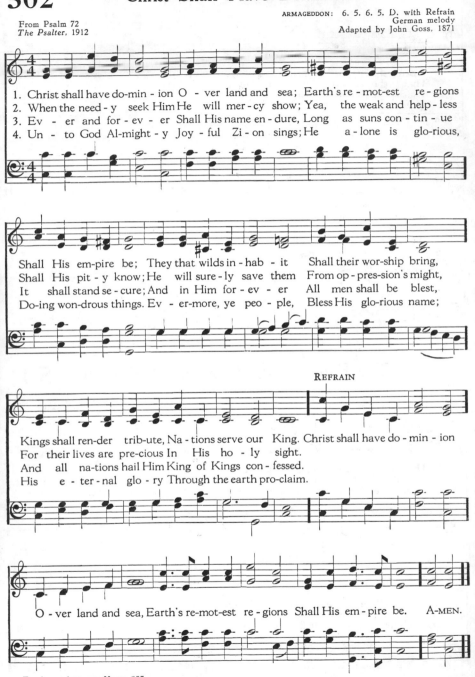

1. Christ shall have do-min-ion O-ver land and sea; Earth's re-mot-est re-gions
2. When the need-y seek Him He will mer-cy show; Yea, the weak and help-less
3. Ev-er and for-ev-er Shall His name en-dure, Long as suns con-tin-ue
4. Un-to God Al-might-y Joy-ful Zi-on sings; He a-lone is glo-rious,

Shall His em-pire be; They that wilds in-hab-it Shall their wor-ship bring,
Shall His pit-y know; He will sure-ly save them From op-pres-sion's might,
It shall stand se-cure; And in Him for-ev-er All men shall be blest,
Do-ing won-drous things. Ev-er-more, ye peo-ple, Bless His glo-rious name;

REFRAIN

Kings shall ren-der trib-ute, Na-tions serve our King. Christ shall have do-min-ion
For their lives are pre-cious In His ho-ly sight.
And all na-tions hail Him King of Kings con-fessed.
His e-ter-nal glo-ry Through the earth pro-claim.

O-ver land and sea, Earth's re-mot-est re-gions Shall His em-pire be. A-MEN.

For lower key, see Hymn 355.

THE KINGDOM OF GOD ON EARTH: MISSIONS

We Have Heard the Joyful Sound 503

Priscilla J. Owens. 1882; alt.

SALVATION: 7. 6. 7. 6. 7. 7. 7. 6.
William J. Kirkpatrick, 1882

1. We have heard the joy-ful sound: Je-sus saves! Je-sus saves!
2. Waft it on the roll-ing tide; Je-sus saves! Je-sus saves!
3. Give the winds a might-y voice, Je-sus saves! Je-sus saves!

Spread the ti-dings all a-round: Je-sus saves! Je-sus saves!
Tell to sin-ners far and wide: Je-sus saves! Je-sus saves!
Let the na-tions now re-joice— Je-sus saves! Je-sus saves!

Bear the news to ev-ery land, Climb the steeps and cross the waves;
Sing, ye is-lands of the sea; Ech-o back, ye o-cean caves;
Shout sal-va-tion full and free To each strand that o-cean laves,

On-ward!—'tis our Lord's com-mand; Je-sus saves! Je-sus saves!
Earth shall keep her ju-bi-lee: Je-sus saves! Je-sus saves!
This our song of vic-to-ry— Je-sus saves! Je-sus saves! A-MEN.

THE KINGDOM OF GOD ON EARTH: MISSIONS

[419]

504 We've a Story to Tell to the Nations

MESSAGE: 10. 8. 8. 7. with Refrain

"Colin Sterne," 1896

H. Ernest Nichol, 1896

1. We've a sto - ry to tell to the na - tions That shall turn their
2. We've a song to be sung to the na - tions That shall lift their
3. We've a mes - sage to give to the na - tions, That the Lord who
4. We've a Sav - iour to show to the na - tions, Who the path of

hearts to the right, A sto - ry of truth and mer - cy,
hearts to the Lord; A song that shall con - quer e - vil
reign - eth a - bove Hath sent us His Son to save us,
sor - row hath trod, That all of the world's great peo - ples

A sto - ry of peace and light, A sto - ry of peace and light.
And shat - ter the spear and sword, And shat - ter the spear and sword.
And show us that God is love, And show us that God is love.
Might come to the truth of God, Might come to the truth of God.

REFRAIN

For the dark-ness shall turn to dawn - ing, And the dawn-ing to noon-day bright,

And Christ's great Kingdom shall come on earth, The King-dom of love and light. A-MEN.

Words and music copyright. Used by permission of H. Ernest Nichol & Son.

THE KINGDOM OF GOD ON EARTH: MISSIONS

[420]

Hail to the Brightness of Zion's Glad Morning! 505

Thomas Hastings, 1832

WESLEY: 11. 10. 11. 10.
Lowell Mason, 1833

1. Hail to the bright-ness of Zi-on's glad morn-ing!
2. Hail to the bright-ness of Zi-on's glad morn-ing,
3. Lo, in the des-ert rich flow-ers are spring-ing,
4. See, from all lands, from the isles of the o-cean,

Joy to the lands that in dark-ness have lain!
Long by the proph-ets of Is-rael fore-told!
Streams ev-er co-pious are glid-ing a-long;
Praise to the Sav-iour as-cend-ing on high;

Hushed be the ac-cents of sor-row and mourn-ing;
Hail to the mil-lions from bond-age re-turn-ing!
Loud from the moun-tain-tops ech-oes are ring-ing,
Fal-len the en-gines of war and com-mo-tion,

Zi-on in tri-umph be-gins her mild reign.
Gen-tiles and Jews the blest vi-sion be-hold.
Wastes rise in ver-dure, and min-gle in song.
Shouts of sal-va-tion are rend-ing the sky. A-MEN.

THE KINGDOM OF GOD ON EARTH: MISSIONS

[421]

506 Fling Out the Banner! Let It Float

From Psalm 60
George W. Doane, 1848

WALTHAM: L. M.
John Baptiste Calkin, 1872

1. Fling out the ban-ner! let it float Sky-ward and sea-ward, high and wide;
2. Fling out the ban-ner! dis-tant lands Shall see from far the glo-rious sight,
3. Fling out the ban-ner! sin-sick souls That sink and per-ish in the strife,
4. Fling out the ban-ner! let it float Sky-ward and sea-ward, high and wide;
5. Fling out the ban-ner! wide and high, Sea-ward and sky-ward, let it shine:

The sun that lights its shin-ing folds, The cross on which the Sav-iour died.
And na-tions, crowd-ing to be born, Bap-tize their spir-its in its light.
Shall touch in faith its ra-diant hem And spring im-mor-tal in-to life.
Our glo-ry, on-ly in the cross; Our on-ly hope, the Cru-ci-fied!
Nor skill, nor might, nor mer-it ours; We con-quer on-ly in that sign. A-MEN.

THE KINGDOM OF GOD ON EARTH: MISSIONS

507 Where Cross the Crowded Ways of Life

Frank Mason North, 1903

GERMANY: L. M.
William Gardiner's *Sacred Melodies*, 1815

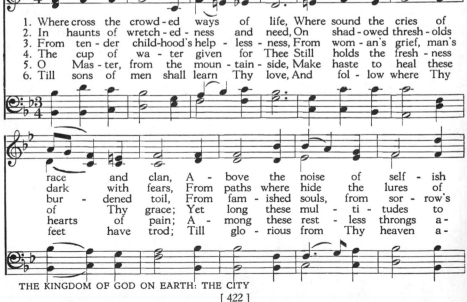

1. Where cross the crowd-ed ways of life, Where sound the cries of
2. In haunts of wretch-ed-ness and need, On shad-owed thresh-olds
3. From ten-der child-hood's help-less-ness, From wom-an's grief, man's
4. The cup of wa-ter given for Thee Still holds the fresh-ness
5. O Mas-ter, from the moun-tain-side, Make haste to heal these
6. Till sons of men shall learn Thy love, And fol-low where Thy

race and clan, A-bove the noise of self-ish
dark with fears, From paths where hide the lures of
bur-dened toil, From fam-ished souls, from sor-row's
of Thy grace; Yet long these mul-ti-tudes to
hearts of pain; A-mong these rest-less throngs a-
feet have trod; Till glo-rious from Thy heaven a-

THE KINGDOM OF GOD ON EARTH: THE CITY

[422]

Where Cross the Crowded Ways of Life

strife, We hear Thy voice, O Son of Man.
greed, We catch the vi - sion of Thy tears.
stress, Thy heart has nev - er known re - coil.
see The sweet com - pas - sion of Thy face.
bide, O tread the cit - y's streets a - gain,
bove Shall come the Cit - y of our God. A - MEN.

O Holy City, Seen of John 508

MORNING SONG: 8. 6. 8. 6. 8. 6.
Melody in *Kentucky Harmony*, 1816
Har. by Charles Winfred Douglas, 1940

Walter Russell Bowie, 1909

1. O Ho - ly Cit - y, seen of John, Where Christ, the Lamb, doth reign,
2. O shame to us who rest con - tent While lust and greed for gain
3. Give us, O God, the strength to build The cit - y that hath stood
4. Al - read - y in the mind of God That cit - y ris - eth fair.

With - in whose four-square walls shall come No night, nor need, nor pain,
In street and shop and ten - e - ment Wring gold from hu - man pain,
Too long a dream, whose laws are love, Whose ways are broth-er-hood,
Lo, how its splen-dor chal - len - ges The souls that great - ly dare—

And where the tears are wiped from eyes That shall not weep a - gain!
And bit - ter lips in blind de - spair Cry, "Christ hath died in vain"!
And where the sun that shin - eth is God's grace for hu - man good.
Yea, bids us seize the whole of life And build its glo - ry there. A-MEN.

Words from *Hymns of the Kingdom of God*, Coffin and Vernon, copyright, 1910. Used by permission of Harper & Brothers, publishers. Music used by permission of The Church Pension Fund.

THE KINGDOM OF GOD ON EARTH: THE CITY

509 From Ocean Unto Ocean

Robert Murray, 1880

MISSIONARY HYMN: 7. 6. 7. 6. D.
Lowell Mason, 1823

1. From o-cean un-to o-cean Our land shall own Thee Lord,
2. O Christ, for Thine own glo-ry, And for our coun-try's weal,
3. Our Sav-iour King, de-fend us, And guide where we should go;

And, filled with true de-vo-tion, O-bey Thy sov-ereign word.
We hum-bly plead be-fore Thee, Thy-self in us re-veal;
Forth with Thy mes-sage send us, Thy love and light to show;

Our prai-ries and our moun-tains, For-est and fer-tile field,
And may we know, Lord Je-sus, The touch of Thy dear hand;
Till, fired with true de-vo-tion, En-kin-dled by Thy word,

Our riv-ers, lakes, and foun-tains, To Thee shall trib-ute yield.
And, healed of our dis-eas-es, The tempt-er's power with-stand.
From o-cean un-to o-cean Our land shall own Thee Lord. A-MEN.

Words used by permission of Mrs. Robert H. Murray.
Alternative tune, "Lancashire," Hymn 208.
THE KINGDOM OF GOD ON EARTH: THE NATION

O Beautiful for Spacious Skies

510

Katharine Lee Bates, 1893, 1904
Descant

MATERNA: C. M. D.
Samuel A. Ward, 1882. Descant by William H. Schutt, 1940

1. O beau - ti - ful for spa - cious skies, For am - ber waves of grain,
2. O beau - ti - ful for pil - grim feet, Whose stern, im - pas - sioned stress
3. O beau - ti - ful for he - roes proved In lib - er - at - ing strife,
4. O beau - ti - ful for pa - triot dream That sees, be - yond the years,

For pur - ple moun - tain maj - es - ties A - bove the fruit - ed plain!
A thor - ough-fare for free - dom beat A - cross the wil - der - ness!
Who more than self their coun - try loved, And mer - cy more than life!
Thine al - a - bas - ter cit - ies gleam, Un-dimmed by hu - man tears!

A - mer - i - ca! A - mer - i - ca! God shed His grace on thee,
A - mer - i - ca! A - mer - i - ca! God mend thine ev - ery flaw,
A - mer - i - ca! A - mer - i - ca! May God thy gold re - fine,
A - mer - i - ca! A - mer - i - ca! God shed His grace on thee,

And crown thy good with broth - er-hood From sea to shin - ing sea!
Con - firm thy soul in self - con-trol, Thy lib - er - ty in law!
Till all suc-cess be no - ble-ness And ev - ery gain di - vine!
And crown thy good with broth - er-hood From sea to shin - ing sea! A-MEN.

Descant from *Hymnal for Christian Worship.* Used by permission of John Knox Press.
THE KINGDOM OF GOD ON EARTH: THE NATION

511 O God of Earth and Altar

LLANGLOFFAN: 7. 6. 7. 6. D.
Welsh hymn melody
D. Evans' *Hymnau a Thonau*, 1865

Gilbert K. Chesterton, 1906

1. O God of earth and al - tar, Bow down and hear our cry;
2. From all that ter - ror teach - es, From lies of tongue and pen;
3. Tie in a liv - ing teth - er The prince and priest and thrall;

Our earth - ly rul - ers fal - ter, Our peo - ple drift and die;
From all the eas - y speech - es That com - fort cru - el men;
Bind all our lives to - geth - er, Smite us and save us all;

The walls of gold en - tomb us, The swords of scorn di - vide;
From sale and prof - a - na - tion Of hon - or and the sword;
In ire and ex - ul - ta - tion A - flame with faith, and free,

Take not Thy thun-der from us, But take a - way our pride.
From sleep and from dam - na - tion, De - liv - er us, good Lord!
Lift up a liv - ing na - tion, A sin - gle sword to Thee. A - MEN.

Words copyright. Reprinted from *The English Hymnal* by permission of Oxford University Press.

THE KINGDOM OF GOD ON EARTH: THE NATION

Not Alone for Mighty Empire

William Pierson Merrill, 1909
In unison

GENEVA: 8. 7. 8. 7. D.
George Henry Day, 1940

1. Not a-lone for might-y em-pire Stretch-ing far o'er land and sea,
2. Not for bat-tle-ship and for-tress, Not for con-quests of the sword,
3. For the ar-mies of the faith-ful, Souls that passed and left no name;
4. God of jus-tice, save the peo-ple From the clash of race and creed,

Not a-lone for boun-teous har-vests, Lift we up our hearts to Thee.
But for con-quests of the spir-it Give we thanks to Thee, O Lord;
For the glo-ry that il-lu-mines Pa-triot lives of death-less fame;
From the strife of class and fac-tion, Make our na-tion free in-deed.

Stand-ing in the liv-ing pres-ent, Mem-o-ry and hope be-tween,
For the price-less gift of free-dom, For the home, the church, the school,
For our proph-ets and a-pos-tles, Loy-al to the liv-ing Word,
Keep her faith in sim-ple man-hood Strong as when her life be-gan,

Lord, we would with deep thanks-giv-ing Praise Thee most for things un-seen.
For the o-pen door to man-hood In a land the peo-ple rule.
For all he-roes of the Spir-it, Give we thanks to Thee, O Lord.
Till it find its full fru-i-tion In the broth-er-hood of man. A-MEN.

Words used by permission of the author. Music copyright, 1942, by The Church Pension Fund. Used by permission.

Alternative tune, "Austrian Hymn," Hymn 434.

THE KINGDOM OF GOD ON EARTH: THE NATION

513 My Country, 'Tis of Thee

Samuel F. Smith, 1832

AMERICA: 6. 6. 4. 6. 6. 6. 4.
Thesaurus Musicus, 1740

1. My coun-try, 'tis of thee, Sweet land of lib-er-ty,
2. My na-tive coun-try, thee, Land of the no-ble free,
3. Let mu-sic swell the breeze, And ring from all the trees
4. Our fa-thers' God, to Thee, Au-thor of lib-er-ty,

Of thee I sing; Land where my fa-thers died, Land of the
Thy name I love; I love thy rocks and rills, Thy woods and
Sweet free-dom's song; Let mor-tal tongues a-wake; Let all that
To Thee we sing; Long may our land be bright With free-dom's

pil-grims' pride, From ev-ery moun-tain-side Let free-dom ring.
tem-pled hills; My heart with rap-ture thrills Like that a-bove.
breathe par-take; Let rocks their si-lence break, The sound pro-long.
ho-ly light; Pro-tect us by Thy might, Great God, our King. A-MEN.

514 God Bless Our Native Land

Stanzas 1, 2, Siegfried A. Mahlmann, 1815
Trans. by Charles T. Brooks and John S. Dwight, c. 1845
Stanza 3, William E. Hickson, 1836

1. God bless our native land;
Firm may she ever stand
Through storm and night:
When the wild tempests rave,
Ruler of wind and wave,
Do Thou our country save
By Thy great might.

2. For her our prayer shall rise
To God above the skies;
On Him we wait;
Thou who art ever nigh,
Guarding with watchful eye,
To Thee aloud we cry,
God save the State!

3. Not for this land alone,
But be God's mercies shown
From shore to shore;
And may the nations see
That men should brothers be,
And form one family
The wide world o'er. AMEN.

This hymn may be sung to the tune "America," above.

THE KINGDOM OF GOD ON EARTH: THE NATION

God of Our Fathers, Whose Almighty Hand 515

Daniel C. Roberts, 1876

NATIONAL HYMN: 10. 10. 10. 10.
George William Warren, 1894

Trumpets, before each stanza
(Optional)

1. God of our fa - thers, whose al-might - y
2. Thy love di - vine hath led us in the
3. From war's a - larms, from dead - ly pes - ti -
4. Re - fresh Thy peo - ple on their toil-some

hand   Leads forth in beau - ty all the star - ry band
past;   In this free land by Thee our lot is cast;
lence, Be Thy strong arm our ev - er-sure de - fense;
way,   Lead us from night to nev - er-end-ing day;

Of shin - ing worlds in splen - dor through the skies,
Be Thou our Rul - er, Guard - ian, Guide, and Stay;
Thy true re - li - gion in our hearts in - crease,
Fill all our lives with love and grace di - vine,

Our grate - ful songs be - fore Thy throne a - rise.
Thy word our law, Thy paths our cho - sen way.
Thy boun-teous good - ness nour - ish us in peace.
And glo - ry, laud, and praise be ev - er Thine. A - MEN.

For higher key, see Hymn 498.

THE KINGDOM OF GOD ON EARTH: THE NATION

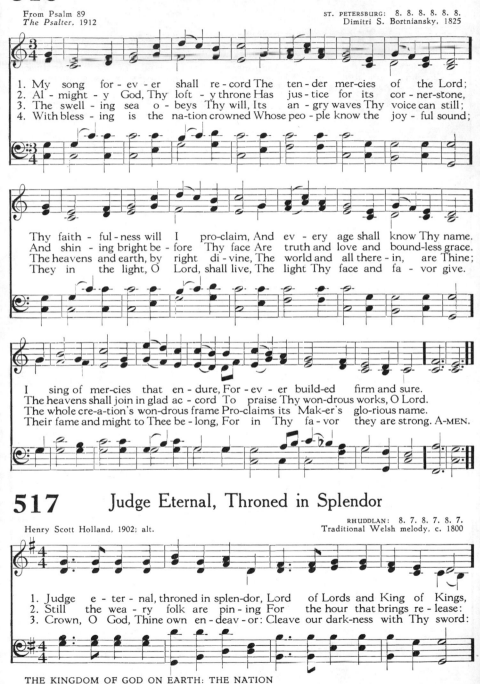

516

My Song Forever Shall Record

From Psalm 89
The Psalter, 1912

ST. PETERSBURG: 8. 8. 8. 8. 8. 8.
Dimitri S. Bortniansky, 1825

1. My song for-ev-er shall re-cord The ten-der mer-cies of the Lord;
2. Al-might-y God, Thy loft-y throne Has jus-tice for its cor-ner-stone;
3. The swell-ing sea o-beys Thy will, Its an-gry waves Thy voice can still;
4. With bless-ing is the na-tion crowned Whose peo-ple know the joy-ful sound;

Thy faith-ful-ness will I pro-claim, And ev-ery age shall know Thy name.
And shin-ing bright be-fore Thy face Are truth and love and bound-less grace.
The heavens and earth, by right di-vine, The world and all there-in, are Thine;
They in the light, O Lord, shall live, The light Thy face and fa-vor give.

I sing of mer-cies that en-dure, For-ev-er build-ed firm and sure.
The heavens shall join in glad ac-cord To praise Thy won-drous works, O Lord.
The whole cre-a-tion's won-drous frame Pro-claims its Mak-er's glo-rious name.
Their fame and might to Thee be-long, For in Thy fa-vor they are strong. A-MEN.

517

Judge Eternal, Throned in Splendor

Henry Scott Holland, 1902; alt.

RHUDDLAN: 8. 7. 8. 7. 8. 7.
Traditional Welsh melody, c. 1800

1. Judge e-ter-nal, throned in splen-dor, Lord of Lords and King of Kings,
2. Still the wea-ry folk are pin-ing For the hour that brings re-lease:
3. Crown, O God, Thine own en-deav-or: Cleave our dark-ness with Thy sword:

THE KINGDOM OF GOD ON EARTH: THE NATION

[430]

Judge Eternal, Throned in Splendor

With Thy liv-ing fire of judg-ment Purge our land of bit-ter things:
And the cit-y's crowd-ed clang-or Cries a-loud for sin to cease;
Feed the faint and hun-gry peo-ple With the rich-ness of Thy word:

Sol-ace all its wide do-min-ion With the heal-ing of Thy wings.
And the home-steads and the wood-lands Plead in si-lence for their peace.
Cleanse the bod-y of this na-tion Through the glo-ry of the Lord. A-MEN.

Words slightly altered from *The English Hymnal.* Used by permission of Oxford University Press.

THE KINGDOM OF GOD ON EARTH: THE NATION

Arise, O Lord, Our God, Arise 518

From Psalm 132
The Psalter, 1912

FEDERAL STREET: L. M.
Henry K. Oliver, 1832

1. A - rise, O Lord, our God, a - rise And en - ter now in - to Thy rest;
2. Thy gra-cious cov - enant, Lord, ful - fill, Turn not a-way from us Thy face;
3. Thy Zi - on Thou hast cho - sen, Lord, And Thou hast said, I love her well,
4. I will a - bun - dant - ly pro - vide For Zi - on's good, the Lord hath said;
5. Sal - va - tion shall a - dorn her priests, Her saints shall shout with joy di - vine,

O let this house be Thy a - bode, For-ev - er with Thy pres-ence blest.
Es - tab-lish Thou Mes-si - ah's throne And let Him reign with-in this place.
This is my con-stant rest - ing place, And here will I de-light to dwell.
I will sup-ply her dai - ly need And sat-is-fy her poor with bread.
Mes - si-ah's power shall be re - vealed, His glo-ry in His Church shall shine. A-MEN.

Alternative tune, "Herr Jesu Christ," Hymn 555.

MISCELLANEOUS: THE DEDICATION OF A CHURCH

519 We Dedicate This Temple

Ernest K. Emurian, 1948

AURELIA: 7. 6. 7. 6. D.
Samuel S. Wesley, 1864

1. We ded - i - cate this tem - ple, O Fa - ther, un - to Thee,
2. We ded - i - cate this tem - ple To Christ, the Lord of love,
3. We ded - i - cate this tem - ple, O Spir - it from on high,
4. We ded - i - cate this tem - ple, This la - bor of our hands,

The God of an - cient a - ges, And a - ges yet to be;
Who brought God's rev - e - la - tion, The King - dom from a - bove;
To Thee, in our thanks - giv - ing That Thou art al - ways nigh;
To Fa - ther, Son, and Spir - it, Whose tem - ple ev - er stands

That here our hearts may wor - ship, And here our songs as - cend,
That we may learn His good - ness, His god - li - ness and grace,
To com - fort us in sor - row, To strength - en in dis - tress;
In hearts that learn to love Thee, And minds that com - pre - hend;

In lov - ing ad - o - ra - tion And praise that knows no end.
Who holds all men and na - tions With - in His love's em - brace.
That we, through truth and mer - cy, May walk in ho - li - ness.
In wills em - powered to wit - ness Thy King - dom with - out end! A - MEN.

Words copyright, 1952, by Ernest K. Emurian. Used by permission.
MISCELLANEOUS: THE DEDICATION OF A CHURCH

God of the Prophets!

Stanzas 1, 3, 4, 5, Denis Wortman, 1884; alt., 1955
Stanza 2, John Underwood Stephens, 1955

TOULON: 10. 10. 10. 10.
Genevan Psalter, 1551

1. God of the proph - ets! Bless the proph - ets' sons;
2. A - noint them proph - ets! Bold and el - o - quent,
3. A - noint them priests! Strong in - ter - ces - sors they
4. A - noint them kings! Aye, king - ly kings, O Lord:
5. Make them a - pos - tles! Her - alds of Thy cross;

E - li - jah's man - tle o'er E - li - sha cast;
Thy whis - pered word from house - tops to pro - claim,
For par - don, and for char - i - ty and peace!
A - noint them with the spir - it of Thy Son:
Forth may they go to tell all realms Thy grace;

Each age its sol - emn task may claim but once;
E - vil to lash with love's pure chas - tise - ment,
O might, with them, the world, though gone a - stray,
Theirs, not a jew - eled crown, a blood-stained sword;
In - spired by Thee, may they count all but loss,

Make each one no - bler, strong - er than the last.
The cap - tive soul to free in Je - sus' name.
Pass in - to Christ's pure life of sac - ri - fice!
Theirs, by sweet love, for Christ a king - dom won.
And stand at last with joy be - fore Thy face. A-MEN.

Stanza 2 copyright, 1955, by John Ribble.

MISCELLANEOUS: THE MINISTRY

521 Eternal Father, Strong to Save

William Whiting, 1860; alt.

MELITA: 8. 8. 8. 8. 8. 8.
John B. Dykes, 1861

1. E - ter - nal Fa - ther, strong to save, Whose arm doth bind the
2. O Sav - iour, whose al - might - y word The winds and waves sub -
3. O sa - cred Spir - it, who didst brood Up - on the cha - os
4. O Trin - i - ty of love and power, Our breth - ren shield in

rest - less wave, Who biddest the might - y o - cean deep
mis - sive heard, Who walk - edst on the foam - ing deep
dark and rude, Who badest its an - gry tu - mult cease,
dan - ger's hour; From rock and tem - pest, fire and foe,

Its own ap - point - ed lim - its keep: O hear us when we
And calm a - mid its rage didst sleep: O hear us when we
And gav - est light and life and peace: O hear us when we
Pro - tect them where - so - e'er they go; And ev - er let there

cry to Thee For those in per - il on the sea.
cry to Thee For those in per - il on the sea.
cry to Thee For those in per - il on the sea.
rise to Thee Glad hymns of praise from land and sea. A-MEN.

MISCELLANEOUS: TRAVELERS

[434]

Almighty Father, Strong to Save

Stanzas 1, 4, William Whiting, 1860; alt., 1937
Stanzas 2, 3, Robert Nelson Spencer, 1937

1. Almighty Father, strong to save,
   Whose arm hath bound the restless wave,
   Who biddest the mighty ocean deep
   Its own appointed limits keep:
   O hear us when we cry to Thee
   For those in peril on the sea.

2. O Christ, the Lord of hill and plain
   O'er which our traffic runs amain
   By mountain pass or valley low;
   Wherever, Lord, Thy brethren go,
   Protect them by Thy guarding hand
   From every peril on the land.

3. O Spirit, whom the Father sent
   To spread abroad the firmament;
   O Wind of heaven, by Thy might
   Save all who dare the eagle's flight,
   And keep them by Thy watchful care
   From every peril in the air.

4. O Trinity of love and power,
   Our brethren shield in danger's hour;
   From rock and tempest, fire and foe,
   Protect them wheresoe'er they go;
   Thus evermore shall rise to Thee
   Glad praise from air and land and sea.
   AMEN.

Used by permission of The Church Pension Fund.
This hymn may be sung to the tune "Melita," on opposite page.

MISCELLANEOUS: TRAVELERS

O God, Beneath Thy Guiding Hand

523

DUKE STREET: L. M.
John Hatton, d. 1793

Leonard Bacon, 1838

1. O   God, be-neath Thy guid - ing hand Our ex-iled fa - thers crossed the sea;
2. Thou heardest, well pleased, the song, the prayer: Thy bless-ing came; and still its power
3. Laws, free-dom, truth, and faith in   God Came with those ex-iles o'er the waves;
4. And   here Thy name, O   God of   love, Their chil-dren's chil-dren shall a - dore,

And when they trod the win-try strand, With prayer and psalm they wor-shiped Thee.
Shall   on-ward, through all a - ges, bear The mem-ory of   that ho - ly hour.
And, where their pil - grim feet have trod, The God they trust-ed guards their graves.
Till   these e - ter-nal hills re-move, And spring a-dorns the earth no more. A-MEN.

For lower key, see Hymn 496.

MISCELLANEOUS: THANKSGIVING

[435]

524 We Plow the Fields

Matthias Claudius, 1782
Trans. by Jane M. Campbell, 1861

DRESDEN: 7. 6. 7. 6. D. with Refrain
Johann A. P. Schulz, 1800

1. We plow the fields, and scat-ter The good seed on the land, But it is
2. He on-ly is the Mak-er Of all things near and far; He paints the
3. We thank Thee, then, O Fa-ther, For all things bright and good, The seed-time

fed and wa-tered By God's al-might-y hand; He sends the snow in
way-side flow-er, He lights the eve-ning star; The winds and waves o-
and the har-vest, Our life, our health, our food; Ac-cept the gifts we

win-ter, The warmth to swell the grain, The breez-es and the sun-shine, And
bey Him, By Him the birds are fed; Much more to us, His chil-dren, He
of-fer, For all Thy love im-parts, And what Thou most de-sir-est, Our

REFRAIN

soft re-fresh-ing rain.
gives our dai-ly bread. All good gifts a-round us Are sent from heaven a-
hum-ble, thank-ful hearts.

bove; Then thank the Lord, O thank the Lord For all His love. A-MEN.

Come, Ye Thankful People, Come

525

Henry Alford, 1844

ST. GEORGE'S, WINDSOR: 7. 7. 7. 7. D.
George J. Elvey, 1859

1. Come, ye thank-ful peo-ple, come, Raise the song of har-vest home:
2. All the world is God's own field, Fruit un-to His praise to yield;
3. For the Lord our God shall come, And shall take His har-vest home;
4. E - ven so, Lord, quick-ly come To Thy fi - nal har-vest home;

All is safe-ly gath-ered in, Ere the win-ter storms be - gin;
Wheat and tares to - geth - er sown, Un - to joy or sor-row grown;
From His field shall in that day All of - fens - es purge a - way;
Gath - er Thou Thy peo - ple in, Free from sor - row, free from sin;

God, our Mak - er, doth pro - vide For our wants to be sup-plied:
First the blade, and then the ear, Then the full corn shall ap - pear:
Give His an - gels charge at last In the fire the tares to cast,
There for - ev - er pu - ri - fied, In Thy pres - ence to a - bide:

Come to God's own tem - ple, come, Raise the song of har-vest home.
Lord of har-vest, grant that we Whole-some grain and pure may be.
But the fruit - ful ears to store In His gar - ner ev - er-more.
Come, with all Thine an - gels, come, Raise the glo-rious har-vest home. A-MEN.

526 Ring Out the Old, Ring In the New

Alfred Tennyson, 1849

DEUS TUORUM MILITUM: L. M.
Grenoble church melody

1. Ring out the old, ring in the new; Ring, hap-py bells, a-cross the snow;
2. Ring out a slow-ly dy-ing cause, And an-cient forms of par-ty strife;
3. Ring out old shapes of foul dis-ease; Ring out the nar-rowing lust of gold;
4. Ring in the val-iant man and free, The larg-er heart, the kind-lier hand;

The year is go-ing, let him go; Ring out the false, ring in the true.
Ring in the no-bler modes of life, With sweet-er man-ners, pur - er laws.
Ring out the thou-sand wars of old; Ring in the thou-sand years of peace.
Ring out the dark-ness of the land; Ring in the Christ that is to be. A - MEN.

Alternative tune, "Mozart," Hymn 388.

527 Great God, We Sing That Mighty Hand

Philip Doddridge (1702-1751)

WAREHAM: L. M.
William Knapp, 1738

1. Great God, we sing that might-y hand By which sup - port-ed still we stand;
2. By day, by night, at home, a-broad, Still are we guard-ed by our God;
3. With grate-ful hearts the past we own; The fu - ture, all to us un-known,
4. In scenes ex - alt - ed or de-pressed, Thou art our Joy, and Thou our Rest;

The o-pening year Thy mer-cy shows; That mer - cy crowns it till it close.
By His in - ces - sant boun-ty fed, By His un - err - ing coun-sel led.
We to Thy guard-ian care com-mit, And peace-ful leave be - fore Thy feet.
Thy good-ness all our hopes shall raise, A-dored through all our chang-ing days. A-MEN.

MISCELLANEOUS: THE NEW YEAR

Let All Who Enter Here

528

Anon.: alt., 1955

ST. ISSEY: Irregular
Traditional English melody
Har. for this book, 1955

Let all who en-ter here Draw nigh to God, Purge your

hearts of sin Through Christ's shed blood; To aid you on your way

Till shad-ows flee, And Christ you see In His e-ter-nal day. A-MEN.

Music copyright, 1955, by John Ribble.

Come, My Soul, Thy Suit Prepare

529

John Newton, 1779

SAVANNAH: 7. 7. 7. 7.
In *The Foundery Collection*, 1742

1. Come, my soul, thy suit pre-pare: Je-sus loves to an-swer prayer;
2. Thou art com-ing to a King, Large pe-ti-tions with Thee bring;

He Him-self has bid thee pray, There-fore will not say thee nay.
For His grace and power are such, None can ev-er ask too much. A-MEN.

SERVICE MUSIC: PREPARATION FOR PRAYER

530 Father, the Watches of the Night Are O'er

Disciples' Hymn Book

SONG 24: 10. 10. 10. 10.
Orlando Gibbons (1583-1625)

1. Fa - ther, the watch - es of the night are o'er; To light and
2. Fa - ther, the watch - es of the day are here; More than from

life the soul has risen once more; Bless - ed be Thou, who, through the
those of night have we to fear; By rude cares trou - bled, by temp -

help - less hours, Hast kept in deep - est peace her slum-bering powers.
ta - tions pressed, Through the day watch - es, Fa - ther, give us rest! A - MEN.

531 Come, Dearest Lord

Isaac Watts, 1709

FEDERAL STREET: L. M.
Henry K. Oliver, 1832

1. Come, dear-est Lord, de - scend and dwell By faith and love in ev - ery breast;
2. Come, fill our hearts with in-ward strength; Make our en - larg - ed souls pos - sess

Then shall we know and taste and feel The joys that can-not be ex-pressed.
And learn the height, the breadth, and length Of Thine un-meas - ur - a - ble grace. A-MEN.

SERVICE MUSIC: OPENING CHORAL PRAYERS

[440]

O Thou Who Hearest Every Heartfelt Prayer 532

MORECAMBE: 10. 10. 10. 10.
Frederick C. Atkinson, 1870

O Thou who hear - est ev - ery heart-felt prayer, With Thy rich grace, Lord, all our hearts pre - pare; Thou art our Life, Thou art our Love and Light, O let this Sab - bath hour with Thee be bright! A - MEN.

Lord, for the Mercies of the Night 533

FARRANT: C. M.

John Mason, 1683; alt.

Ascribed to Richard Farrant (c. 1530-c. 1580)

1. Lord, for the mer - cies of the night Our hum - ble thanks we pay,
2. Let this day praise Thee, O Lord God, And so let all our days;

And un - to Thee we ded - i - cate The first fruits of the day.
And O let heaven's e - ter - nal day Be Thine e - ter - nal praise! A - MEN.

SERVICE MUSIC: OPENING CHORAL PRAYERS

[441]

534 Let the Words of My Mouth

Psalm 19:14

Joseph Barnby (1838-1896)

Let the words of my mouth and the meditation of my heart be acceptable in Thy sight, O Lord, my Strength and my Re - deem - er. A-MEN.

535 Hear Our Prayer, O Lord

George Whelpton, 1897

Hear our prayer, O Lord, Hear our prayer, O Lord,

In - cline Thine ear to us, And grant us Thy peace. A-MEN.

536 To My Humble Supplication

MON DIEU, PRÊTE-MOI L'OREILLE: 8. 8. 7. 7.

Joseph Bryan, c. 1620; alt., 1955

Genevan Psalter, 1543

1. To my hum-ble sup-pli - ca - tion, Lord, give ear and ac - cep - ta - tion;
2. Heaven-ly Tu-tor, of Thy kind-ness, Teach my dull-ness, guide my blind-ness,

Save Thy serv-ant, who doth own Help and hope in Thee a - lone.
That my steps Thy paths may tread, Which to end-less bliss do lead. A-MEN.

SERVICE MUSIC: CHORAL PRAYERS

[442]

Create in Me a Clean Heart

537

Psalm 51: 10-12

Tonus Regius

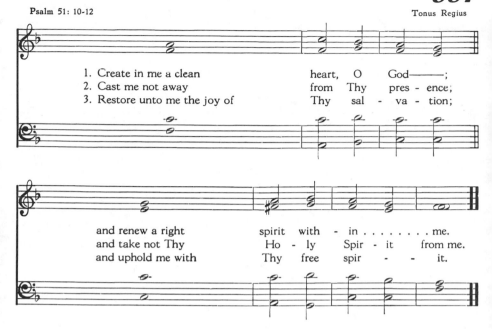

1. Create in me a clean heart, O God———;
2. Cast me not away from Thy pres - ence;
3. Restore unto me the joy of Thy sal - va - tion;

and renew a right spirit with - in . . . . me.
and take not Thy Ho - ly Spir - it from me.
and uphold me with Thy free spir - - it.

Father, Fill Us with Thy Love

538

HORSHAM: 7. 7. 7. 7.
Traditional English melody

Fa - ther, fill us with Thy love; Nev - er from our souls re - move;

Dwell in us, and may we be Thine through all e - ter - ni - ty.

Music copyright. Reprinted from *Songs of Praise* by permission of Oxford University Press.

SERVICE MUSIC: CHORAL PRAYERS

539 Lead Me, Lord, in Thy Righteousness

From Psalm 5: 8; 4: 8

Samuel S. Wesley (1810-1876)

Lead me, Lord, lead me in Thy right-eous-ness; make Thy way plain be - fore my face. For it is Thou, Lord, Thou, Lord, on - ly that mak - est me dwell in safe - ty. A-MEN.

Words and music from *The Concord Anthem Book* (Concord Series No. 13), copyright, 1925, 1952, by E. C. Schirmer Music Company, Boston. Used by permission.

540 The Lone, Wild Fowl in Lofty Flight

Henry Richard McFadyen, 1925

CWMAFON: L. M.
Philip James, 1927

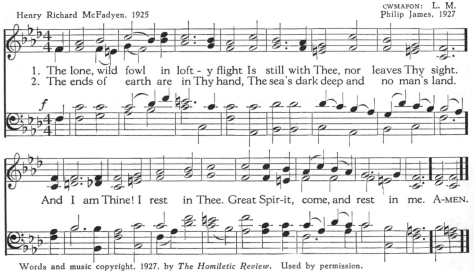

1. The lone, wild fowl in loft - y flight Is still with Thee, nor leaves Thy sight.
2. The ends of earth are in Thy hand, The sea's dark deep and no man's land.

And I am Thine! I rest in Thee. Great Spir-it, come, and rest in me. A-MEN.

Words and music copyright, 1927, by *The Homiletic Review*. Used by permission.
SERVICE MUSIC: CHORAL PRAYERS

[444]

Day by Day, Dear Lord

541

Richard of Chichester (c. 1197-1253)

STONETHWAITE: 3. 8. 6. 5. 6. 3.
Arthur Somervell, 1931

Day by day, Dear Lord, of Thee three things I pray: To see Thee more clear-ly, Love Thee more dear-ly, Fol-low Thee more near-ly, Day by day. A-MEN.

Music copyright. Used by permission of Oxford University Press.

Almighty Father, Hear Our Prayer

542

Arr. from Felix Mendelssohn, 1846

Al-might-y Fa-ther, hear our prayer, and bless all souls that wait be-fore Thee. A-MEN.

SERVICE MUSIC: CHORAL PRAYERS

Part in Peace

543

Sarah F. Adams, 1841

PAX VOBISCUM: 7. 7. 8. 7.
Edward Arthur, 1927

Part in peace: Christ's life was peace, Let us live our life in Him;

Part in peace, our du-ties call us; We must serve as well as praise. A-MEN.

Music copyright. Reprinted from *The Church Hymnary*, Revised Edition, by permission of Oxford University Press.

SERVICE MUSIC: CLOSING EXHORTATION

544 Praise God from Whom All Blessings Flow

OLD HUNDREDTH (altered rhythm): L. M.
Louis Bourgeois, *Genevan Psalter*, 1551

Thomas Ken, 1695, 1709

Praise God from whom all bless-ings flow; Praise Him, all crea-tures here be - low;

Praise Him a - bove, ye heaven-ly host: Praise Fa-ther, Son, and Ho - ly Ghost. A-MEN.

545 Glory Be to the Father

Old Scottish chant

Glory be to the Father, and to the Son, and to the Ho - ly Ghost;
As it was in the beginning, is now, and ev - er shall be, world without end. A - men.

546 Glory Be to the Father

Henry W. Greatorex, 1851

Glo - ry be to the Fa-ther, and to the Son, and to the Ho - ly Ghost; As it

was in the be-gin-ning, is now, and ev-er shall be, world with-out end. A-men, A - men.

SERVICE MUSIC: DOXOLOGIES

[446]

Let Thy Word Abide in Us

547

George Dyson. 1930

Let Thy Word a - bide in us, O Lord.

Music copyright. Used by permission of D. Tait Patterson.

O Lord, Open Thou Our Eyes

548

From Psalm 119: 18

John Camidge (1735-1803)

O Lord, o-pen Thou our eyes, That we may be-hold won-drous things out of Thy law.

Father of Mercies

549

GRÄFENBERG: C. M.
Ascribed to Johann Crüger
Praxis Pietatis Melica, 1653

Anne Steele. 1760

Fa - ther of mer - cies, in Thy Word What end - less glo - ry shines;

For - ev - er be Thy name a-dored For these ce - les - tial lines. A-MEN.

Write These Words in Our Hearts

550

Ancient tone

Write these words in our hearts, we be - seech Thee, O Lord.

SERVICE MUSIC: RESPONSES TO SCRIPTURES

[447]

551 The Sacrifices of God

Psalm 51: 17

Tonus Regius

{ The sacrifices / of God are a } bro-ken spir-it. { A broken and a con- / trite heart, O God, } Thou wilt not de-spise.

552 We Give Thee but Thine Own

WINDERMERE: S. M.
Arthur Somervell, 1906

William Walsham How, 1858

We give Thee but Thine own, What-e'er the gift may be:

All that we have is Thine a-lone, A trust, O Lord, from Thee. A-MEN.

Music copyright. Used by permission of Oxford University Press.
Alternative tune, "Schumann," Hymn 443.

553 Bless Thou the Gifts Our Hands Have Brought

DEUS TUORUM MILITUM: L. M.
Grenoble church melody

Samuel Longfellow, 1886

Bless Thou the gifts our hands have brought; Bless Thou the work our hearts have planned;

Ours is the faith, the will, the thought; The rest, O God, is in Thy hand. A-MEN.

Alternative tune, "Canonbury," Hymn 298.
SERVICE MUSIC: OFFERTORY RESPONSES

[448]

O Dearest Lord

554

Maurice F. Bell, 1906; adapted

MIT FREUDEN ZART (abridged): 4. 8. 8. 7.
Pre-Reformation melody
From the Bohemian Brethren's *Gesangbuch*, 1566

O dear-est Lord, Ac-cept to-day the gifts we bring, Our songs of praise, the prayers we raise; And grant us, Lord, Thy bless-ing. A-MEN.

All Things Are Thine

555

John Greenleaf Whittier, 1873

HERR JESU CHRIST: L. M.
Pensum Sacrum, 1648
Arr. by Johann Sebastian Bach (1685-1750)

All things are Thine; no gift have we, Lord of all gifts, to of-fer Thee; And hence with grate-ful hearts to-day Thine own be-fore Thy feet we lay. A-MEN.

Words used by permission of Houghton Mifflin Company, authorized publishers.
Alternative tune, "Germany," Hymn 313.

All Things Come of Thee, O Lord

556

From I Chronicles 29: 14

Ascribed to Ludwig van Beethoven (1770-1827)

All things come of Thee, O Lord, and of Thine own have we giv-en Thee. A-MEN.

SERVICE MUSIC: OFFERTORY RESPONSES

[449]

557 Father, Give Thy Benediction

Samuel Longfellow, 1864

ALLA TRINITA BEATA: 8. 7. 8. 7.
Arr. from *Laudi Spirituali*, 1336

Fa - ther, give Thy ben - e - dic - tion, Give Thy peace be - fore we part;

Still our minds with truth's con-vic-tion, Calm with trust each anx-ious heart. A-MEN.

SERVICE MUSIC: CLOSING CHORAL PRAYER

558 Amen

Robert Ramsey, 1635

A - - - - - - - men.

Amen **559**

From William Byrd (c. 1543-1623)

A - - - - - - - men.

560 Twofold Amen

Dresden

A - men, A - - men.

Twofold Amen **561**

Greek

A - - men, A - men.

SERVICE MUSIC: AMENS

[450]

Anon.

A — — men, A-men, A - men.

Danish

Amen, A-men, A — — men.

564 Threefold Amen   Threefold Amen **565**

Walter Henry Hall (1862-1935)

David Hugh Jones, 1934

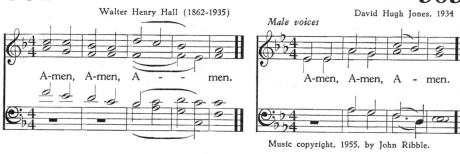

A-men, A-men, A — men.

Male voices

A-men, A-men, A - men.

Music copyright, 1955, by John Ribble.

Sevenfold Amen   **567**

John Stainer, 1873

A - men,   A — — — — men,

A - men, A - men, A - men, A — — men, A-

A — men, A - men,

A — — — men,

- - - men, A — - men, A - men.

A — — men,

568 Lord, Have Mercy Upon Us

Edward C. Bairstow, 1923

In unison

After each Commandment, except the Tenth

Lord, have mer-cy up-on us, and in-cline our hearts to keep this law.

Organ, 1, 4, 7

Organ, 2, 5, 8

Organ, 3, 6, 9

After the Tenth Commandment

Lord, have mer-cy up-on us, and write all

these Thy laws in our hearts, we be-seech Thee.

Music copyright, 1923, by Oxford University Press. Used by permission.

SERVICE MUSIC: THE COMMUNION SERVICE

Lord, Have Mercy Upon Us 569

George J. Elvey (1816-1893)

After each Commandment, except the Tenth

Lord, have mer-cy, have mer-cy up-on us, and in-cline our hearts to

After the Tenth Commandment

keep this law. Lord, have mer-cy, have mer-cy up-on us, and write all

these Thy laws in our hearts, Thy laws in our hearts, we be-seech Thee.

Lord, Have Mercy Upon Us 570

John Merbecke, 1550
Arr. by Healey Willan, 1930

In unison

Lord, have mer-cy up-on us; Christ, have mer-cy up-on us; Lord, have mer-cy up-on us.

Music used by permission of The United Church Publishing House.

Lord, Have Mercy Upon Us 571

From a Lutheran service of 1528

In unison

Lord, have mer-cy up-on us; Christ, have mer-cy up-on us; Lord, have mer-cy up-on us.

SERVICE MUSIC: THE COMMUNION SERVICE

Glory Be to God on High

Old Scottish chant

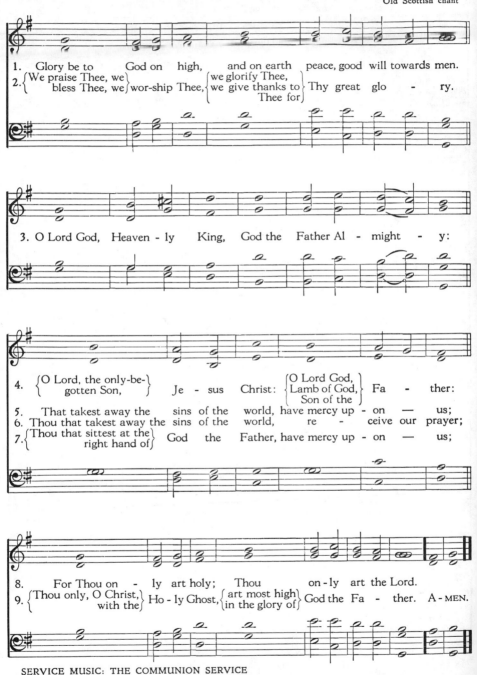

1. Glory be to God on high, and on earth peace, good will towards men.
2. {We praise Thee, we bless Thee, we} wor-ship Thee, {we glorify Thee, we give thanks to Thee for} Thy great glo - ry.

3. O Lord God, Heaven - ly King, God the Father Al - might - y:

4. {O Lord, the only-be-gotten Son,} Je - sus Christ: {O Lord God, Lamb of God, Son of the} Fa - ther:
5. That takest away the sins of the world, have mercy up - on — us;
6. Thou that takest away the sins of the world, re - ceive our prayer;
7. {Thou that sittest at the right hand of} God the Father, have mercy up - on — us;

8. For Thou on - ly art holy; Thou on - ly art the Lord.
9. {Thou only, O Christ, with the} Ho - ly Ghost, {art most high in the glory of} God the Fa - ther. A - MEN.

SERVICE MUSIC: THE COMMUNION SERVICE

Lift Up Your Hearts 573

To be read or sung by minister or soloist

Choir or congregation

John Merbecke, 1550

Lift up your hearts. We lift them up un-to the Lord.

Lift Up Your Hearts 574

To be read or sung by minister or soloist

Choir or congregation

John Camidge (1735-1803)

Lift up your hearts. We lift them up un-to the Lord.

575 Glory Be to Thee

John Merbecke, 1550

Glo-ry be to Thee, O Lord.

Glory Be to Thee 576

Anon.

Glo-ry be to Thee, O Lord.

577 Glory Be to Thee

Thomas Tallis (c. 1510-1585)

Glo-ry be to Thee, O Lord.

Thanks Be to Thee 578

Thomas Tallis (c. 1510-1585)

Thanks be to Thee, O Christ, for this Thy ho-ly gos-pel.

579 Glory Be to Thee

Before the Gospel

Thomas Tallis (c. 1510-1585)

Glo-ry be to Thee, O Lord.

Praise Be to Thee 580

After the Gospel

John Playford (1674-1730)

Praise be to Thee, O Christ.

SERVICE MUSIC: THE COMMUNION SERVICE

[455]

581

Holy, Holy, Holy

Edward C. Bairstow, 1923

Ho - ly, ho - ly, ho - ly, Lord God of Hosts,
Heaven and earth are full of Thy glo - ry: Glo - ry be to
Thee, O Lord Most High. A - - - men.

Music copyright, 1923, by Oxford University Press. Used by permission.

582

Holy, Holy, Holy

John Merbecke, 1550
Arr. by Healey Willan, 1930

In unison

Ho-ly, ho-ly, ho-ly, Lord God of Hosts, Heaven and earth are full of Thy glo - ry:

SERVICE MUSIC: THE COMMUNION SERVICE

[456]

Holy, Holy, Holy

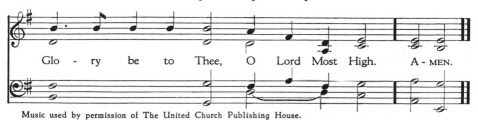

Glo - ry be to Thee, O Lord Most High. A - MEN.

Music used by permission of The United Church Publishing House.

Holy, Holy, Holy

583

Peter C. Lutkin (1858-1931)

In unison

Ho - ly, ho - ly, ho - ly, Lord

God of Hosts, Heaven and earth are full of Thy

glo - ry: Glo - ry be to Thee, O Lord Most High. A - MEN.

Music used by permission of The Parish Press.

SERVICE MUSIC: THE COMMUNION SERVICE

584

Holy, Holy, Holy

Samuel Wesley (1766-1837)

Ho - ly, ho - ly, ho - ly, Lord God of Hosts, Heaven and earth are full of Thy glo - ry: Glo - ry be to Thee, O Lord Most High. A - MEN.

585

O Lamb of God

John Merbecke, 1550
Arr. by Healey Willan, 1930

In unison

O Lamb of God, that tak-est a - way the sins of the world, have mer-cy up-on us.

O Lamb of God, that tak-est a-way the sins of the world, have mer-cy up-on us.

O Lamb of God, that tak-est a-way the sins of the world, grant us Thy peace.

Music used by permission of The United Church Publishing House.
SERVICE MUSIC: THE COMMUNION SERVICE

O Come, Let Us Sing

586

From Psalm 95: 1-7; 96: 9, 13

William Boyce (1710-1779)

1. O come, let us sing unto the Lord; {let us heartily / rejoice in the / strength of} our sal - va - - - tion.

3. For the Lord is a great — God; and a great King a - bove all gods.

5. The sea is His and He made it; and His hands pre-pared the dry — land.

7. For He is the Lord our God; {and we are the / people of His / pasture, and the} sheep of His — hand.

{Glory be to the / Father, and} to the Son, and to the Ho - ly Ghost;

2. {Let us come before / His presence with} thanks - giving; {and show our- / selves} glad in Him with psalms.

4. {In His hand are all / the corners} of the earth; {and the strength / of the hills is} His — al - - - so.

6. {O come, let us / worship and} fall — down, {and kneel before / the} Lord our Mak - - er.

8. {O worship the Lord / in the} beauty of holiness; let the whole earth stand in awe of Him.

9. {For He cometh, for / He cometh to} judge the earth; {and with right - / eousness to judge / the world, and the} peo - ples with His truth.

{As it was in the / beginning, is now, / and} ever shall be, world without end. — A - - - men.

587

Richard Tomlinson (1822-?)

588

Richard Goodson (1655-1718)

SERVICE MUSIC: MORNING CANTICLES

589   We Praise Thee, O God

Edwin George Monk (1819-1900)

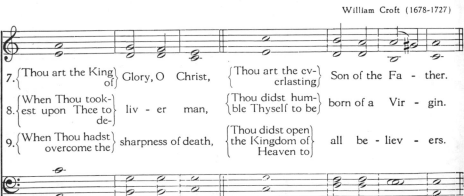

William Croft (1678-1727)

We Praise Thee, O God

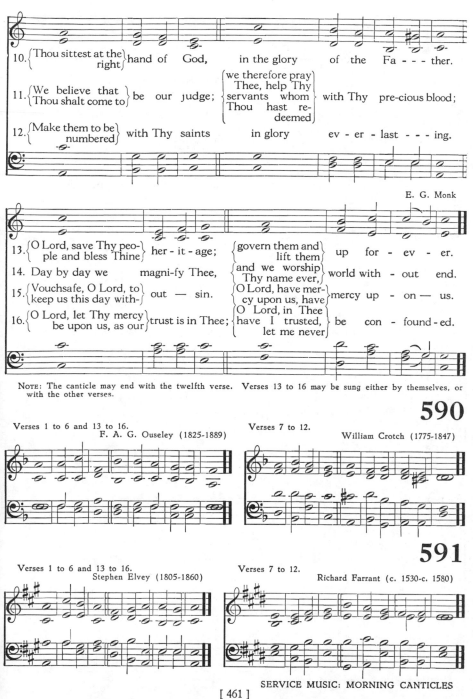

10. {Thou sittest at the / right} hand of God, in the glory of the Fa - - - ther.

11. {We believe that / Thou shalt come to} be our judge; {we therefore pray / Thee, help Thy / servants whom / Thou hast re- / deemed} with Thy pre-cious blood;

12. {Make them to be / numbered} with Thy saints in glory ev - er - last - - - ing.

E. G. Monk

13. {O Lord, save Thy peo- / ple and bless Thine} her - it - age; {govern them and / lift them} up for - ev - er.

14. Day by day we magni-fy Thee, {and we worship / Thy name ever,} world with - out end.

15. {Vouchsafe, O Lord, to / keep us this day with-} out — sin. {O Lord, have mer- / cy upon us, have} mercy up - on — us.

16. {O Lord, let Thy mercy / be upon us, as our} trust is in Thee; {O Lord, in Thee / have I trusted, / let me never} be con - found - ed.

NOTE: The canticle may end with the twelfth verse. Verses 13 to 16 may be sung either by themselves, or with the other verses.

590

Verses 1 to 6 and 13 to 16.
F. A. G. Ouseley (1825-1889)

Verses 7 to 12.
William Crotch (1775-1847)

591

Verses 1 to 6 and 13 to 16.
Stephen Elvey (1805-1860)

Verses 7 to 12.
Richard Farrant (c. 1530-c. 1580)

SERVICE MUSIC: MORNING CANTICLES

[461]

592 Blessed Be the Lord

From Luke 1: 68-79

Joseph Barnby (1838-1896)

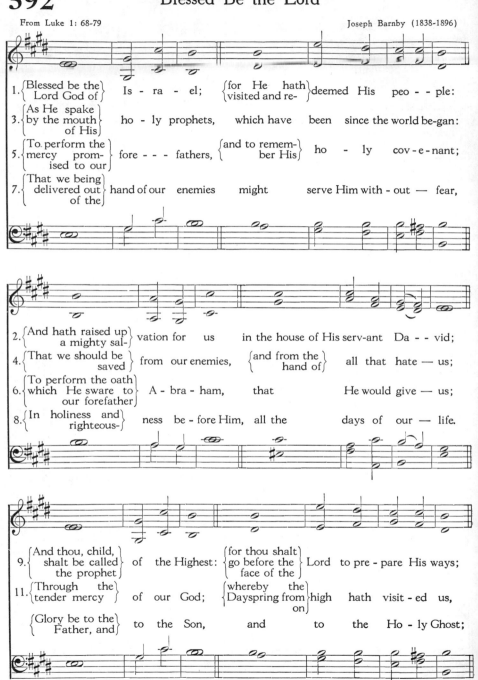

1. {Blessed be the / Lord God of} Is - ra - el; {for He hath / visited and re-} deemed His peo - - ple:

3. {As He spake / by the mouth / of His} ho - ly prophets, which have been since the world be-gan:

5. {To perform the / mercy prom- / ised to our} fore - - - fathers, {and to remem- / ber His} ho - ly cov-e-nant;

7. {That we being / delivered out / of the} hand of our enemies might serve Him with - out — fear,

2. {And hath raised up / a mighty sal-} vation for us in the house of His serv-ant Da - - vid;

4. {That we should be / saved} from our enemies, {and from the / hand of} all that hate — us;

6. {To perform the oath / which He sware to / our forefather} A - bra - ham, that He would give — us;

8. {In holiness and / righteous-} ness be - fore Him, all the days of our — life.

9. {And thou, child, / shalt be called / the prophet} of the Highest: {for thou shalt / go before the / face of the} Lord to pre - pare His ways;

11. {Through the / tender mercy} of our God; {whereby the / Dayspring from / on} high hath visit-ed us,

{Glory be to the / Father, and} to the Son, and to the Ho - ly Ghost;

SERVICE MUSIC: MORNING CANTICLES

[462]

Blessed Be the Lord

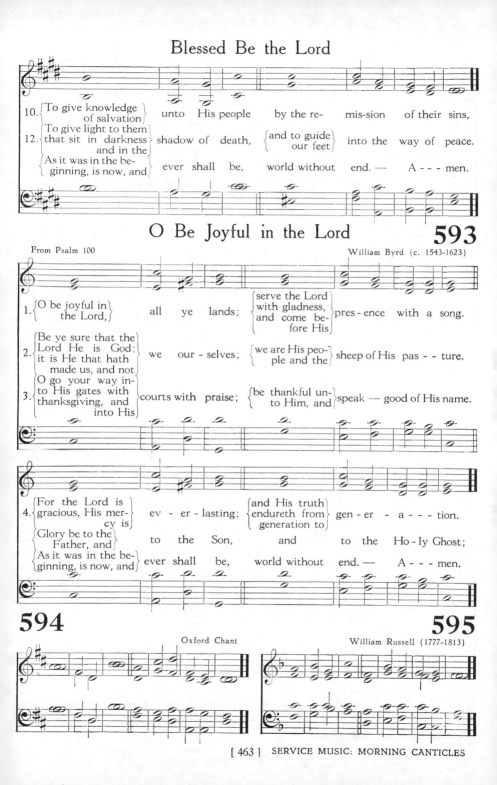

10. {To give knowledge of salvation} unto His people by the re- mis-sion of their sins,
12. {To give light to them that sit in darkness and in the} shadow of death, {and to guide our feet} into the way of peace.
{As it was in the be- ginning, is now, and} ever shall be, world without end. — A - - - men.

O Be Joyful in the Lord

593

From Psalm 100

William Byrd (c. 1543-1623)

1. {O be joyful in the Lord,} all ye lands; {serve the Lord with gladness, and come be- fore His} pres - ence with a song.

2. {Be ye sure that the Lord He is God; it is He that hath made us, and not} we our - selves; {we are His peo- ple and the} sheep of His pas - - ture.

3. {O go your way in- to His gates with thanksgiving, and into His} courts with praise; {be thankful un- to Him, and} speak — good of His name.

4. {For the Lord is gracious, His mer- cy is} ev - er - lasting; {and His truth endureth from generation to} gen - er - a - - - tion.

{Glory be to the Father, and} to the Son, and to the Ho - ly Ghost;
{As it was in the be- ginning, is now, and} ever shall be, world without end. — A - - - men.

594

595

Oxford Chant

William Russell (1777-1813)

596   My Soul Doth Magnify the Lord

From Luke 1: 46-55

John Robinson (1682-1762)

1. My soul doth magni - fy the Lord, {and my spirit hath rejoiced in} God my Sav - - - iour.

3. For be - hold, from henceforth all generations shall call me bless - - - ed.

5. And His mercy is on them that fear Him, throughout all gener - a - - - tions.

7. {He hath put down the mighty} from their seat; and hath ex - alted the humble and meek.

{Glory be to the Fa- ther, and} to the Son, and to the Ho - ly Ghost;

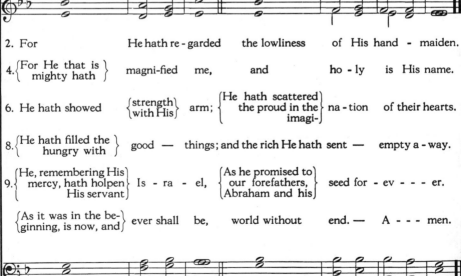

2. For He hath re - garded the lowliness of His hand - maiden.

4. {For He that is mighty hath} magni-fied me, and ho - ly is His name.

6. He hath showed {strength with His} arm; {He hath scattered the proud in the imagi-} na - tion of their hearts.

8. {He hath filled the hungry with} good — things; and the rich He hath sent — empty a - way.

9. {He, remembering His mercy, hath holpen His servant} Is - ra - el, {As he promised to our forefathers, Abraham and his} seed for - ev - - - er.

{As it was in the be- ginning, is now, and} ever shall be, world without end. — A - - - men.

SERVICE MUSIC: EVENING CANTICLES

Lord, Now Lettest Thou Thy Servant Depart 597

From Luke 2: 29-32

Joseph Barnby (1838-1896)

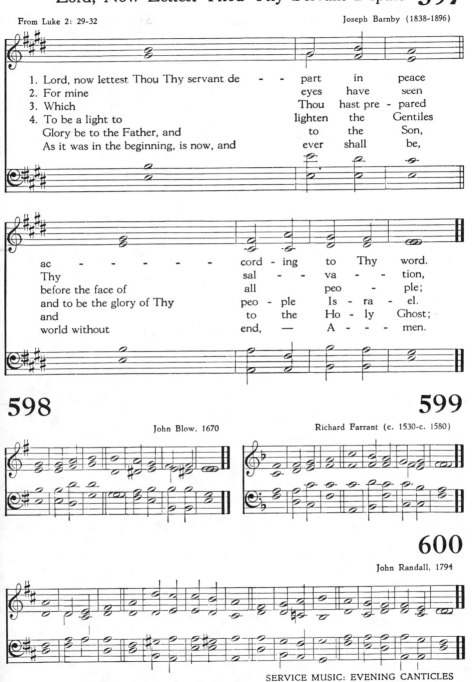

1. Lord, now lettest Thou Thy servant de - - part in peace
2. For mine eyes have seen
3. Which Thou hast pre - pared
4. To be a light to lighten the Gentiles
Glory be to the Father, and to the Son,
As it was in the beginning, is now, and ever shall be,

ac - - - - - cord - ing to Thy word.
Thy sal - - va - - tion,
before the face of all peo - ple;
and to be the glory of Thy peo - ple Is - ra - el.
and to the Ho - ly Ghost;
world without end, — A - - - men.

598

John Blow, 1670

599

Richard Farrant (c. 1530-c. 1580)

600

John Randall, 1794

SERVICE MUSIC: EVENING CANTICLES

[465]

SCRIPTURE READINGS

The Christian Year

The Christian Life

The Civil Year

NOTE: These readings are from the Revised Standard Version of the Bible, except Selections 1 and 5, which are from the King James Version.

SCRIPTURE READINGS

1

Psalm 1 (*Unison*)

Blessed is the man that walketh not in the counsel of the ungodly, nor standeth in the way of sinners, nor sitteth in the seat of the scornful. But his delight is in the law of the Lord; and in his law doth he meditate day and night. And he shall be like a tree planted by the rivers of water, that bringeth forth his fruit in his season; his leaf also shall not wither; and whatsoever he doeth shall prosper.

The ungodly are not so: but are like the chaff which the wind driveth away. Therefore the ungodly shall not stand in the judgment, nor sinners in the congregation of the righteous. For the Lord knoweth the way of the righteous: but the way of the ungodly shall perish. [*End*]

2

Psalm 2 (*Unison*)

Why do the nations conspire,
    And the peoples plot in vain?
The kings of the earth set themselves,
    And the rulers take counsel together,
    Against the Lord and his anointed, saying,
" Let us burst their bonds asunder,
    And cast their cords from us."
He who sits in the heavens laughs;
    The Lord has them in derision.
Then he will speak to them in his wrath,
    And terrify them in his fury, saying,
" I have set my king
    On Zion, my holy hill."

I will tell of the decree of the Lord:
He said to me, " You are my son,
   Today I have begotten you.
Ask of me, and I will make the nations your heritage,
   And the ends of the earth your possession.
You shall break them with a rod of iron,
   And dash them in pieces like a potter's vessel."
Now therefore, O kings, be wise;
   Be warned, O rulers of the earth.
Serve the Lord with fear,
   With trembling kiss his feet,
Lest he be angry, and you perish in the way;
   For his wrath is quickly kindled.
Blessed are all who take refuge in him.

                                        [*End*]

3

Psalm 8

O Lord, our Lord, how majestic is thy name in all the earth!

   Thou whose glory above the heavens is chanted by the mouth of
   babes and infants,
Thou hast founded a bulwark because of thy foes,

   To still the enemy and the avenger.
When I look at thy heavens, the work of thy fingers,

   The moon and the stars which thou hast established;
What is man that thou art mindful of him,

   And the son of man that thou dost care for him?
Yet thou hast made him little less than God,

   And dost crown him with glory and honor.
Thou hast given him dominion over the works of thy hands;

   Thou hast put all things under his feet,

All sheep and oxen, and also the beasts of the field,

The birds of the air, and the fish of the sea, whatever passes along the paths of the sea.

(*Unison*)

O Lord, our Lord, how majestic is thy name in all the earth!

[*End*]

4

Psalm 19

The heavens are telling the glory of God;

And the firmament proclaims his handiwork.

Day to day pours forth speech,

And night to night declares knowledge.

There is no speech, nor are there words;

Their voice is not heard;

Yet their voice goes out through all the earth,

And their words to the end of the world.

In them he has set a tent for the sun, which comes forth like a bridegroom leaving his chamber,

And like a strong man runs its course with joy.

Its rising is from the end of the heavens, and its circuit to the end of them;

And there is nothing hid from its heat.

The law of the Lord is perfect, reviving the soul;

The testimony of the Lord is sure, making wise the simple;

The precepts of the Lord are right, rejoicing the heart;

The commandment of the Lord is pure, enlightening the eyes;

The fear of the Lord is clean, enduring for ever;

The ordinances of the Lord are true, and righteous altogether.
More to be desired are they than gold, even much fine gold;

Sweeter also than honey and drippings of the honeycomb.
Moreover by them is thy servant warned;

In keeping them there is great reward.
But who can discern his errors?

Clear thou me from hidden faults.
Keep back thy servant also from presumptuous sins;

Let them not have dominion over me!
Then I shall be blameless,

And innocent of great transgression.
(*Unison*)

Let the words of my mouth and the meditation of my heart be acceptable in thy sight, O Lord, my rock and my redeemer.

[*End*]

5

Psalm 23 (*Unison*)

The Lord is my shepherd; I shall not want. He maketh me to lie down in green pastures: he leadeth me beside the still waters. He restoreth my soul: he leadeth me in the paths of righteousness for his name's sake.

Yea, though I walk through the valley of the shadow of death, I will fear no evil: for thou art with me; thy rod and thy staff they comfort me.

Thou preparest a table before me in the presence of mine enemies: thou anointest my head with oil; my cup runneth over. Surely goodness and mercy shall follow me all the days of my life: and I will dwell in the house of the Lord for ever.

[*End*]

6

Psalm 24

The earth is the Lord's and the fulness thereof,

The world and those who dwell therein;

For he has founded it upon the seas,

And established it upon the rivers.

Who shall ascend the hill of the Lord?

And who shall stand in his holy place?

He who has clean hands and a pure heart,

Who does not lift up his soul to what is false, and does not swear deceitfully.

He will receive blessing from the Lord,

And vindication from the God of his salvation.

Such is the generation of those who seek him,

Who seek the face of the God of Jacob.

Lift up your heads, O gates! and be lifted up, O ancient doors!

That the King of glory may come in.

Who is the King of glory?

The Lord, strong and mighty, the Lord, mighty in battle!

Lift up your heads, O gates! and be lifted up, O ancient doors!

That the King of glory may come in!

Who is this King of glory?

The Lord of hosts, he is the King of glory!

[*End*]

7

Psalm 27

The Lord is my light and my salvation; whom shall I fear?

The Lord is the stronghold of my life; of whom shall I be afraid?

When evildoers assail me, uttering slanders against me, my adversaries and foes,

They shall stumble and fall.
Though a host encamp against me, my heart shall not fear;

Though war arise against me, yet I will be confident.
One thing have I asked of the Lord, that will I seek after;

That I may dwell in the house of the Lord all the days of my life,
To behold the beauty of the Lord,

And to inquire in his temple.
For he will hide me in his shelter in the day of trouble;

He will conceal me under the cover of his tent,
He will set me high upon a rock.

And now my head shall be lifted up above my enemies round about me;
And I will offer in his tent sacrifices with shouts of joy;

I will sing and make melody to the Lord.
Hear, O Lord, when I cry aloud,

Be gracious to me and answer me!
Thou hast said, " Seek ye my face."

My heart says to thee, " Thy face, Lord, do I seek."
Hide not thy face from me.

Turn not thy servant away in anger, thou who hast been my help.
Cast me not off, forsake me not, O God of my salvation!

For my father and my mother have forsaken me, but the Lord will take me up.
Teach me thy way, O Lord;

And lead me on a level path because of my enemies.
Give me not up to the will of my adversaries;

For false witnesses have risen against me, and they breathe out violence.

I believe that I shall see the goodness of the Lord in the land of the living!

Wait for the Lord; be strong, and let your heart take courage; yea, wait for the Lord!   [*End*]

8

Psalm 32:1, 2, 5–8, 10, 11

Blessed is he whose transgression is forgiven, whose sin is covered.

Blessed is the man to whom the Lord imputes no iniquity, and in whose spirit there is no deceit.

I acknowledged my sin to thee,

And I did not hide my iniquity;

I said, " I will confess my transgressions to the Lord ";

Then thou didst forgive the guilt of my sin.

Therefore let every one who is godly offer prayer to thee;

At a time of distress, in the rush of great waters, they shall not reach him.

Thou art a hiding place for me, thou preservest me from trouble;

Thou dost encompass me with deliverance.

I will instruct you and teach you the way you should go;

I will counsel you with my eye upon you.

Many are the pangs of the wicked;

But steadfast love surrounds him who trusts in the Lord.

Be glad in the Lord, and rejoice, O righteous,

And shout for joy, all you upright in heart!

[*End*]

9

Psalm 34
I will bless the Lord at all times;

His praise shall continually be in my mouth.
My soul makes its boast in the Lord;

Let the afflicted hear and be glad.
O magnify the Lord with me,

And let us exalt his name together!
I sought the Lord, and he answered me,

And delivered me from all my fears.
Look to him, and be radiant;

So your faces shall never be ashamed.
This poor man cried, and the Lord heard him, and saved him out of
all his troubles.

The angel of the Lord encamps around those who fear him, and
delivers them.
O taste and see that the Lord is good!

Happy is the man who takes refuge in him!
O fear the Lord, you his saints,

For those who fear him have no want!
The young lions suffer want and hunger;

But those who seek the Lord lack no good thing.
Come, O sons, listen to me,

I will teach you the fear of the Lord.
What man is there who desires life, and covets many days, that he
may enjoy good?

Keep your tongue from evil, and your lips from speaking deceit.

Depart from evil, and do good;

    Seek peace, and pursue it.

The eyes of the Lord are toward the righteous,

    And his ears toward their cry.

The face of the Lord is against evildoers,

    To cut off the remembrance of them from the earth.

When the righteous cry for help, the Lord hears,

    And delivers them out of all their troubles.

The Lord is near to the brokenhearted,

    And saves the crushed in spirit.

Many are the afflictions of the righteous;

    But the Lord delivers him out of them all.

He keeps all his bones;

    Not one of them is broken.

Evil shall slay the wicked;

    And those who hate the righteous will be condemned.

The Lord redeems the life of his servants;

    None of those who take refuge in him will be condemned.

[End]

10

Psalm 37:1–9, 23–31, 37–40

Fret not yourself because of the wicked,

    Be not envious of wrongdoers!

For they will soon fade like the grass,

    And wither like the green herb.

Trust in the Lord, and do good;

    So you will dwell in the land, and enjoy security.

Take delight in the Lord,

> And he will give you the desires of your heart.

Commit your way to the Lord;

> Trust in him, and he will act.

He will bring forth your vindication as the light,

> And your right as the noonday.

Be still before the Lord, and wait patiently for him;

> Fret not yourself over him who prospers in his way, over the man who carries out evil devices!

Refrain from anger, and forsake wrath!

> Fret not yourself; it tends only to evil.

For the wicked shall be cut off;

> But those who wait for the Lord shall possess the land.

The steps of a man are from the Lord,

> And he establishes him in whose way he delights;

Though he fall, he shall not be cast headlong,

> For the Lord is the stay of his hand.

I have been young, and now am old; yet I have not seen the righteous forsaken or his children begging bread.

> He is ever giving liberally and lending, and his children become a blessing.

Depart from evil, and do good;

> So shall you abide for ever.

For the Lord loves justice; he will not forsake his saints.

> The righteous shall be preserved for ever, but the children of the wicked shall be cut off.

The righteous shall possess the land,

> And dwell upon it for ever.

The mouth of the righteous utters wisdom,

> And his tongue speaks justice.

The law of his God is in his heart;
  His steps do not slip.

Mark the blameless man, and behold the upright,
  For there is posterity for the man of peace.

But transgressors shall be altogether destroyed;
  The posterity of the wicked shall be cut off.

The salvation of the righteous is from the Lord;
  He is their refuge in the time of trouble.

The Lord helps them and delivers them;
  He delivers them from the wicked, and saves them, because they
  take refuge in him.   [*End*]

11

Psalm 40:1–12, 16, 17
I waited patiently for the Lord;
  He inclined to me and heard my cry.

He drew me up from the desolate pit, out of the miry bog,
  And set my feet upon a rock, making my steps secure.

He put a new song in my mouth, a song of praise to our God.
  Many will see and fear, and put their trust in the Lord.

Blessed is the man who makes the Lord his trust,
  Who does not turn to the proud, to those who go astray after
  false gods!

Thou hast multiplied, O Lord my God, thy wondrous deeds
  And thy thoughts toward us; none can compare with thee!

Were I to proclaim and tell of them,
  They would be more than can be numbered.

Sacrifice and offering thou dost not desire; but thou hast given me an open ear.

Burnt offering and sin offering thou hast not required.
Then I said, " Lo, I come; in the roll of the book it is written of me;

I delight to do thy will, O my God; thy law is within my heart."
I have told the glad news of deliverance in the great congregation;

Lo, I have not restrained my lips, as thou knowest, O Lord.
I have not hid thy saving help within my heart, I have spoken of thy faithfulness and thy salvation;

I have not concealed thy steadfast love and thy faithfulness from the great congregation.
Do not thou, O Lord, withhold thy mercy from me,

Let thy steadfast love and thy faithfulness ever preserve me!
For evils have encompassed me without number; my iniquities have overtaken me, till I cannot see;

They are more than the hairs of my head; my heart fails me.
But may all who seek thee rejoice and be glad in thee;

May those who love thy salvation say continually, " Great is the Lord! "
As for me, I am poor and needy; but the Lord takes thought for me.

Thou art my help and my deliverer; do not tarry, O my God!
                                                    [*End*]

12

Psalm 42:1-5, 8-11; 43
As a hart longs for flowing streams,

So longs my soul for thee, O God.
My soul thirsts for God, for the living God.

When shall I come and behold the face of God?

My tears have been my food day and night,

While men say to me continually, "Where is your God?"

These things I remember, as I pour out my soul:

How I went with the throng, and led them in procession to the house of God, with glad shouts and songs of thanksgiving, a multitude keeping festival.

Why are you cast down, O my soul, and why are you disquieted within me?

Hope in God; for I shall again praise him, my help and my God.

By day the Lord commands his steadfast love;

And at night his song is with me, a prayer to the God of my life.

I say to God, my rock: "Why hast thou forgotten me? Why go I mourning because of the oppression of the enemy?"

As with a deadly wound in my body, my adversaries taunt me, while they say to me continually, "Where is your God?"

Why are you cast down, O my soul, and why are you disquieted within me?

Hope in God; for I shall again praise him, my help and my God.

Vindicate me, O God, and defend my cause against an ungodly people;

From deceitful and unjust men deliver me!

For thou art the God in whom I take refuge;

Why hast thou cast me off? Why go I mourning because of the oppression of the enemy?

Oh send out thy light and thy truth; let them lead me,

Let them bring me to thy holy hill and to thy dwelling!

Then I will go to the altar of God, to God my exceeding joy;

And I will praise thee with the lyre, O God, my God.

Why are you cast down, O my soul, and why are you disquieted within me?

Hope in God; for I shall again praise him, my help and my God.

[*End*]

13

Psalm 46

God is our refuge and strength,
  A very present help in trouble.

Therefore we will not fear though the earth should change,
  Though the mountains shake in the heart of the sea;

Though its waters roar and foam,
  Though the mountains tremble with its tumult.

There is a river whose streams make glad the city of God,
  The holy habitation of the Most High.

God is in the midst of her, she shall not be moved;
  God will help her right early.

The nations rage, the kingdoms totter;
  He utters his voice, the earth melts.

The Lord of hosts is with us;
  The God of Jacob is our refuge.

Come, behold the works of the Lord, how he has wrought desolations
in the earth.
  **He makes wars cease to the end of the earth; he breaks the bow,
  and shatters the spear, he burns the chariots with fire!**

" Be still, and know that I am God.
  I am exalted among the nations, I am exalted in the earth! "

The Lord of hosts is with us;
  The God of Jacob is our refuge.   *[End]*

14

Psalm 51:1–17

Have mercy on me, O God, according to thy steadfast love; according to thy abundant mercy blot out my transgressions.

Wash me thoroughly from my iniquity, and cleanse me from my sin!
For I know my transgressions, and my sin is ever before me.

Against thee, thee only, have I sinned, and done that which is evil in thy sight, so that thou art justified in thy sentence and blameless in thy judgment.
Behold, I was brought forth in iniquity, and in sin did my mother conceive me.

Behold, thou desirest truth in the inward being; therefore teach me wisdom in my secret heart.
Purge me with hyssop, and I shall be clean; wash me, and I shall be whiter than snow.

Fill me with joy and gladness; let the bones which thou hast broken rejoice.
Hide thy face from my sins, and blot out all my iniquities.

Create in me a clean heart, O God, and put a new and right spirit within me.
Cast me not away from thy presence, and take not thy holy Spirit from me.

Restore to me the joy of thy salvation, and uphold me with a willing spirit.
Then I will teach transgressors thy ways, and sinners will return to thee.

Deliver me from bloodguiltiness, O God, thou God of my salvation, and my tongue will sing aloud of thy deliverance.

O Lord, open thou my lips, and my mouth shall show forth thy praise.

For thou hast no delight in sacrifice; were I to give a burnt offering, thou wouldst not be pleased.

The sacrifice acceptable to God is a broken spirit;

A broken and contrite heart, O God, thou wilt not despise.

[End]

15

Psalm 67

May God be gracious to us and bless us and make his face to shine upon us,

That thy way may be known upon earth, thy saving power among all nations.

Let the peoples praise thee, O God; let all the peoples praise thee!

Let the nations be glad and sing for joy,

For thou dost judge the peoples with equity and guide the nations upon earth.

Let the peoples praise thee, O God; let all the peoples praise thee!

The earth has yielded its increase; God, our God, has blessed us.

God has blessed us; let all the ends of the earth fear him!

[End]

16

Psalm 72:1-19

Give the king thy justice, O God,

And thy righteousness to the royal son!

May he judge thy people with righteousness,

And thy poor with justice!

Let the mountains bear prosperity for the people, and the hills, in righteousness!

> May he defend the cause of the poor of the people, give deliverance to the needy, and crush the oppressor!

May he live while the sun endures,

> And as long as the moon, throughout all generations!

May he be like rain that falls on the mown grass,

> Like showers that water the earth!

In his days may righteousness flourish,

> And peace abound, till the moon be no more!

May he have dominion from sea to sea,

> And from the River to the ends of the earth!

May his foes bow down before him,

> And his enemies lick the dust!

May the kings of Tarshish and of the isles render him tribute, may the kings of Sheba and Seba bring gifts!

> May all kings fall down before him, all nations serve him!

For he delivers the needy when he calls, the poor and him who has no helper.

> He has pity on the weak and the needy, and saves the lives of the needy.

From oppression and violence he redeems their life;

> And precious is their blood in his sight.

Long may he live, may gold of Sheba be given to him!

> May prayer be made for him continually, and blessings invoked for him all the day!

May there be abundance of grain in the land; on the tops of the mountains may it wave;

> May its fruit be like Lebanon; and may men blossom forth from the cities like the grass of the field!

May his name endure for ever, his fame continue as long as the sun!

> May men bless themselves by him, all nations call him blessed!

Blessed be the Lord, the God of Israel, who alone does wondrous things.

(*Unison*)
Blessed be his glorious name for ever; may his glory fill the whole earth! Amen and Amen!   [*End*]

17

Psalm 73:1-26

Truly God is good to the upright, to those who are pure in heart.
  But as for me, my feet had almost stumbled, my steps had well nigh slipped.

For I was envious of the arrogant, when I saw the prosperity of the wicked.
  For they have no pangs; their bodies are sound and sleek.

They are not in trouble as other men are; they are not stricken like other men.
  Therefore pride is their necklace; violence covers them as a garment.

Their eyes swell out with fatness, their hearts overflow with follies.
  They scoff and speak with malice; loftily they threaten oppression.

They set their mouths against the heavens, and their tongue struts through the earth.
  Therefore the people turn and praise them; and find no fault in them.

And they say, "How can God know? Is there knowledge in the Most High?"
  Behold, these are the wicked; always at ease, they increase in riches.

All in vain have I kept my heart clean and washed my hands in innocence.

For all the day long I have been stricken, and chastened every morning.

If I had said. " I will speak thus," I would have been untrue to the generation of thy children.

But when I thought how to understand this, it seemed to me a wearisome task,

Until I went into the sanctuary of God; then I perceived their end.

Truly thou dost set them in slippery places; thou dost make them fall to ruin.

How they are destroyed in a moment, swept away utterly by terrors!

They are like a dream when one awakes, on awaking you despise their phantoms.

When my soul was embittered, when I was pricked in heart,

I was stupid and ignorant, I was like a beast toward thee.

Nevertheless I am continually with thee; thou dost hold my right hand.

Thou dost guide me with thy counsel, and afterward thou wilt receive me to glory.

Whom have I in heaven but thee? And there is nothing upon earth that I desire besides thee.

My flesh and my heart may fail, but God is the strength of my heart and my portion for ever.   [*End*]

18

Psalm 84
How lovely is thy dwelling place, O Lord of hosts!

My soul longs, yea, faints for the courts of the Lord; my heart and flesh sing for joy to the living God.

Even the sparrow finds a home, and the swallow a nest for herself,

Where she may lay her young, at thy altars, O Lord of hosts, my king and my God.

Blessed are those who dwell in thy house, ever singing thy praise!

Blessed are the men whose strength is in thee, in whose heart are the highways to Zion.

As they go through the valley of Baca they make it a place of springs;

The early rain also covers it with pools.

They go from strength to strength;

The God of gods will be seen in Zion.

O Lord God of hosts, hear my prayer; give ear, O God of Jacob!

Behold our shield, O God; look upon the face of thine anointed!

For a day in thy courts is better than a thousand elsewhere.

I would rather be a doorkeeper in the house of my God than dwell in the tents of wickedness.

For the Lord God is a sun and shield; he bestows favor and honor.

No good thing does the Lord withhold from those who walk uprightly.

(*Unison*)

O Lord of hosts, blessed is the man who trusts in thee!

[*End*]

19

Psalm 86

Incline thy ear, O Lord, and answer me,

For I am poor and needy.

Preserve my life, for I am godly;

Save thy servant who trusts in thee.

Thou art my God; be gracious to me, O Lord, for to thee do I cry all the day.

Gladden the soul of thy servant, for to thee, O Lord, do I lift up my soul.

For thou, O Lord, art good and forgiving,

Abounding in steadfast love to all who call on thee.

Give ear, O Lord, to my prayer;

Hearken to my cry of supplication.

In the day of my trouble I call on thee,

For thou dost answer me.

There is none like thee among the gods, O Lord,

Nor are there any works like thine.

All the nations thou hast made shall come and bow down before thee, O Lord, and shall glorify thy name.

For thou art great and doest wondrous things, thou alone art God.

Teach me thy way, O Lord, that I may walk in thy truth;

Unite my heart to fear thy name.

I give thanks to thee, O Lord my God, with my whole heart,

And I will glorify thy name for ever.

For great is thy steadfast love toward me;

Thou hast delivered my soul from the depths of Sheol.

O God, insolent men have risen up against me; a band of ruthless men seek my life, and they do not set thee before them.

But thou, O Lord, art a God merciful and gracious, slow to anger and abounding in steadfast love and faithfulness.

Turn to me and take pity on me;

Give thy strength to thy servant, and save the son of thy handmaid.

Show me a sign of thy favor, that those who hate me may see and be put to shame

Because thou, Lord, hast helped me and comforted me.

[*End*]

20

Psalm 90

Lord, thou hast been our dwelling place in all generations.

Before the mountains were brought forth, or ever thou hadst formed the earth and the world, from everlasting to everlasting thou art God.

Thou turnest man back to the dust, and sayest, " Turn back, O children of men! "

For a thousand years in thy sight are but as yesterday when it is past, or as a watch in the night.

Thou dost sweep men away; they are like a dream, like grass which is renewed in the morning:

In the morning it flourishes and is renewed; in the evening it fades and withers.

For we are consumed by thy anger; by thy wrath we are overwhelmed.

Thou hast set our iniquities before thee, our secret sins in the light of thy countenance.

For all our days pass away under thy wrath, our years come to an end like a sigh.

The years of our life are threescore and ten, or even by reason of strength fourscore; yet their span is but toil and trouble; they are soon gone, and we fly away.

Who considers the power of thy anger, and thy wrath according to the fear of thee?

So teach us to number our days that we may get a heart of wisdom.

Return, O Lord! How long? Have pity on thy servants!

Satisfy us in the morning with thy steadfast love, that we may rejoice and be glad all our days.

Make us glad as many days as thou hast afflicted us, and as many years as we have seen evil.

Let thy work be manifest to thy servants, and thy glorious power to their children.

Let the favor of the Lord our God be upon us, and establish thou the work of our hands upon us,

Yea, the work of our hands establish thou it.

[End]

21

Psalm 91

He who dwells in the shelter of the Most High, who abides in the shadow of the Almighty, will say to the Lord, " My refuge and my fortress; my God, in whom I trust."

For he will deliver you from the snare of the fowler and from the deadly pestilence;

He will cover you with his pinions, and under his wings you will find refuge;

His faithfulness is a shield and buckler.

You will not fear the terror of the night,

Nor the arrow that flies by day,

Nor the pestilence that stalks in darkness,

Nor the destruction that wastes at noonday.

A thousand may fall at your side, ten thousand at your right hand; but it will not come near you.

You will only look with your eyes and see the recompense of the wicked.

Because you have made the Lord your refuge, the Most High your habitation,

No evil shall befall you, no scourge come near your tent.

For he will give his angels charge of you to guard you in all your ways.

> On their hands they will bear you up, lest you dash your foot against a stone.

You will tread on the lion and the adder,

> The young lion and the serpent you will trample under foot.

Because he cleaves to me in love, I will deliver him;

> I will protect him, because he knows my name.

When he calls to me, I will answer him; I will be with him in trouble, I will rescue him and honor him.

> With long life I will satisfy him, and show him my salvation.
>
> > *[End]*

22

Psalm 95:1–7a; 96

O come, let us sing to the Lord;

> Let us make a joyful noise to the rock of our salvation!

Let us come into his presence with thanksgiving;

> Let us make a joyful noise to him with songs of praise!

For the Lord is a great God,

> And a great King above all gods.

In his hand are the depths of the earth; the heights of the mountains are his also.

> The sea is his, for he made it; for his hands formed the dry land.

O come, let us worship and bow down, let us kneel before the Lord, our Maker!

> For he is our God, and we are the people of his pasture, and the sheep of his hand.

O sing to the Lord a new song;
  Sing to the Lord, all the earth!

Sing to the Lord, bless his name;
  Tell of his salvation from day to day.

Declare his glory among the nations,
  His marvelous works among all the peoples!

For great is the Lord, and greatly to be praised;
  He is to be feared above all gods.

For all the gods of the peoples are idols;
  But the Lord made the heavens.

Honor and majesty are before him;
  Strength and beauty are in his sanctuary.

Ascribe to the Lord, O families of the peoples,
  Ascribe to the Lord glory and strength!

Ascribe to the Lord the glory due his name;
  Bring an offering, and come into his courts!

Worship the Lord in holy array;
  Tremble before him, all the earth!

Say among the nations, " The Lord reigns!
  Yea, the world is established, it shall never be moved; he will judge the peoples with equity."

Let the heavens be glad, and let the earth rejoice;
  Let the sea roar, and all that fills it;

Let the field exult, and everything in it!
  Then shall all the trees of the wood sing for joy before the Lord,

For he comes, for he comes to judge the earth.
  He will judge the world with righteousness. and the peoples with his truth.   *[End]*

23

Psalm 98

O sing to the Lord a new song, for he has done marvelous things!
His right hand and his holy arm have gotten him victory.

The Lord has made known his victory,
He has revealed his vindication in the sight of the nations.

He has remembered his steadfast love and faithfulness to the house
of Israel.
All the ends of the earth have seen the victory of our God.

Make a joyful noise to the Lord, all the earth;
Break forth into joyous song and sing praises!

Sing praises to the Lord with the lyre, with the lyre and the sound
of melody!
With trumpets and the sound of the horn make a joyful noise be-
fore the King, the Lord!

Let the sea roar, and all that fills it;
The world and those who dwell in it!

Let the floods clap their hands;
Let the hills sing for joy together before the Lord,

For he comes to rule the earth.
He will judge the world with righteousness, and the peoples with
equity.   [*End*]

24

Psalm 100

Make a joyful noise to the Lord, all the lands!
Serve the Lord with gladness!

Come into his presence with singing!

Know that the Lord is God!

It is he that made us, and we are his;

We are his people, and the sheep of his pasture.

Enter his gates with thanksgiving, and his courts with praise!

Give thanks to him, bless his name!

For the Lord is good; his steadfast love endures for ever,

And his faithfulness to all generations.

[*End*]

25

Psalm 103

Bless the Lord, O my soul;

And all that is within me, bless his holy name!

Bless the Lord, O my soul,

And forget not all his benefits,

Who forgives all your iniquity,

Who heals all your diseases,

Who redeems your life from the Pit,

Who crowns you with steadfast love and mercy,

Who satisfies you with good as long as you live

So that your youth is renewed like the eagle's.

The Lord works vindication and justice for all who are oppressed.

He made known his ways to Moses, his acts to the people of Israel.

The Lord is merciful and gracious,

Slow to anger and abounding in steadfast love.

He will not always chide,
   Nor will he keep his anger for ever.

He does not deal with us according to our sins,
   Nor requite us according to our iniquities.

For as the heavens are high above the earth, so great is his steadfast
love toward those who fear him;
   As far as the east is from the west, so far does he remove our
   transgressions from us.

As a father pities his children, so the Lord pities those who fear him.
   For he knows our frame; he remembers that we are dust.

As for man, his days are like grass;
   He flourishes like a flower of the field;

For the wind passes over it, and it is gone,
   And its place knows it no more.

But the steadfast love of the Lord is from everlasting to everlasting
upon those who fear him,
   And his righteousness to children's children, to those who keep his
   covenant and remember to do his commandments.

The Lord has established his throne in the heavens,
   And his kingdom rules over all.

Bless the Lord, O you his angels, you mighty ones who do his word,
hearkening to the voice of his word!
   Bless the Lord, all his hosts, his ministers that do his will!

Bless the Lord, all his works, in all places of his dominion.
   Bless the Lord, O my soul!   [*End*]

26

Psalm 107:1-22
O give thanks to the Lord, for he is good;
   For his steadfast love endures for ever!

Let the redeemed of the Lord say so, whom he has redeemed from trouble

And gathered in from the lands, from the east and from the west, from the north and from the south.

Some wandered in desert wastes, finding no way to a city to dwell in;

Hungry and thirsty, their soul fainted within them.

Then they cried to the Lord in their trouble, and he delivered them from their distress;

He led them by a straight way, till they reached a city to dwell in.

Let them thank the Lord for his steadfast love,

For his wonderful works to the sons of men!

For he satisfies him who is thirsty,

And the hungry he fills with good things.

Some sat in darkness and in gloom,

Prisoners in affliction and in irons,

For they had rebelled against the words of God,

And spurned the counsel of the Most High

Their hearts were bowed down with hard labor;

They fell down, with none to help.

Then they cried to the Lord in their trouble,

And he delivered them from their distress;

He brought them out of darkness and gloom, and broke their bonds asunder.

Let them thank the Lord for his steadfast love, for his wonderful works to the sons of men!

For he shatters the doors of bronze,

And cuts in two the bars of iron.

Some were sick through their sinful ways, and because of their iniquities suffered affliction;

They loathed any kind of food, and they drew near to the gates of death.

Then they cried to the Lord in their trouble, and he delivered them from their distress;

He sent forth his word, and healed them, and delivered them from destruction.

Let them thank the Lord for his steadfast love, for his wonderful works to the sons of men!

And let them offer sacrifices of thanksgiving, and tell of his deeds in songs of joy!   [End]

27

Psalm 116

I love the Lord, because he has heard my voice and my supplications.

Because he inclined his ear to me, therefore I will call on him as long as I live.

The snares of death encompassed me; the pangs of Sheol laid hold on me; I suffered distress and anguish.

Then I called on the name of the Lord: "O Lord, I beseech thee, save my life!"

Gracious is the Lord, and righteous; our God is merciful.

The Lord preserves the simple; when I was brought low, he saved me.

Return, O my soul, to your rest;

For the Lord has dealt bountifully with you.

For thou hast delivered my soul from death, my eyes from tears, my feet from stumbling;

I walk before the Lord in the land of the living.

I kept my faith, even when I said, " I am greatly afflicted ";

I said in my consternation, "Men are all a vain hope."

What shall I render to the Lord for all his bounty to me?

I will lift up the cup of salvation and call on the name of the Lord,

I will pay my vows to the Lord in the presence of all his people.

Precious in the sight of the Lord is the death of his saints.

O Lord, I am thy servant; I am thy servant, the son of thy handmaid. Thou hast loosed my bonds.

I will offer to thee the sacrifice of thanksgiving and call on the name of the Lord.

I will pay my vows to the Lord in the presence of all his people,

In the courts of the house of the Lord, in your midst, O Jerusalem. Praise the Lord!   *[End]*

28

Psalm 118:1–9, 14–24, 28, 29

O give thanks to the Lord, for he is good; his steadfast love endures for ever!

Let Israel say, " His steadfast love endures for ever."

Let the house of Aaron say, " His steadfast love endures for ever."

Let those who fear the Lord say, " His steadfast love endures for ever."

Out of my distress I called on the Lord;

The Lord answered me and set me free.

With the Lord on my side I do not fear.

What can man do to me?

The Lord is on my side to help me;

I shall look in triumph on those who hate me.

It is better to take refuge in the Lord than to put confidence in man.

It is better to take refuge in the Lord than to put confidence in princes.

The Lord is my strength and my song;

He has become my salvation.

Hark, glad songs of victory in the tents of the righteous: " The right hand of the Lord does valiantly,

The right hand of the Lord is exalted, the right hand of the Lord does valiantly! "

I shall not die, but I shall live, and recount the deeds of the Lord.

The Lord has chastened me sorely, but he has not given me over to death.

Open to me the gates of righteousness,

That I may enter through them and give thanks to the Lord.

This is the gate of the Lord; the righteous shall enter through it.

I thank thee that thou hast answered me and hast become my salvation.

The stone which the builders rejected has become the chief corner-stone.

This is the Lord's doing; it is marvelous in our eyes.

This is the day which the Lord has made;

Let us rejoice and be glad in it.

Thou art my God, and I will give thanks to thee;

Thou art my God, I will extol thee.

O give thanks to the Lord, for he is good;

For his steadfast love endures for ever!

[End]

29

Psalm 121; 122

I lift up my eyes to the hills. From whence does my help come?

My help comes from the Lord, who made heaven and earth.

He will not let your foot be moved, he who keeps you will not slumber.

Behold, he who keeps Israel will neither slumber nor sleep.

The Lord is your keeper; the Lord is your shade on your right hand.

The sun shall not smite you by day, nor the moon by night.

The Lord will keep you from all evil; he will keep your life.

The Lord will keep your going out and your coming in from this time forth and for evermore.

I was glad when they said to me, " Let us go to the house of the Lord! "

Our feet have been standing within your gates, O Jerusalem!

Jerusalem, built as a city which is bound firmly together,

To which the tribes go up, the tribes of the Lord,

As was decreed for Israel, to give thanks to the name of the Lord.

There thrones for judgment were set, the thrones of the house of David.

Pray for the peace of Jerusalem! " May they prosper who love you!

Peace be within your walls, and security within your towers! "

For my brethren and companions' sake I will say, " Peace be within you! "

For the sake of the house of the Lord our God, I will seek your good.   *[End]*

30

Psalm 130 (*Unison*)

Out of the depths I cry to thee, O Lord!
   Lord, hear my voice!
Let thy ears be attentive
   To the voice of my supplications!
If thou, O Lord, shouldst mark iniquities,
   Lord, who could stand?
But there is forgiveness with thee,
   That thou mayest be feared.
I wait for the Lord, my soul waits,
   And in his word I hope;
My soul waits for the Lord
   More than watchmen for the morning,
   More than watchmen for the morning.
O Israel, hope in the Lord!
   For with the Lord there is steadfast love,
   And with him is plenteous redemption.
And he will redeem Israel   *[End]*
   From all his iniquities.

31

Psalm 137:1-6 (*Unison*)

By the waters of Babylon,
   There we sat down and wept,
   When we remembered Zion.
On the willows there
   We hung up our lyres.
For there our captors
   Required of us songs,
And our tormentors, mirth, saying,
   " Sing us one of the songs of Zion! "

How shall we sing the Lord's song
  In a foreign land?
If I forget you, O Jerusalem,
  Let my right hand wither!
Let my tongue cleave to the roof of my mouth,
  If I do not remember you,
If I do not set Jerusalem
  Above my highest joy!   [*End*]

32

Psalm 139:1–12, 17, 18, 23, 24

O Lord, thou hast searched me and known me! Thou knowest when
I sit down and when I rise up;

Thou discernest my thoughts from afar.

Thou searchest out my path and my lying down, and art acquainted
with all my ways.

**Even before a word is on my tongue, lo, O Lord, thou knowest it
altogether.**

Thou dost beset me behind and before, and layest thy hand upon me.

**Such knowledge is too wonderful for me; it is high, I cannot
attain it.**

Whither shall I go from thy Spirit?

Or whither shall I flee from thy presence?

If I ascend to heaven, thou art there!

If I make my bed in Sheol, thou art there!

If I take the wings of the morning and dwell in the uttermost parts
of the sea, even there thy hand shall lead me,

And thy right hand shall hold me.

If I say, " Let only darkness cover me, and the light about me be
night,"

**Even the darkness is not dark to thee, the night is bright as the
day; for darkness is as light with thee.**

How precious to me are thy thoughts, O God! How vast is the sum of them!

If I would count them, they are more than the sand. When I awake, I am still with thee.

Search me, O God, and know my heart! Try me and know my thoughts!

And see if there be any wicked way in me, and lead me in the way everlasting!   [End]

33

Psalm 145

I will extol thee, my God and King, and bless thy name for ever and ever.

Every day I will bless thee, and praise thy name for ever and ever. Great is the Lord, and greatly to be praised, and his greatness is unsearchable.

One generation shall laud thy works to another, and shall declare thy mighty acts.

Of the glorious splendor of thy majesty, and of thy wondrous works, I will meditate.

Men shall proclaim the might of thy terrible acts, and I will declare thy greatness.

They shall pour forth the fame of thy abundant goodness, and shall sing aloud of thy righteousness.

The Lord is gracious and merciful, slow to anger and abounding in steadfast love.

The Lord is good to all, and his compassion is over all that he has made.

All thy works shall give thanks to thee, O Lord, and all thy saints shall bless thee!

They shall speak of the glory of thy kingdom, and tell of thy power,

To make known to the sons of men thy mighty deeds, and the glorious splendor of thy kingdom.

Thy kingdom is an everlasting kingdom, and thy dominion endures throughout all generations.

The Lord is faithful in all his words, and gracious in all his deeds.

The Lord upholds all who are falling, and raises up all who are bowed down.

The eyes of all look to thee, and thou givest them their food in due season.

Thou openest thy hand, thou satisfiest the desire of every living thing.

The Lord is just in all his ways, and kind in all his doings.

The Lord is near to all who call upon him, to all who call upon him in truth.

He fulfils the desire of all who fear him, he also hears their cry, and saves them.

The Lord preserves all who love him; but all the wicked he will destroy.

My mouth will speak the praise of the Lord, and let all flesh bless his holy name for ever and ever.   [*End*]

34

Psalm 148

Praise the Lord! Praise the Lord from the heavens, praise him in the heights!

Praise him, all his angels, praise him, all his host!

Praise him, sun and moon, praise him, all you shining stars!

Praise him, you highest heavens, and you waters above the heavens!

Let them praise the name of the Lord!

For he commanded and they were created.

And he established them for ever and ever;

He fixed their bounds which cannot be passed.

Praise the Lord from the earth, you sea monsters and all deeps,

Fire and hail, snow and frost, stormy wind fulfilling his command!

Mountains and all hills, fruit trees and all cedars!

Beasts and all cattle, creeping things and flying birds!

Kings of the earth and all peoples, princes and all rulers of the earth!

Young men and maidens together, old men and children!

Let them praise the name of the Lord,

For his name alone is exalted; his glory is above earth and heaven.

He has raised up a horn for his people,

Praise for all his saints, for the people of Israel who are near to him.

(*Unison*)

Praise the Lord!   [*End*]

35

Psalm 150

Praise the Lord! Praise God in his sanctuary;

Praise him in his mighty firmament!

Praise him for his mighty deeds;

Praise him according to his exceeding greatness!

Praise him with trumpet sound;

Praise him with lute and harp!

Praise him with timbrel and dance;

Praise him with strings and pipe!

Praise him with sounding cymbals;

Praise him with loud clashing cymbals!

Let everything that breathes praise the Lord!

Praise the Lord! [*End*]

36

Job 28:12–28 (*Unison*)
" Where shall wisdom be found?
    And where is the place of understanding?
Man does not know the way to it,
    And it is not found in the land of the living.
The deep says, ' It is not in me,'
    And the sea says, ' It is not with me.'
It cannot be gotten for gold,
    And silver cannot be weighed as its price.
It cannot be valued in the gold of Ophir,
    In precious onyx or sapphire.
Gold and glass cannot equal it,
    Nor can it be exchanged for jewels of fine gold.
No mention shall be made of coral or of crystal;
    The price of wisdom is above pearls.
The topaz of Ethiopia cannot compare with it,
    Nor can it be valued in pure gold.
Whence then comes wisdom?
    And where is the place of understanding?
It is hid from the eyes of all living,
    And concealed from the birds of the air.
Destruction and Death say,
    ' We have heard a rumor of it with our ears.'
God understands the way to it,
    And he knows its place.
For he looks to the ends of the earth,
    And sees everything under the heavens.

When he gave to the wind its weight,
  And meted out the waters by measure;
When he made a decree for the rain,
  And a way for the lightning of the thunder;
Then he saw it and declared it;
  He established it, and searched it out.
And he said to man,
' Behold, the fear of the Lord, that is wisdom;
  And to depart from evil is understanding.' "

[End]

37

Proverbs 3:13-26
Happy is the man who finds wisdom,
  And the man who gets understanding,

For the gain from it is better than gain from silver
  And its profit better than gold.

She is more precious than jewels,
  And nothing you desire can compare with her.

Long life is in her right hand;
  In her left hand are riches and honor.

Her ways are ways of pleasantness,
  And all her paths are peace.

She is a tree of life to those who lay hold of her;
  Those who hold her fast are called happy.

The Lord by wisdom founded the earth;
  By understanding he established the heavens;

By his knowledge the deeps broke forth,
  And the clouds drop down the dew.

My son, keep sound wisdom and discretion;
  Let them not escape from your sight,

And they will be life for your soul
  And adornment for your neck.

Then you will walk on your way securely
  And your foot will not stumble.

If you sit down, you will not be afraid;
  When you lie down, your sleep will be sweet.

Do not be afraid of sudden panic, or of the ruin of the wicked, when
it comes;
  For the Lord will be your confidence and will keep your foot
  from being caught.   [*End*]

38

Isaiah 9:2-7 (*Unison*)
The people who walked in darkness
  Have seen a great light;
Those who dwelt in a land of deep darkness,
  On them has light shined.
Thou hast multiplied the nation,
  Thou hast increased its joy;
They rejoice before thee
  As with joy at the harvest,
  As men rejoice when they divide the spoil.
For the yoke of his burden,
  And the staff for his shoulder,
  The rod of his oppressor,
  Thou hast broken as on the day of Midian.
For every boot of the tramping warrior in battle tumult
  And every garment rolled in blood
  Will be burned as fuel for the fire.

For to us a child is born,
　To us a son is given;
And the government will be upon his shoulder,
　And his name will be called
" Wonderful Counselor, Mighty God,
　Everlasting Father, Prince of Peace."
Of the increase of his government and of peace
　There will be no end,
Upon the throne of David, and over his kingdom,
　To establish it, and to uphold it
With justice and with righteousness
　From this time forth and for evermore.
The zeal of the Lord of hosts will do this.

[*End*]

39

Isaiah 11:1-9 (*Unison*)

There shall come forth a shoot from the stump of Jesse,
　And a branch shall grow out of his roots.
And the Spirit of the Lord shall rest upon him,
　The spirit of wisdom and understanding,
　The spirit of counsel and might,
The spirit of knowledge and the fear of the Lord.
And his delight shall be in the fear of the Lord.
He shall not judge by what his eyes see,
　Or decide by what his ears hear;
But with righteousness he shall judge the poor,
　And decide with equity for the meek of the earth;
And he shall smite the earth with the rod of his mouth,
　And with the breath of his lips he shall slay the wicked.
Righteousness shall be the girdle of his waist,
　And faithfulness the girdle of his loins.
The wolf shall dwell with the lamb,
　And the leopard shall lie down with the kid,

And the calf and the lion and the fatling together,
  And a little child shall lead them.
The cow and the bear shall feed;
  Their young shall lie down together;
  And the lion shall eat straw like the ox.
The sucking child shall play over the hole of the asp,
  And the weaned child shall put his hand on the adder's **den.**
They shall not hurt or destroy
  In all my holy mountain;
For the earth shall be full of the knowledge of the Lord
  As the waters cover the sea.   [*End*]

40

Isaiah, Ch. 35 (*Unison*)
The wilderness and the dry land shall be **glad,**
  The desert shall rejoice and blossom;
Like the crocus it shall blossom abundantly,
  And rejoice with joy and singing.
The glory of Lebanon shall be given to it,
  The majesty of Carmel and Sharon.
They shall see the glory of the Lord,
  The majesty of our God.
Strengthen the weak hands,
  And make firm the feeble knees.
Say to those who are of a fearful heart,
  " Be strong, fear not!
Behold, your God
  Will come with vengeance,
With the recompense of God.
  He will come and save you."
Then the eyes of the blind shall be opened,
  And the ears of the deaf unstopped;
Then shall the lame man leap like a hart,
  And the tongue of the dumb sing for joy.

For waters shall break forth in the wilderness,
   And streams in the desert;
The burning sand shall become a pool,
   And the thirsty ground springs of water;
The haunt of jackals shall become a swamp,
   The grass shall become reeds and rushes.
And a highway shall be there,
   And it shall be called the Holy Way;
The unclean shall not pass over it,
   And fools shall not err therein.
No lion shall be there,
   Nor shall any ravenous beast come up on it;
They shall not be found there,
   But the redeemed shall walk there.
And the ransomed of the Lord shall return,
   And come to Zion with singing,
   With everlasting joy upon their heads;
They shall obtain joy and gladness,
   And sorrow and sighing shall flee away.

                                         [*End*]

41

Isaiah 40:1-11, 27-31 (*Unison*)

Comfort, comfort my people,
   Says your God.
Speak tenderly to Jerusalem,
   And cry to her
That her warfare is ended,
   That her iniquity is pardoned,
That she has received from the Lord's hand
   Double for all her sins.
A voice cries:
" In the wilderness prepare the way of the Lord,
   Make straight in the desert a highway for our God.

Every valley shall be lifted up,
  And every mountain and hill be made low;
The uneven ground shall become level,
  And the rough places a plain.
And the glory of the Lord shall be revealed,
  And all flesh shall see it together,
  For the mouth of the Lord has spoken."
A voice says, " Cry! "
  And I said, " What shall I cry? "
All flesh is grass,
  And all its beauty is like the flower of the field.
The grass withers, the flower fades,
  When the breath of the Lord blows upon it;
  Surely the people is grass.
The grass withers, the flower fades;
  But the word of our God will stand for ever.
Get you up to a high mountain,
  O Zion, herald of good tidings;
Lift up your voice with strength,
  O Jerusalem, herald of good tidings,
  Lift it up, fear not;
Say to the cities of Judah,
  " Behold your God! "
Behold, the Lord God comes with might,
  And his arm rules for him;   .
Behold, his reward is with him,
  And his recompense before him.
He will feed his flock like a shepherd,
  He will gather the lambs in his arms,
He will carry them in his bosom,
  And gently lead those that are with young.
Why do you say, O Jacob,
  And speak, O Israel,
" My way is hid from the Lord,
  And my right is disregarded by my God "?
Have you not known? Have you not heard?
The Lord is the everlasting God,

The Creator of the ends of the earth.
He does not faint or grow weary,
   His understanding is unsearchable.
He gives power to the faint,
   And to him who has no might he increases strength.
Even youths shall faint and be weary,
   And young men shall fall exhausted;
But they who wait for the Lord shall renew their strength,
   They shall mount up with wings like eagles,
They shall run and not be weary,
   They shall walk and not faint.   *[End]*

42

Isaiah 42:1-7 (*Unison*)

Behold my servant, whom I uphold,
   My chosen, in whom my soul delights;
I have put my spirit upon him,
   He will bring forth justice to the nations.
He will not cry or lift up his voice,
   Or make it heard in the street;
A bruised reed he will not break,
   And a dimly burning wick he will not quench;
   He will faithfully bring forth justice.
He will not fail or be discouraged
   Till he has established justice in the earth;
   And the coastlands wait for his law.
Thus says God, the Lord,
   Who created the heavens and stretched them out,
   Who spread forth the earth and what comes from it,
Who gives breath to the people upon it
   And spirit to those who walk in it:
" I am the Lord, I have called you in righteousness,
   I have taken you by the hand and kept you;

I have given you as a covenant to the people,
  A light to the nations,
  To open the eyes that are blind,
To bring out the prisoners from the dungeon,
  From the prison those who sit in darkness."

  [End]

43

Isaiah 52:13-15; Ch. 53 (*Unison*)

Behold, my servant shall prosper,
  He shall be exalted and lifted up,
  And shall be very high.
As many were astonished at him —
  His appearance was so marred, beyond human semblance,
  And his form beyond that of the sons of men —
So shall he startle many nations;
  Kings shall shut their mouths because of him;
For that which has not been told them they shall see,
  And that which they have not heard they shall understand.
Who has believed what we have heard?
  And to whom has the arm of the Lord been revealed?
For he grew up before him like a young plant,
  And like a root out of dry ground;
He had no form or comeliness that we should look at him,
  And no beauty that we should desire him.
He was despised and rejected by men;
  A man of sorrows, and acquainted with grief;
And as one from whom men hide their faces
  He was despised, and we esteemed him not.
Surely he has borne our griefs
  And carried our sorrows;
Yet we esteemed him stricken,
  Smitten by God, and afflicted.
But he was wounded for our transgressions,
  He was bruised for our iniquities;

Upon him was the chastisement that made us whole,
    And with his stripes we are healed.
All we like sheep have gone astray;
    We have turned every one to his own way;
And the Lord has laid on him
    The iniquity of us all.
He was oppressed, and he was afflicted,
    Yet he opened not his mouth;
Like a lamb that is led to the slaughter,
    And like a sheep that before its shearers is dumb,
    So he opened not his mouth.
By oppression and judgment he was taken away;
    And as for his generation, who considered
That he was cut off out of the land of the living,
    Stricken for the transgression of my people?
And they made his grave with the wicked
    And with a rich man in his death,
Although he had done no violence,
    And there was no deceit in his mouth.
Yet it was the will of the Lord to bruise him;
    He has put him to grief;
When he makes himself an offering for sin,
    He shall see his offspring, he shall prolong his days;
The will of the Lord shall prosper in his hand;
    He shall see the fruit of the travail of his soul and be satisfied;
By his knowledge shall the righteous one, my servant,
    Make many to be accounted righteous;
    And he shall bear their iniquities.
Therefore I will divide him a portion with the great,
    And he shall divide the spoil with the strong;
Because he poured out his soul to death,
    And was numbered with the transgressors;
Yet he bore the sin of many,
    And made intercession for the transgressors.

                                        [*End*]

44

Isaiah, Ch. 55 (*Unison*)

" Ho, every one who thirsts,
  Come to the waters;
And he who has no money,
  Come, buy and eat!
Come, buy wine and milk
  Without money and without price.
Why do you spend your money for that which is not bread,
  And your labor for that which does not satisfy?
Hearken diligently to me, and eat what is good,
  And delight yourselves in fatness.
Incline your ear, and come to me;
  Hear, that your soul may live;
And I will make with you an everlasting covenant,
  My steadfast, sure love for David.
Behold, I made him a witness to the peoples,
  A leader and commander for the peoples.
Behold, you shall call nations that you know not,
  And nations that knew you not shall run to you,
Because of the Lord your God, and of the Holy One of Israel,
  For he has glorified you.
Seek the Lord while he may be found,
  Call upon him while he is near;
Let the wicked forsake his way,
  And the unrighteous man his thoughts;
Let him return to the Lord, that he may have mercy on him,
  And to our God, for he will abundantly pardon.
For my thoughts are not your thoughts,
  Neither are your ways my ways, says the Lord.
For as the heavens are higher than the earth,
  So are my ways higher than your ways
  And my thoughts than your thoughts.
For as the rain and the snow come down from heaven,
  And return not thither but water the earth,

Making it bring forth and sprout,
　Giving seed to the sower and bread to the eater,
So shall my word be that goes forth from my mouth;
　It shall not return to me empty,
But it shall accomplish that which I purpose,
　And prosper in the thing for which I sent it.
For you shall go out in joy,
　And be led forth in peace;
The mountains and the hills before you
　Shall break forth into singing,
　And all the trees of the field shall clap their hands.
Instead of the thorn shall come up the cypress;
　Instead of the brier shall come up the myrtle;
And it shall be to the Lord for a memorial,
　For an everlasting sign which shall not be cut off."

[End]

45

Matthew 5:3-16 (*Unison*)

" Blessed are the poor in spirit, for theirs is the kingdom of heaven.

" Blessed are those who mourn, for they shall be comforted.

" Blessed are the meek, for they shall inherit the earth.

" Blessed are those who hunger and thirst for righteousness, for they shall be satisfied.

" Blessed are the merciful, for they shall obtain mercy.

" Blessed are the pure in heart, for they shall see God.

" Blessed are the peacemakers, for they shall be called sons of God.

" Blessed are those who are persecuted for righteousness' sake, for theirs is the kingdom of heaven.

" Blessed are you when men revile you and persecute you and utter all kinds of evil against you falsely on my account. Rejoice and be glad, for your reward is great in heaven, for so men persecuted the prophets who were before you.

" You are the salt of the earth; but if salt has lost its taste, how shall its saltness be restored? It is no longer good for anything except to be thrown out and trodden under foot by men.

" You are the light of the world. A city set on a hill cannot be hid. Nor do men light a lamp and put it under a bushel, but on a stand, and it gives light to all in the house. Let your light so shine before men, that they may see your good works and give glory to your Father who is in heaven." [*End*]

46

Matthew 6:19–34 (*Unison*)

" Do not lay up for yourselves treasures on earth, where moth and rust consume and where thieves break in and steal, but lay up for yourselves treasures in heaven, where neither moth nor rust consumes and where thieves do not break in and steal. For where your treasure is, there will your heart be also.

" The eye is the lamp of the body. So, if your eye is sound, your whole body will be full of light; but if your eye is not sound, your whole body will be full of darkness. If then the light in you is darkness, how great is the darkness!

" No one can serve two masters; for either he will hate the one and love the other, or he will be devoted to the one and despise the other. You cannot serve God and mammon.

" Therefore I tell you, do not be anxious about your life, what you shall eat or what you shall drink, nor about your body, what you shall put on. Is not life more than food, and the body more than clothing? Look at the birds of the air: they neither sow nor reap nor gather into barns, and yet your heavenly Father feeds them. Are you not of more value than they? And which of you by being anxious can add one cubit to his span of life? And why are you anxious about clothing? Consider the lilies of the field, how they grow; they neither toil nor spin; yet I tell you, even Solomon in all his glory was not arrayed like one of these. But if God so clothes the grass of the field, which today is alive and tomorrow is thrown into the oven, will he not much more clothe you, O men of little faith? Therefore do not be anxious, saying, ' What shall we eat? ' or ' What shall we drink? ' or ' What shall we wear? ' For the Gentiles seek all these things; and your heavenly Father knows that you need them all. But seek first his kingdom and his righteousness, and all these things shall be yours as well.

" Therefore do not be anxious about tomorrow, for tomorrow will be anxious for itself. Let the day's own trouble be sufficient for the day."   [*End*]

47

Luke 2:1–20 (*Unison*)

In those days a decree went out from Caesar Augustus that all the world should be enrolled. This was the first enrollment, when Quirinius was governor of Syria. And all went to be enrolled, each to his own city. And Joseph also went up from Galilee, from the city of Nazareth, to Judea, to the city of David, which is called Bethlehem, because he was of the house and lineage of David, to be enrolled with Mary, his betrothed, who was with child. And while they were there, the time came for her to be delivered. And she gave birth to her first-born son and wrapped him in swaddling cloths, and laid him in a manger, because there was no place for them in the inn.

And in that region there were shepherds out in the field, keeping watch over their flock by night. And an angel of the Lord appeared to them, and the glory of the Lord shone around them, and they were filled with fear. And the angel said to them, " Be not afraid; for behold, I bring you good news of a great joy which will come to all the people; for to you is born this day in the city of David a Savior, who is Christ the Lord. And this will be a sign for you: you will find a babe wrapped in swaddling cloths and lying in a manger." And suddenly there was with the angel a multitude of the heavenly host praising God and saying, " Glory to God in the highest, and on earth peace among men with whom he is pleased! "

When the angels went away from them into heaven, the shepherds said to one another, " Let us go over to Bethlehem and see this thing that has happened, which the Lord has made known to us." And they went with haste, and found Mary and Joseph, and the babe lying in a manger. And when they saw it they made known the saying which had been told them concerning this child; and all who heard it wondered at what the shepherds told them. But Mary kept all these things, pondering them in her heart. And the shepherds returned, glorifying and praising God for all they had heard and seen, as it had been told them. *[End]*

48

John 1:1-14 (*Unison*)

In the beginning was the Word, and the Word was with God, and the Word was God. He was in the beginning with God; all things were made through him, and without him was not anything made that was made. In him was life, and the life was the light of men. The light shines in the darkness, and the darkness has not overcome it.

There was a man sent from God, whose name was John. He came for testimony, to bear witness to the light, that all might believe through him. He was not the light, but came to bear witness to the light.

The true light that enlightens every man was coming into the world. He was in the world, and the world was made through him, yet the world knew him not. He came to his own home, and his own people received him not. But to all who received him, who believed in his name, he gave power to become children of God; who were born, not of blood nor of the will of the flesh nor of the will of man, but of God.

And the Word became flesh and dwelt among us, full of grace and truth; we have beheld his glory, glory as of the only Son from the Father. *[End]*

49

John 10:1-18 (*Unison*)

" Truly, truly, I say to you, he who does not enter the sheepfold by the door but climbs in by another way, that man is a thief and a robber; but he who enters by the door is the shepherd of the sheep. To him the gatekeeper opens; the sheep hear his voice, and he calls his own sheep by name and leads them out. When he has brought out all his own, he goes before them, and the sheep follow him, for they know his voice. A stranger they will not follow, but they will flee from him, for they do not know the voice of strangers." This figure Jesus used with them, but they did not understand what he was saying to them.

So Jesus again said to them, " Truly, truly, I say to you, I am the door of the sheep. All who came before me are thieves and robbers; but the sheep did not heed them. I am the door; if any one enters by me, he will be saved, and will go in and out and find pasture. The thief comes only to steal and kill and destroy; I came that they may have life, and have it abundantly. I am the good shepherd. The good shepherd lays down his life for the sheep. He who is a hireling and not a shepherd, whose own the sheep are not, sees the wolf coming and leaves the sheep and flees; and the wolf snatches them and scatters them. He flees because he is a hireling and cares nothing for the sheep. I am the good shepherd; I know my own and my own know me, as the Father knows me and I know the Father; and I lay down my life for the sheep. And I have other sheep, that are not of this fold; I must bring them also, and they will heed my voice. So there shall be one flock, one shepherd. For this reason the Father loves me, because I lay down my life, that I may take it again. No one takes it from me, but I lay it down of my own accord. I have power to lay it down, and I have power to take it again; this charge I have received from my Father."   **[*End*]**

50

John 14:1–21 (*Unison*)

" Let not your hearts be troubled; believe in God, believe also in me. In my Father's house are many rooms; if it were not so, would I have told you that I go to prepare a place for you? And when I go and prepare a place for you, I will come again and will take you to myself, that where I am you may be also. And you know the way where I am going." Thomas said to him, " Lord, we do not know where you are going; how can we know the way? " Jesus said to him, " I am the way, and the truth, and the life; no one comes to the Father, but by me. If you had known me, you would have known my Father also; henceforth you know him and have seen him."

Philip said to him, " Lord, show us the Father, and we shall be satisfied." Jesus said to him, " Have I been with you so long, and yet you do not know me, Philip? He who has seen me has seen the Father; how can you say, ' Show us the Father '? Do you not believe that I am in the Father and the Father in me? The words that I say to you I do not speak on my own authority; but the Father who dwells in me does his works. Believe me that I am in the Father and the Father in me; or else believe me for the sake of the works themselves.

" Truly, truly, I say to you, he who believes in me will also do the works that I do; and greater works than these will he do, because I go to the Father. Whatever you ask in my name, I will do it, that the Father may be glorified in the Son; if you ask anything in my name, I will do it.

" If you love me, you will keep my commandments. And I will pray the Father, and he will give you another Counselor, to be with you for ever, even the Spirit of truth, whom the world cannot receive, because it neither sees him nor knows him; you know him, for he dwells with you, and will be in you.

" I will not leave you desolate; I will come to you. Yet a little while, and the world will see me no more, but you will see me; because I live, you will live also. In that day you will know that I am in my Father, and you in me, and I in you. He who has my commandments and keeps them, he it is who loves me; and he who loves me will be loved by my Father, and I will love him and manifest myself to him."　　　　　　　　　　　　　　*[End]*

51

John 14:25–27; 15:26, 27; 16:7–13 (*Unison*)

" These things I have spoken to you, while I am still with you. But the Counselor, the Holy Spirit, whom the Father will send in my name, he will teach you all things, and bring to your remembrance all that I have said to you. Peace I leave with you; my peace I give to you; not as the world gives do I give to you. Let not your hearts be troubled, neither let them be afraid.

" But when the Counselor comes, whom I shall send to you from the Father, even the Spirit of truth, who proceeds from the Father, he will bear witness to me; and you also are witnesses, because you have been with me from the beginning.

" Nevertheless I tell you the truth: it is to your advantage that I go away, for if I do not go away, the Counselor will not come to you; but if I go, I will send him to you. And when he comes, he will convince the world of sin and of righteousness and of judgment: of sin, because they do not believe in me; of righteousness, because I go to the Father, and you will see me no more; of judgment, because the ruler of this world is judged.

" I have yet many things to say to you, but you cannot bear them now. When the Spirit of truth comes, he will guide you into all the truth; for he will not speak on his own authority, but whatever he hears he will speak, and he will declare to you the things that are to come."　　　　　　　　　　　　*[End]*

52

John 15:1–17 (*Unison*)

" I am the true vine, and my Father is the vinedresser. Every branch of mine that bears no fruit, he takes away, and every branch that does bear fruit he prunes, that it may bear more fruit. You are already made clean by the word which I have spoken to you. Abide in me, and I in you. As the branch cannot bear fruit by itself, unless it abides in the vine, neither can you, unless you abide in me. I am the vine, you are the branches. He who abides in me, and I in him, he it is that bears much fruit, for apart from me you can do nothing. If a man does not abide in me, he is cast forth as a branch and withers; and the branches are gathered, thrown into the fire and burned. If you abide in me, and my words abide in you, ask whatever you will, and it shall be done for you. By this my Father is glorified, that you bear much fruit, and so prove to be my disciples. As the Father has loved me, so have I loved you; abide in my love. If you keep my commandments, you will abide in my love, just as I have kept my Father's commandments and abide in his love. These things I have spoken to you, that my joy may be in you, and that your joy may be full.

" This is my commandment, that you love one another as I have loved you. Greater love has no man than this, that a man lay down his life for his friends. You are my friends if you do what I command you. No longer do I call you servants, for the servant does not know what his master is doing; but I have called you friends, for all that I have heard from my Father I have made known to you. You did not choose me, but I chose you and appointed you that you should go and bear fruit and that your fruit should abide; so that whatever you ask the Father in my name, he may give it to you. This I command you, to love one another." *[End]*

53

John 17:3-6, 16-26 (*Unison*)

" And this is eternal life, that they know thee the only true God, and Jesus Christ whom thou hast sent. I glorified thee on earth, having accomplished the work which thou gavest me to do; and now, Father, glorify thou me in thy own presence with the glory which I had with thee before the world was made.

" I have manifested thy name to the men whom thou gavest me out of the world; thine they were, and thou gavest them to me, and they have kept thy word. They are not of the world, even as I am not of the world. Sanctify them in the truth; thy word is truth. As thou didst send me into the world, so I have sent them into the world. And for their sake I consecrate myself, that they also may be consecrated in truth.

" I do not pray for these only, but also for those who are to believe in me through their word, that they may all be one; even as thou, Father, art in me, and I in thee, that they also may be in us, so that the world may believe that thou hast sent me. The glory which thou hast given me I have given to them, that they may be one even as we are one, I in them and thou in me, that they may become perfectly one, so that the world may know that thou hast sent me and hast loved them even as thou hast loved me. Father, I desire that they also, whom thou hast given me, may be with me where I am, to behold my glory which thou hast given me in thy love for me before the foundation of the world. O righteous Father, the world has not known thee, but I have known thee; and these know that thou hast sent me. I made known to them thy name, and I will make it known, that the love with which thou hast loved me may be in them, and I in them."   [*End*]

54

Mark 15:22–39 (*Unison*)

And they brought him to the place called Golgotha (which means the place of a skull). And they offered him wine mingled with myrrh; but he did not take it. And they crucified him, and divided his garments among them, casting lots for them, to decide what each should take. And it was the third hour, when they crucified him. And the inscription of the charge against him read, " The King of the Jews." And with him they crucified two robbers, one on his right and one on his left. And those who passed by derided him, wagging their heads, and saying, " Aha! You who would destroy the temple and build it in

three days, save yourself, and come down from the cross!" So also
the chief priests mocked him to one another with the scribes, saying,
" He saved others; he cannot save himself. Let the Christ, the King
of Israel, come down now from the cross, that we may see and believe." Those who were crucified with him also reviled him.

And when the sixth hour had come, there was darkness over the
whole land until the ninth hour. And at the ninth hour Jesus cried
with a loud voice, " E'lo-i, E'lo-i, la'ma sabach-tha'ni? " which means,
" My God, my God, why hast thou forsaken me? " And some of the
bystanders hearing it said, " Behold, he is calling Elijah." And one
ran and, filling a sponge full of vinegar, put it on a reed and gave it to
him to drink, saying, " Wait, let us see whether Elijah will come to
take him down." And Jesus uttered a loud cry, and breathed his last.
And the curtain of the temple was torn in two, from top to bottom.
And when the centurion, who stood facing him, saw that he thus
breathed his last, he said, " Truly this man was a son of God! "

[End]

55

Matthew, Ch. 28 (*Unison*)

Now after the sabbath, toward the dawn of the first day of the
week, Mary Magdalene and the other Mary went to see the sepulchre.
And behold, there was a great earthquake; for an angel of the Lord
descended from heaven and came and rolled back the stone, and sat
upon it. His appearance was like lightning, and his raiment white
as snow. And for fear of him the guards trembled and became like
dead men. But the angel said to the women, " Do not be afraid; for I
know that you seek Jesus who was crucified. He is not here; for he
has risen, as he said. Come, see the place where he lay. Then go
quickly and tell his disciples that he has risen from the dead, and
behold, he is going before you to Galilee; there you will see him. Lo,
I have told you." So they departed quickly from the tomb with fear
and great joy, and ran to tell his disciples. And behold, Jesus met

them and said, " Hail! " And they came up and took hold of his feet and worshiped him. Then Jesus said to them, " Do not be afraid; go and tell my brethren to go to Galilee, and there they will see me."

While they were going, behold, some of the guard went into the city and told the chief priests all that had taken place. And when they had assembled with the elders and taken counsel, they gave a sum of money to the soldiers and said, " Tell people, ' His disciples came by night and stole him away while we were asleep.' And if this comes to the governor's ears, we will satisfy him and keep you out of trouble." So they took the money and did as they were directed; and this story has been spread among the Jews to this day.

Now the eleven disciples went to Galilee, to the mountain to which Jesus had directed them. And when they saw him they worshiped him; but some doubted. And Jesus came and said to them, " All authority in heaven and on earth has been given to me. Go therefore and make disciples of all nations, baptizing them in the name of the Father and of the Son and of the Holy Spirit, teaching them to observe all that I have commanded you; and lo, I am with you always, to the close of the age."   [End]

56

Romans 5:1-11 (*Unison*)

Therefore, since we are justified by faith, we have peace with God through our Lord Jesus Christ. Through him we have obtained access to this grace in which we stand, and we rejoice in our hope of sharing the glory of God. More than that, we rejoice in our sufferings, knowing that suffering produces endurance, and endurance produces character, and character produces hope, and hope does not disappoint us, because God's love has been poured into our hearts through the Holy Spirit which has been given to us.

While we were yet helpless, at the right time Christ died for the ungodly. Why, one will hardly die for a righteous man—though perhaps for a good man one will dare even to die. But God shows his love for us in that while we were yet sinners Christ died for us. Since, therefore, we are now justified by his blood, much more shall

we be saved by him from the wrath of God. For if while we were
enemies we were reconciled to God by the death of his Son, much
more, now that we are reconciled, shall we be saved by his life. Not
only so, but we also rejoice in God through our Lord Jesus Christ,
through whom we have now received our reconciliation.

[*End*]

57

Romans 8:14-18, 26-39 (*Unison*)

For all who are led by the Spirit of God are sons of God. For you
did not receive the spirit of slavery to fall back into fear, but you
have received the spirit of sonship. When we cry, " Abba! Father! "
it is the Spirit himself bearing witness with our spirit that we are
children of God, and if children, then heirs, heirs of God and fellow
heirs with Christ, provided we suffer with him in order that we may
also be glorified with him.

I consider that the sufferings of this present time are not worth
comparing with the glory that is to be revealed to us.

Likewise the Spirit helps us in our weakness; for we do not know
how to pray as we ought, but the Spirit himself intercedes for us with
sighs too deep for words. And he who searches the hearts of men
knows what is the mind of the Spirit, because the Spirit intercedes
for the saints according to the will of God.

We know that in everything God works for good with those who
love him, who are called according to his purpose. For those whom
he foreknew he also predestined to be conformed to the image of his
Son, in order that he might be the first-born among many brethren.
And those whom he predestined he also called; and those whom he
called he also justified; and those whom he justified he also glorified.

What then shall we say to this? If God is for us, who is against
us? He who did not spare his own Son but gave him up for us all,
will he not also give us all things with him? Who shall bring any
charge against God's elect? It is God who justifies; who is to con-
demn? Is it Christ Jesus, who died, yes, who was raised from the

dead, who is at the right hand of God, who indeed intercedes for us? Who shall separate us from the love of Christ? Shall tribulation, or distress, or persecution, or famine, or nakedness, or peril, or sword? As it is written, " For thy sake we are being killed all the day long; we are regarded as sheep to be slaughtered." No, in all these things we are more than conquerors through him who loved us. For I am sure that neither death, nor life, nor angels, nor principalities, nor things present, nor things to come, nor powers, nor height, nor depth, nor anything else in all creation will be able to separate us from the love of God in Christ Jesus our Lord.

[*End*]

58

Romans 12:1, 2, 9–21 (*Unison*)

I appeal to you therefore, brethren, by the mercies of God, to present your bodies as a living sacrifice, holy and acceptable to God, which is your spiritual worship. Do not be conformed to this world but be transformed by the renewal of your mind, that you may prove what is the will of God, what is good and acceptable and perfect.

Let love be genuine; hate what is evil, hold fast to what is good; love one another with brotherly affection; outdo one another in showing honor. Never flag in zeal, be aglow with the Spirit, serve the Lord. Rejoice in your hope, be patient in tribulation, be constant in prayer. Contribute to the needs of the saints, practice hospitality.

Bless those who persecute you; bless and do not curse them. Rejoice with those who rejoice, weep with those who weep. Live in harmony with one another; do not be haughty, but associate with the lowly; never be conceited. Repay no one evil for evil, but take thought for what is noble in the sight of all. If possible, so far as it depends upon you, live peaceably with all. Beloved, never avenge yourselves, but leave it to the wrath of God; for it is written, " Vengeance is mine, I will repay, says the Lord." No, " if your enemy is hungry, feed him; if he is thirsty, give him drink; for by so doing you will heap burning coals upon his head." Do not be overcome by evil, but overcome evil with good.   [*End*]

59

I Corinthians 12:31; Ch. 13; 14:1a (*Unison*)

Earnestly desire the higher gifts.

And I will show you a still more excellent way.

If I speak in the tongues of men and of angels, but have not love, I am a noisy gong or a clanging cymbal. And if I have prophetic powers, and understand all mysteries and all knowledge, and if I have all faith, so as to remove mountains, but have not love, I am nothing. If I give away all I have, and if I deliver my body to be burned, but have not love, I gain nothing.

Love is patient and kind; love is not jealous or boastful; it is not arrogant or rude. Love does not insist on its own way; it is not irritable or resentful; it does not rejoice at wrong, but rejoices in the right. Love bears all things, believes all things, hopes all things, endures all things.

Love never ends; as for prophecy, it will pass away; as for tongues, they will cease; as for knowledge, it will pass away. For our knowledge is imperfect and our prophecy is imperfect; but when the perfect comes, the imperfect will pass away. When I was a child, I spoke like a child, I thought like a child, I reasoned like a child; when I became a man, I gave up childish ways. For now we see in a mirror dimly, but then face to face. Now I know in part; then I shall understand fully, even as I have been fully understood. So faith, hope, love abide, these three; but the greatest of these is love.

Make love your aim. [*End*]

60

1 Corinthians 15:17–26, 50–52, 54b–58 (*Unison*)

If Christ has not been raised, your faith is futile and you are still in your sins. Then those also who have fallen asleep in Christ have perished. If in this life we who are in Christ have only hope, we are of all men most to be pitied.

But in fact Christ has been raised from the dead, the first fruits of those who have fallen asleep. For as by a man came death, by a man has come also the resurrection of the dead. For as in Adam all die, so also in Christ shall all be made alive. But each in his own order: Christ the first fruits, then at his coming those who belong to Christ. Then comes the end, when he delivers the kingdom to God the Father after destroying every rule and every authority and power. For he must reign until he has put all his enemies under his feet. The last enemy to be destroyed is death.

I tell you this, brethren: flesh and blood cannot inherit the kingdom of God, nor does the perishable inherit the imperishable.

Lo! I tell you a mystery. We shall not all sleep, but we shall all be changed, in a moment, in the twinkling of an eye, at the last trumpet. For the trumpet will sound, and the dead will be raised imperishable, and we shall be changed. Then shall come to pass the saying that is written: " Death is swallowed up in victory." " O death, where ·is thy victory? O death, where is thy sting? " The sting of death is sin, and the power of sin is the law. But thanks be to God, who gives us the victory through our Lord Jesus Christ.

Therefore, my beloved brethren, be steadfast, immovable, always abounding in the work of the Lord, knowing that in the Lord your labor is not in vain. [*End*]

61

Philippians 4:1, 4–8, 9b, 13, 19, 20 (*Unison*)

Therefore, my brethren, whom I love and long for, my joy and crown, stand firm thus in the Lord, my beloved.

Rejoice in the Lord always; again I will say, Rejoice. Let all men know your forbearance. The Lord is at hand. Have no anxiety about anything, but in everything by prayer and supplication with thanksgiving let your requests be made known to God. And the peace of God, which passes all understanding, will keep your hearts and your minds in Christ Jesus.

Finally, brethren, whatever is true, whatever is honorable, whatever is just, whatever is pure, whatever is lovely, whatever is gracious, if there is any excellence, if there is anything worthy of praise, think about these things and the God of peace will be with you. I can do all things in him who strengthens me.

And my God will supply every need of yours according to his riches in glory in Christ Jesus. To our God and Father be glory for ever and ever. Amen.   [*End*]

62

Hebrews 11:1–6, 32–40; 12:1, 2 (*Unison*)

Now faith is the assurance of things hoped for, the conviction of things not seen. For by it the men of old received divine approval. By faith we understand that the world was created by the word of God, so that what is seen was made out of things which do not appear.

By faith Abel offered to God a more acceptable sacrifice than Cain, through which he received approval as righteous, God bearing witness by accepting his gifts; he died, but through his faith he is still speaking. By faith Enoch was taken up so that he should not see death; and he was not found, because God had taken him. Now before he was taken he was attested as having pleased God. And without faith it is impossible to please him. For whoever would draw near to God must believe that he exists and that he rewards those who seek him.

And what more shall I say? For time would fail me to tell of Gideon, Barak, Samson, Jephthah, of David and Samuel and the prophets — who through faith conquered kingdoms, enforced justice, received promises, stopped the mouths of lions, quenched raging fire, escaped the edge of the sword, won strength out of weakness, became mighty in war, put foreign armies to flight. Women received their dead by resurrection. Some were tortured, refusing to accept release, that they might rise again to a better life. Others suffered mocking and scourging, and even chains and imprisonment. They were stoned, they were sawn in two, they were killed with the sword; they went about in skins of sheep and goats, destitute, afflicted, ill-treated — of whom the world was not worthy — wandering over deserts and mountains, and in dens and caves of the earth.

And all these, though well attested by their faith, did not receive what was promised, since God had foreseen something better for us, that apart from us they should not be made perfect.

Therefore, since we are surrounded by so great a cloud of witnesses, let us also lay aside every weight, and sin which clings so closely, and let us run with perseverance the race that is set before us, looking to Jesus the pioneer and perfecter of our faith, who for the joy that was set before him endured the cross, despising the shame, and is seated at the right hand of the throne of God.

[End]

63

I John 4:7-21 (*Unison*)

Beloved, let us love one another; for love is of God, and he who loves is born of God and knows God. He who does not love does not know God; for God is love. In this the love of God was made manifest among us, that God sent his only Son into the world, so that we might live through him. In this is love, not that we loved God but that he loved us and sent his Son to be the expiation for our sins. Beloved, if God so loved us, we also ought to love one another. No man has ever seen God; if we love one another, God abides in us and his love is perfected in us.

By this we know that we abide in him and he in us, because he has given us of his own Spirit. And we have seen and testify that the Father has sent his Son as the Savior of the world. Whoever confesses that Jesus is the Son of God, God abides in him, and he in God. So we know and believe the love God has for us. God is love, and he who abides in love abides in God, and God abides in him. In this is love perfected with us, that we may have confidence for the day of judgment, because as he is so are we in this world. There is no fear in love, but perfect love casts out fear. For fear has to do with punishment, and he who fears is not perfected in love. We love, because he first loved us. If any one says, " I love God," and hates his brother, he is a liar; for he who does not love his brother whom he has seen, cannot love God whom he has not seen. And this commandment we have from him, that he who loves God should love his brother also.   [*End*]

64

Acts 17:24-28; Romans 10:12-15; Matthew 9:37, 38 (*Unison*)

" The God who made the world and everything in it, being Lord of heaven and earth, does not live in shrines made by man, nor is he served by human hands, as though he needed anything, since he himself gives to all men life and breath and everything. And he made from one every nation of men to live on all the face of the earth, having determined allotted periods and the boundaries of their habitation, that they should seek God, in the hope that they might feel after him and find him. Yet he is not far from each one of us, for ' In him we live and move and have our being '; as even some of your poets have said, ' For we are indeed his offspring.' "

For there is no distinction between Jew and Greek; the same Lord is Lord of all and bestows his riches upon all who call upon him. For, " every one who calls upon the name of the Lord will be saved."

But how are men to call upon him in whom they have not believed? And how are they to believe in him of whom they have never heard? And how are they to hear without a preacher? And how can men preach unless they are sent? As it is written, " How beautiful are the feet of those who preach good news! "

Then he said to his disciples, " The harvest is plentiful, but the laborers are few; pray therefore the Lord of the harvest to send out laborers into his harvest."   [*End*]

65

Ephesians 1:3-14 (*Unison*)

Blessed be the God and Father of our Lord Jesus Christ, who has blessed us in Christ with every spiritual blessing in the heavenly places, even as he chose us in him before the foundation of the world, that we should be holy and blameless before him. He destined us in love to be his sons through Jesus Christ, according to the purpose of his will, to the praise of his glorious grace which he freely bestowed on us in the Beloved. In him we have redemption through his blood, the forgiveness of our trespasses, according to the riches of his grace which he lavished upon us. For he has made known to us in all wisdom and insight the mystery of his will, according to his purpose which he set forth in Christ as a plan for the fullness of time, to unite all things in him, things in heaven and things on earth.

In him, according to the purpose of him who accomplishes all things according to the counsel of his will, we who first hoped in Christ have been destined and appointed to live for the praise of his glory. In him you also, who have heard the word of truth, the gospel of your salvation, and have believed in him, were sealed with the promised Holy Spirit, which is the guarantee of our inheritance until we acquire possession of it, to the praise of his glory.

[End]

66

Matthew 25:31-40 (*Unison*)

" When the Son of man comes in his glory, and all the angels with him, then he will sit on his glorious throne. Before him will be gathered all the nations, and he will separate them one from another as a shepherd separates the sheep from the goats, and he will place the sheep at his right hand, but the goats at the left. Then the King will say to those at his right hand, ' Come, O blessed of my Father, inherit the kingdom prepared for you from the foundation of the world; for I was hungry and you gave me food, I was thirsty and you gave me drink, I was a stranger and you welcomed me, I was naked and you clothed me, I was sick and you visited me, I was in prison and you came to me.' Then the righteous will answer him, ' Lord, when did we see thee hungry and feed thee, or thirsty and give thee drink? And when did we see thee a stranger and welcome thee, or naked and clothe thee? And when did we see thee sick or

in prison and visit thee? ' And the King will answer them, ' Truly,
I say to you, as you did it to one of the least of these my brethren,
you did it to me.' "   *[End]*

67

Revelation 21:1-7, 22-27; 22:1-5 (*Unison*)

Then I saw a new heaven and a new earth; for the first heaven
and the first earth had passed away, and the sea was no more. And
I saw the holy city, new Jerusalem, coming down out of heaven
from God, prepared as a bride adorned for her husband; and I heard
a great voice from the throne saying, " Behold, the dwelling of God
is with men. He will dwell with them, and they shall be his people,
and God himself will be with them; he will wipe away every tear
from their eyes, and death shall be no more, neither shall there be
mourning nor crying nor pain any more, for the former things have
passed away."

And he who sat upon the throne said, " Behold, I make all things
new." Also he said, " Write this, for these words are trustworthy and
true." And he said to me, " It is done! I am the Alpha and the
Omega, the beginning and the end. To the thirsty I will give water
without price from the fountain of the water of life. He who con-
quers shall have this heritage, and I will be his God and he shall
be my son.

And I saw no temple in the city, for its temple is the Lord God
the Almighty and the Lamb. And the city has no need of sun or
moon to shine upon it, for the glory of God is its light, and its lamp
is the Lamb. By its light shall the nations walk; and the kings of
the earth shall bring their glory into it, and its gates shall never be
shut by day — and there shall be no night there; they shall bring into
it the glory and the honor of the nations. But nothing unclean shall
enter it, nor any one who practices abomination or falsehood, but
only those who are written in the Lamb's book of life.

Then he showed me the river of the water of life, bright as crystal,
flowing from the throne of God and of the Lamb through the middle
of the street of the city; also, on either side of the river, the tree of

life with its twelve kinds of fruit, yielding its fruit each month; and the leaves of the tree were for the healing of the nations. There shall no more be anything accursed, but the throne of God and of the Lamb shall be in it, and his servants shall worship him; they shall see his face, and his name shall be on their foreheads. And night shall be no more; they need no light of lamp or sun, for the Lord God will be their light, and they shall reign for ever and ever.

[End]

Topical Index

Index of Scriptural Allusions

Index of Authors, Translators, and Sources of Hymns

Index of Composers, Arrangers, and Sources of Tunes

Metrical Index of Tunes

S.M. (6. 6. 8. 6.)
Aylesbury, 118
Boylston, 301
Dennis, 105, 473
Festal Song, 352
Franconia, 94, 226
Greenwood, 218
Laban, 363
St. Bride, 233, 308, 364
St. Michael, 493
St. Thomas (Williams), 408, 435
Schumann, 312, 443
Southwell, 270
Swabia, 72
Trentham, 235
Windermere, 552

S.M. with Refrain
Marion, 407

S.M.D. (6. 6. 8. 6. 6. 6. 8. 6.)
Diademata, 213, 362, 469
Terra beata, 101

C.M. (8. 6. 8. 6.)
Abridge, 413
Amazing Grace, 275
Antioch, 161
Arlington, 69, 275, 353
Azmon, 141, 227
Ballerma, 386
Beatitudo, 249, 319, 325
Belmont, 104, 260, 292
Boardman, 38
Caddo, 82
Chopin, 29
Christmas, 169, 346
Cleansing Fountain, 276
Coronation, 132
Covenanters, 153
Crimond, 104
Dalehurst, 319, 444
Downs, 422
Dundee (French), 112, 342, 377, 477
Dunfermline, 95
Evan, 104
Exeter, 224
Farrant, 533
Georgetown, 421
Glasgow, 257
Gräfenberg, 243, 549
Heber (Kingsley), 255
Howard, 121
Irish, 29, 440
Kilmarnock, 125, 219
Lambeth, 32, 254
McKee, 479
Maitland, 68, 290
Manoah, 86
Martyrdom (Avon), 199, 396
Meditation, 202
Miles' Lane, 132

Old 107th, 230
Ortonville, 142
Prayer, 126
Richmond, 436
St. Agnes, 239, 391, 401
St. Anne, 111, 431
St. Flavian, 113, 181, 446, 484
St. James, 221
St. Magnus, 211, 468
St. Paul, 328
St. Peter, 130, 309, 315, 479
St. Stephen, 49, 120, 232
Serenity, 229
Song 67 (Gibbons), 37, 277
Spohr, 322
Stracathro, 327
Tallis' Ordinal, 119
This Endris Nyght, 180
Walsall, 129
Winchester Old, 381
Zerah, 71, 84

C.M. with Refrain
McAfee, 318
Martin, 124

C.M.D. (8. 6. 8. 6. 8. 6. 8. 6.)
All Saints New, 354
Amesbury, 178
Ancyra, 296
Bethlehem, 23
Carol, 160
Ellacombe, 84
Forest Green, 96, 256, 485
Kingsfold, 177
Materna, 510
Minerva, 36
Pentatone, 109, 406
St. Matthew, 179
Vox dilecti, 280

L.M. (8. 8. 8. 8.)
Abends, 62
Adesto sancta Trinitas, 245
Ames, 412
Andre, 19
Angelus, 55
Arizona, 87
Breslau, 293
Cannock, 359
Cannons, 392
Canonbury, 298
Church Triumphant, 497
Cwmafon, 540
Deo gracias, 182
Deus tuorum militum, 83, 526, 553
Duke Street, 5, 496, 523
Federal Street, 518, 531
Germany, 313, 507
Hamburg, 198
Hebron, 289

Herr Jesu Christ, 555
Hursley, 56
Illsley, 335
Maryton, 304
Melcombe, 45, 323
Mendon, 370
Missionary Chant, 494
Morning Hymn (Barthélémon), 50
Morning Hymn (Boyce), 439
Mozart, 388
Old Hundredth, 24, 544
Olive's Brow, 189
Onslow, 467
Park Street, 8, 35, 81
Pentecost, 283, 359, 480
Plain Song, 245
Preston (Doane), 258
Puer nobis nascitur, 46
Quebec, 215, 483
Retreat, 419
Rockingham Old, 387, 448
St. Crispin, 116, 228
St. Cross, 192
St. Drostane, 188
St. John's Highlands, 438
Soldau, 389
Solothurn, 305
Tallis' Canon, 63
Truro, 152, 481
Uxbridge, 259
Veni Creator, 237
Vision, 501
Vom Himmel hoch, 173, 452
Waltham, 506
Wareham, 527
Winchester New, 242
Woodworth, 272

L.M. with Refrain
He Leadeth Me, 338
More About Jesus, 316
Solid Rock, 368

L.M.D. (8. 8. 8. 8. 8. 8. 8. 8.)
Creation, 97
Sweet Hour, 398

3. 8. 6. 5. 6. 3.
Stonethwaite, 541

4. 4. 7. 4. 4. 7. 4. 4. 4. 7.
W zlobie lezy, 164

4. 8. 8. 7.
Mit Freuden zart, 554

4. 10. 10. 10. 4.
Ora labora, 287

5. 4. 5. 4. D.
Adelaide, 302

5. 5. 5. 4. D.
Bunessan, 464

5. 5. 5. 5.
Hubbard, 223

5. 5. 6. 5. 6. 5. 6. 5. with Refrain
Judas Maccabeus, 209

5. 5. 8. 8. 5. 5.
Seelenbräutigam, 334

5. 6. 6. 4.
Cura Dei, 466

5. 6. 8. 5. 5. 8.
Crusader's Hymn, 135
Schönster Herr Jesu, 135

6. 4. 6. 4. with Refrain
Need, 324

6. 4. 6. 4. D.
Bread of Life, 250

6. 4. 6. 4. 6. 6. 4.
Love's Offering, 299

6. 4. 6. 4. 6. 6. 4. 4.
More Love to Thee, 397

6. 4. 6. 4. 6. 6. 6. 4.
Bethany, 326
St. Edmund, 284
Something for Jesus, 311

6. 4. 6. 4. 10. 10.
Sursum corda, 295

6. 5. 6. 5.
Bemerton (Caswall), 222
Eudoxia, 225
Merrial, 51

6. 5. 6. 5. D.
King's Weston, 143
Longstaff, 300
Penitence, 52, 394
St. Andrew of Crete, 360

6. 5. 6. 5. D. with Refrain
Armageddon, 502
Hermas, 80
St. Gertrude, 350

6. 5. 6. 5. 6. 5. D.
Armageddon, 355

6. 5. 6. 5. 6. 6. 6. 5.
Moab, 337
St. Dunstan's, 345

8. 7. 8. 7. 4. 4. 8. 8.
Was Gott thut das ist Wohlgethan, 366

8. 7. 8. 7. 4. 7.
Bryn Calfaria, 90
Coronae, 133

8. 7. 8. 7. 6. 6. 6. 6. 7.
Ein' feste Burg, 91

8. 7. 8. 7. 7. 7.
Il buon Pastor, 12

8. 7. 8. 7. 7. 7.
Unser Herrscher (Neander), 40

8. 7. 8. 7. 8. 6. 8. 7.
Vesper Hymn, 67

8. 7. 8. 7. 8. 7.
Bradbury, 380
Cwm Rhondda, 339, 358
Dulce carmen (Corinth), 343
Holywood, 234
Irby, 462
Lauda anima (Benedic anima mea), 31
Picardy, 148
Regent Square, 168, 433
Rhuddlan, 517
Segur, 339
Sicilian Mariners, 79, 451

8. 7. 8. 7. 8. 7. 7.
Divinum mysterium, 7

8. 7. 8. 7. 8. 8. 7.
Mit Freuden zart, 15
Nun freut euch, 16

8. 8. 4. 4. 8. 8. with Alleluias
Lasst uns erfreuen, 33, 100

8. 8. 6. D.
Ariel, 134
Meribah, 329

8. 8. 7. D.
Ascendit Deus, 212

8. 8. 7. 7.
Mon Dieu, prête-moi l'oreille, 536

8. 8. 7. 8.
P'u T'o, 75

8.8.7.8.8.7.4.8.4.8.
Frankfort, 415

8. 8. 8.
O Mensch sieh, 476

8. 8. 8. with Alleluias
O filii et filiae, 206
Victory, 203

8. 8. 8. 6.
Childhood, 461
Flemming, 214
Just as I Am, 472

8. 8. 8. 6. with Refrain
Kings of Orient, 176

8. 8. 8. 8. 6.
St. Margaret, 400

8. 8. 8. 8. 8. 8.
Melita, 521
St. Catherine, 88, 348, 404
St. Petersburg, 145, 423, 516
Veni Emmanuel, 147

8. 8. 8. 8. 8. 8. 8.
Built on the Rock, 432

8. 8. 9. 8. 8. 8. 8. 4.
Open My Eyes, 390

8. 8. 10. 10.
Wallin, 25

9. 8. 8. 9.
God Be with You, 78
Randolph, 78

9. 8. 9. 8.
Commandments, 59
Eucharistic Hymn, 445
St. Clement, 59
Sunset, 57

9. 8. 9. 8. 8. 8.
Neumark, 344

9. 8. 9. 9.
Sheng En, 450

9. 10. 9. 9. with Refrain
Assurance, 139

10. 4. 6. 6. 6. 6. 10. 4.
High Road, 22

10. 4. 10. 4. 10. 10.
Lux benigna, 331
Sandon, 108

10. 7. 10. 7. with Refrain
I Am Thine, 320

10. 8. 8. 7. with Refrain
Message, 504

10. 8. 10. 7. with Refrain
Jesus Is Calling, 267

10. 10.
Pax tecum, 420

10. 10. 9. 10.
Slane, 303

10. 10. 10. 4.
Sarum, 425
Sine nomine, 425

10. 10. 10. 6.
Peace, 274, 402

10. 10. 10. 10.
Ellers, 77, 393
Eventide, 64
Field, 294
Hall, 306
Langran, 341
Morecambe, 236, 442, 532
National Hymn, 498, 515
O quanta qualia, 137, 424
Song 24, 530
Toulon, 144, 520

10. 10. 10. 10. 10.
Old 124th, 357, 490

10. 10. 10. 10. 10. 10.
Finlandia, 374, 470

10. 10. 11. 11.
Hanover, 27
Lyons, 26

11. 10. 11. 9.
Russian Hymn, 487

11. 10. 11. 10.
Ancient of Days, 246
Charterhouse, 217, 247

Consolation (Mendelssohn), 455
Consolation (Webbe), 373
Cushman, 183
Donne secours, 285, 291
Henley, 384
Morning Star, 175
Perfect Love, 453
Welwyn, 150, 288, 474
Wesley, 505

11. 10. 11. 10. with Refrain
Pilgrims (Smart), 426
Tidings, 491

11. 10. 11. 10. 10.
Langham, 486

11. 11. 11. 5.
Christe sanctorum, 43
Flemming, 53
Herzliebster Jesu, 191

11. 11. 11. 11.
Adeste fideles, 369
Foundation, 369
Gordon, 405
Joanna, 85
Mueller, 157
O quanta qualia, 122

11. 11. 11. 11. with Refrain
Fortunatus, 207

11. 12. 12. 10.
Nicaea, 11

12. 11. 12. 11.
Kremser, 17

14. 14. 4. 7. 8.
Lobe den Herren, 1

Irregular
God Be in My Head, 395
God Rest You Merry (with Refrain), 166
I Want to Be a Christian, 317
Luke (Sweet Story), 460
Margaret, 184
Purpose, 500
St. Issey, 528
Stille Nacht, 154
The First Noel (with Refrain), 156
Were You There, 201

Alphabetical Index of Tunes

KEY: (AH) Alternative harmonization; (D) Descant; (FB) Faux-bourdon

KEY: (AH) Alternative harmonization; (D) Descant; (FB) Faux-bourdon

KEY: (AH) Alternative harmonization; (D) Descant; (FB) Faux-bourdon

Index of First Lines